PHYSICS

AN INTRODUCTION

PHYSICS

AN INTRODUCTION

Poets' Physics

ERNEST C. POLLARD
Evan Pugh Professor of Biophysics
The Pennsylvania State University

DOUGLAS C. HUSTON
Assistant Professor of Physics
Skidmore College

New York
OXFORD UNIVERSITY PRESS
London   Toronto   1969

The illustration on the cover is a micrograph showing bend contours in a tungsten foil about 100 nm thick. This micrograph was taken with the high-voltage electron micro-scope at the Cavendish Laboratory, Cambridge, England, by M. S. Spring. The micro-graph originally appeared in the article "High-Voltage Electron Microscopy," by V. E. Cosslett, in the July 1968 issue of *Physics Today*. The authors are grateful to Mr. Spring, Mr. Cosslett, and *Physics Today* for permission to reproduce it.

Acknowledgments

We would like to acknowledge, as a kind of dedication, the formative teachers in our lives. They are A. S. Kendrick, E. S. Walton, T. J. Baker, A. S. Langley, S. Pollard, Alex Wood, C. D. Ellis, G. F. C. Searle, P. M. S. Blackett, E. Rutherford, J. Chadwick, A. Sommerfeld, D. R. Hartree, Leigh Page, E. J. Miles, H. B. Williams, and R. W. Dressel.

Preface

There are three well-known statements of the problem of science for the educated nonscientist. One of the ones best known today has been made by C. P. Snow, formally in his little book "The Two Cultures" and informally in many of his novels. C. P. Snow is no problem to the scientist, but rather a help. His books do show relationship between the scientist as a man and as a person caught in the scheme of his national and international interests, and they are definitely a help. A second statement is an article by Robert Graves which appeared in *The Saturday Review* called "A Poet Investigates Science." In it he makes perhaps one key brief statement. He inquires as to what is the mystique of science. And this is answerable. The answer is that *Physical Science reveals a real unseen world, and that this world is beautiful.* It is because he pursues this beauty that the physical scientist works so hard. Finally, and much the most thought-provoking is, the extremely sharp statement of the whole problem by William Blake. Blake's caricature of Newton is very hard indeed to take. We have lived with it in our office for a number of years, and it is reproduced in this book. It is really the statement of the position that man has aspirations beyond the details of the knowledge of the world around him, and it is a good deal harder to look at and to refute than anything else. There is really only one way to answer Blake. It is to say that there is Humanism in Science: that science does develop values and that they are of great importance to us. It is not easy to say this and the reason is that all the values that derive from science are *inferred:* they are not clearly asserted.

Nevertheless, in this mid-century time of a search for values, the basis for inference given by science is most useful. Educated men need to realize it is there, and to use science in developing a new morality. So even Blake's caricature can be faced with courage and integrity.

The central theme of this book is the message that the unseen real world, revealed by science, is beautiful. The problem is to make this a true appreciation of beauty. To do so one cannot simply say it, because then it is not felt. So in order to make some appreciation of the beauty of the real world apparent, we have to decide on some method of presenting it. We have to find some example where revelation of order and regularity has been achieved and show the manner in which it is done. Doing this is extremely tricky and not something in which we necessarily feel any pride of achievement. We have tried, but still many better ways may be found. Nevertheless, we do not think we have misjudged the fundamental thing that needs to be taught.

The approach that is used in this book is in terms of four elements. The first is the decision that the content of the course is not really important but the contact of a scientist with the students is vital. This means that arguing as to whether the course should contain some geology, some astronomy, some modern physics, some reference to molecular structure, etc. is not important. What the individual teacher feels he can use to illustrate the central point, that the unseen real world is beautiful, is the thing that matters. Anything which is concerned with total content is much less stringent. So, in this book the second element is one logical development of science, essentially the science of motion and the related forces, with an addition of a little electricity plus a story of later developments. The numerical aspect in terms of simple numbers is not stressed very much at all. On the other hand, students are required to retain and give back concepts exactly. One might say that the fundamental objective is to teach the elements of theoretical physics rather than the elements of experimental physics.

The third aspect is that the relationship of science to people is important. Thus the study of biographies is urged, and we use a continual explanation of the way scientists do things and the kind of individuals they are.

Finally, the last element of the approach is the relationship to society.

Many people have been most helpful. Students, faculty associates, graduate assistants and office staff have advised, criticized, and worked hard. We can single out Wallace Snipes, Paul Scheie, Mary Osborn, Rick Bockrath, and Lynn Kashuba. To them and to all the others we owe sincere thanks.

August 1968

ERNEST C. POLLARD
DOUGLAS C. HUSTON

Contents

PHYSICS

AN INTRODUCTION

I

Introduction

The topic we consider in this book is Physical Science: the body of knowledge that concerns motion; gravitation; electricity; radiation; the structure of solids, liquids, and gases; radioactivity; astronomy; geology; and cosmology. It might seem strange to ask the question—"Why is it necessary to know something about Physical Science?"—because the list of subjects it encompasses is so obviously comprehensive and so basic that it would seem to be impossible to be educated in the most elementary sense of the word without knowing something about all these matters. In fact, the question is most important, for at the present time most students, let alone most people, are profoundly ignorant of these subjects, and are also quite firmly set on a pathway through life in such a way that they will avoid, as completely as possible, any knowledge of Physical Science whatsoever.

It is quite easy to have a reasonable understanding of the affairs of Man, to read the daily newspaper, to consider politics, to go to church, to manage one's money affairs, to bring up children (up to a point where their questions begin to be worrisome), and to be respected in society without any of the knowledge we are going to develop in this book. The authors remember two separate occasions when presidents of Yale were dedicating some scientific addition to the University. Both stated, in almost the same words, that as college students their main objective had been to get as little science as they could get away with. Both admitted regret, but it cannot be denied that they had won the respect of an academic community with an avowed minimum of scientific knowledge. It has become so easy to operate without knowledge of science that a very real danger now threatens us if we are to continue with a democratic form of government: the danger that only a few can bring any wisdom at all to forming policies that concern techniques and

"forces" which can be used to destroy us all. Up to the present the few
we speak of above, who by and large are scientists, have not had very
separate group ambitions. Surely this is not a typical state of affairs, and
surely it is unwise to expect a continuation of this benevolent attitude of
men who are, after all, having to strive to reach their eminent positions,
and who may easily think that this striving entitles them to something
more than the disrespect which goes with being largely ignored.

When approached in this way, an individual who operates without any
knowledge of or feeling for science usually points out that we are, of
necessity, in a time of specialization and that experts are necessary for
all phases of life: he is just not an expert in any kind of science, but
there are plenty who are, and he will leave it to them. This is quite true,
and in this book we propose to avoid any attempt to develop any kind of
expert skill in physical science. What is not true is that an educated
individual can delegate the knowledge of who he is as a person and what
environment he lives in to somebody else. To take a more specific
illustration, he may not need to know how the water supply reaches
him, or how to fix it inside his house, but he does need to know that the
water supply is essential, that it is elaborate, that it has necessary safe-
guards, and that it will cost him money both to secure and to maintain.
In the same way we can approach the subject of physical science. To
quote J. H. Jeans:

The last hundred years have seen more change than a thousand years of the
stone age. This change has resulted in large part from the applications of
physical science which, through the use of steam, electricity and gasoline, and by
way of the various industrial arts, now affects almost every moment of our
existences. Its use in medicine and surgery may save our lives; its use in warfare
may involve us in utter ruination. In its more abstract aspects, it has exerted a
powerful influence on our philosophies, our religions and our general outlook
on life.

A subject of so great and general an influence, both on society and on
individual philosophy, cannot be dismissed as a subject only for the
expert: it should at least be understood in its scope, power, and promise
for the future, by every educated person.

Very often the educated non-scientist will accept the truth of the above,
but will rejoin that it is very difficult indeed to communicate with
scientists, particularly modern, rather specialized scientists; and so the
effort required to learn what science can tell him about who he is as a
person and what kind of environment he lives in is greater than he can
exert and he must take refuge in hoping he can live without the knowledge. We take the attitude that there is much truth in this objection
also. We reject, in our turn, the notion that the effort necessary to get

some feeling for physical science, and for what it tells us about the environment in which we live, and for its promise and perhaps its threat, is too great for a normal educated person. It is our purpose in this book to show that such knowledge can be obtained. We would like to think that at the end of reading it the student would welcome the chance that might seat him next to Bethe or Herb or Glaser on an airplane trip, and find him able to communicate on the affairs of the day as seen by a great scientist, instead of having to resort to reading the instructions for safety in overwater flights and relapsing into gloom. He should be able to look at news items on science in the daily paper and ask his scientific friends about their significance. Most of all, he should begin to make his acquaintance among scientists much more pleasant and understanding.

In order to achieve these objectives we propose to ask the student to conform to one or two rules in return for one or two concessions on our part. Let us take the concessions first. We said earlier that we do not propose to develop in the student any expert skill in physical science. Therefore, we do not propose to ask the student to solve any problems, unless he wants to, except perhaps a few in mathematics where problems may prove to be the fastest and easiest way to acquire familiarity with certain ideas and ways of expressing them. We do not propose to cover anything like the whole of physical science: we shall leave out vast segments. We intend to devote one half of the course to the development of a limited part of physical science, in which we treat the subject both logically and historically, and the other half to a kind of descriptive account of material which is important in the modern era, but which cannot be treated fully and logically in the time we have available. We cannot, however, give an inch on the point that the real beauty of physical science is its precision of ideas—ideas which work exactly and universally. So we shall ask that the student learn a certain number of basic principles and some of their applications. He should be able to discuss their significance, not vaguely, but precisely and to the point.

Before bringing this introductory part to a close and moving into the subject matter, we would like to make a comment on the scientist and the artist.

Perhaps the best recent discussion of the two worlds involved has been given by C. P. Snow in *The Two Cultures*. He speaks there of moving among two groups, writers and scientists, and of finding "Greenwich Village talking precisely the same language as Chelsea, and both having about as much communication with M.I.T. as though the scientist spoke nothing but Tibetan." It is indeed one of the rather sad features of our present society that there is a sort of conflict between the artist and the scientist. It is worthwhile to look for a little time at what constitutes the area of conflict, and to see whether it is sensible to be very much occupied with it. The emotional climate which the conflict is capable of generating is shown in the remarkable painting of Newton by William Blake, which is reproduced adequately, for our purposes, in Figure 1.1. Blake, the mystic poet and artist, did not like the surge of materialistic thinking that followed from the successful interpretation of the motion of the moon and of planets by purely mechanical laws. So he fixed his resentment on Newton. The narrow, stupid concentration on a trivial design, with the cramped use of the probably too magnificent human figure, expresses about perfectly the feeling many art-centered people have for the scientist.

Let us look at it dispassionately for a moment.

If we think of the early stages of an artist's work, they are mostly self-expression. On the other hand, a scientist has a strong complication in this matter of expressing himself. While he undoubtedly wants his work to be his individually, and he wants credit for it, sometimes desperately, his work cannot really be concerned with expressing himself. He is seeking for some property that can also be found by others. It is tremendously important to him that what he discovers can also be discovered by others—in scientific terms, be repeatable by others, even those who have had very little experience with the subject. When Newton pro-

Fig. 1.1. Newton, by William Blake.

pounded the Law of Gravitation, what was important to him was the fact that anyone, even his severest critic, would recognize the truth of it, accept it, and use it. Thus, the scientist as regards expressing *himself* is relatively humble. This does not mean that he has no pride in his achievement, but it does mean that he urgently seeks to share his achievement with others and that he also regards himself as revealing a universal value, rather than expressing himself.

This point, about the attitude of the scientist toward his work, is very important. It would not be true to say that the scientist regards himself in some way subservient to a vaguely defined "Nature," and that he must at all times play down his personal involvement with his work. In fact, most scientists approach their work very emotionally. The manner in which the emotion appears is not always easy to see, but the truth is that a man cannot spend fourteen hours a day in the laboratory, often on the most menial and painstaking work, without being strongly motivated emotionally as well as intellectually. When he appears in public to discuss his work at meetings of scientific societies, the emotion often flares out; and some of the most bitter discussions we have ever heard have been between people who have conducted work on the same subject and reached different conclusions. The essential feature of the scientist with regard to his work is his acceptance of the idea that it imposes a very rigorous discipline on him. It is essentially true that all the great innovators in science—men who by their discoveries have profoundly changed our way of thought—have been most conservative in their approach to their science. Koch and Pasteur laid the foundation for the idea that communicable disease is due to infection by microorganisms. Here are some words from Pasteur:

When you believe you have found an important scientific fact and are feverishly curious to publish it, constrain yourself for days, weeks, years sometimes; fight yourself, try to ruin your own experiments, and only proclaim your discovery after having exhausted all contrary hypothesis.

In a modern setting, the basic experiments which directly revealed the form of nuclear forces, done by Tuve, Heydenburg, and Hafstad, were reported with the following words:

. . . we spent the period from early February to the middle of April endeavoring to "break down" the results of our survey, to see whether [they could] be explained in terms of an unsuspected contamination . . . or other spurious cause.

To complete the story, it is also part of the faith of the scientist that following the discipline can result in real reward. To finish the quotation from Pasteur:

But when after so many efforts you have at last arrived at certainty, your joy is one of the greatest that can be felt by the human soul.

At first sight, what we have described about the scientist is in some measure of contrast to the artist. Nevertheless the contrast diminishes when the higher qualities of art are looked at. Even though J. S. Bach may have written his Mass in B Minor as an example of his own personal musical skill, and even though in his own age most of it was never heard except in his own mind, there is clearly a universal appeal in the tremendous musical structure which he created. The same is true of Shakespeare. Portia says:

> . . . consider this,
> That in the course of justice none of us
> Should see salvation: we do pray for mercy,
> And that same prayer doth teach us all to render
> The deeds of mercy.

When Shakespeare writes on mercy he is not simply writing a speech for a lawyer in court. He is actually stating in his words the nature of one of the highest human attributes, for all who will read it. The artist, if he is great, also touches the universal very closely; and the separation between him and the scientist is not really so deep.

This point, which is really absolutely major in this book, needs some more elaboration. The word "universal" is too cold, the statement too factual. The real essence of what we are saying is that when the great artist paints or writes or composes, he starts by doing it for himself, and ends by doing it for us all. As Charles Lamb wrote of *King Lear*, " . . . while we read it, we see not Lear, but we are Lear,—we are in his mind."

Look at Michelangelo's famous depiction of the creation of Adam. There is the hand of God, the fingertip just moving toward the hand of Adam. Adam lies finished in body, but listless, unaware, looking across at God. Everything that moves with the finger of God is alive, God himself, the Angels watching in sharp suspense this greatest of all moments. The author, as a scientist, without any claim to knowledge of painting, and writing, has no doubt that he can capture some of Michelangelo's thoughts as he created this painting. Michelangelo would certainly care about the anatomy of the figures, about the accuracy of expression, about the color—but he would care fervently that he was painting *all* creative moments as he painted this one. He wanted the figures, the expression, the listless hand of Adam and the finger of God to remind those who saw it of those great moments in their lives, when something ready and fully endowed *came to life*. To any teacher, to pick an example, the painting has profound meaning. Surely no teacher thinks of himself as God, and yet the moments which repay the teacher are those when he sees some student "take-off." When he knows that from that moment on his exposition, analysis, and program of learning have become secondary —the student will go on his own, and when he also knows that without his contribution it might not have happened.

If now we say that great science involves intensely personal moments of great insight, followed by discovery which can be shared by all, and that great art involves moments of great inspiration followed by work which leaves a message for all, the two do not seem so very far apart. This is the position we take, and the whole book is written in this spirit.

Before we conclude this chapter and proceed to the development of the subject, it is worth another moment to comment on the scientist and the "ascent of Man." By these three words, we mean the growth of the ability of Man to control his environment: to master hunger, to house himself, to travel fast, to communicate instantly, to improve health, and to aid his thought processes when they become too slow or tedious. This ascent of man is something the scientist takes very seriously. He believes that he has had a very large part in bringing it about, and he thinks that it is a major contribution to the welfare of man. He thinks that life would be intolerable without the possibility of understanding Nature and the advance that can be made because of the understanding. Today many scientists will go further. They will say that with the removal of parasites from man's body and with the provision of food and housing for him, science has made it possible for man to become *himself;* that the "ascent" operation has really been a liberation. It is not at all trivial that in the room where the greatest respect to science is paid in this country, the main hall of the National Academy of Sciences, some of these words from *Prometheus Bound* appear:

> Harken to the miseries that beset mankind.
> They were witless erst and I made them to have sense
> And be endowed with reason. Though they had eyes to
> See they saw in vain. They had ears but heard not,
> But like to shapes in dreams. Throughout their
> Length of days without purpose they wrought all things
> In confusion. ——They had no sign either of
> Winter or of flowery spring or of fruitful summer,
> Whereon they could depend, but in everything
> They wrought without judgement until such time as
> I taught them to discern the risings of the stars
> And their settings. Aye and numbers too, chiefest

Of sciences I invented for them, and the combining
Of letters, creative mother of the muses arts wherewith
To hold all things in memory. . . Twas I and no one else
That contrived the mariner's flaxen-winged car to roam
the sea. . . If ever man fell ill there was no defense
But for lack of medicine they wasted away until I showed
Them how to mix soothing remedies wherewith they now ward
Off their disorders. Hear the sum of the whole matter—
Every art possessed by man comes from Prometheus.

It is true that most scientists are too matter-of-fact to express their attitude toward the ascent of man with this kind of imagery, but when presented with it, they acknowledge that it expresses one major result of the careful study of Nature. And because they do take this aspect seriously, they often stress the importance of seemingly irrelevant work. So very often the most off-the-track discoveries have led to great advances in man's ability to influence his environment, that scientists will sturdily say that any research which adds definitely to man's understanding of the way things work is urgent, even though it seemingly bears no relation to any desired end. One of the most famous reversals of expectation is that of the release of nuclear energy, which has totally altered warfare, and which its discoverer, Rutherford, was convinced was of purely intellectual interest. Even he, the man of science himself, could not credit the idea that the little, feeble manifestation which he had discovered in his laboratory would, within less than twenty-five years, be a dominant force in the policy of the nations of the world. Realizations of the cumulative value of accurate knowledge, of even the most inconsequential properties of Nature have made men of science anxious to protect what they call "basic research." Some of the most valuable research in the post World War II years has been supported by far-sighted men who are willing to gamble on the future utility of the esoteric discoveries now being made.

It should not surprise anyone, therefore, that the topics of research in universities, for example, seem strange, overspecial, and esoteric. The scientific community has learned that these subjects, when honestly and competently studied, and with results published so that they are accessible, can be of value, not only because they are intellectually interesting, but because they may be of crucial importance in some future great advance in man's ability.

With these preliminary thoughts, let us set about the business of finding out about physical science.

Suggestions for Further Thought

1. Give and discuss two instances of social change imposed by scientific discovery. Do not include material improvement in comfort.

References

Sir J. H. Jeans, *The Growth of Physical Science,* 2nd ed. (New York: Cambridge University Press, 1948).

C. P. Snow, *The Two Cultures* (New York: Cambridge University Press, 1959).

Hans Zinsser, *Rats, Lice, and History* (New York: Bantam Books, 1960).

For the artist and for the scientist there is a special problem and a special hope, for in their extraordinarily different ways, in their lives that have increasingly divergent character, there is still a sensed bond, a sensed analogy. Both the man of science and the man of art live always at the edge of mystery, surrounded by it; both always, as the measure of their creation, have had to do with the harmonization of what is new with what is familiar, with the balance between novelty and synthesis, with the struggle to make partial order in total chaos. They can, in their work and in their lives, help themselves, help one another, and help all men. They can make the paths that connect the villages of arts and sciences with each other and with the world at large the multiple, varied, precious bonds of a true and world-wide community.

This cannot be an easy life. We shall have a rugged time of it to keep our minds open and to keep them deep, to keep our sense of beauty and our ability to make it, and our occasional ability to see it in places remote and strange and unfamiliar; we shall have a rugged time of it, all of us, in keeping these gardens in our villages, in keeping open the manifold, intricate, casual paths, to keep these flourishing in a great, open, windy world; but this, as I see it, is the condition of man; and in this condition we can help, because we can love, one another.

J. ROBERT OPPENHEIMER

2

Abstract Thinking, Algebra and Calculus

What I prophesied two-and-twenty years ago, as soon as I discovered the five solids among the heavenly orbits—what I firmly believed long before I had seen Ptolemy's Harmonies—what I had promised my friends in the title of this book, which I named before I was sure of my discovery— what sixteen years ago, I urged as a thing to be sought—that for which I joined Tycho Brahe, for which I settled in Prague, for which I have devoted the best part of my life to astronomical contemplations, at length I have brought to light, and recognized its truth beyond my most sanguine expectations. It is not eighteen months since I got the first glimpse of light, three months since the dawn, very few days since the unveiled sun, most admirable to gaze upon, burst upon me. Nothing holds me; I will indulge my sacred fury; I will triumph over mankind by the honest confession that I have stolen the golden vases of the Egyptians to build up a tabernacle for my God far away from the confines of Egypt. If you forgive me, I rejoice; if you are angry, I can bear it; the die is cast, the book is written, to be read either now or by posterity, I care not which; it may well wait a century for a reader, as God has waited six thousand years for an observer.

JOHANNES KEPLER

One essential feature of the advance of physical science, and a feature which is becoming increasingly dominant in the whole of modern science, is the use of the process of thinking about abstractions which are related to reality, rather than directly about reality itself. In many of the areas of modern physics, notably in those areas which concern the nucleus of

12

the atom, the possibility of thinking about the tangible object is so remote that a nuclear physicist will look at you in amazement if you suggest it. And the truth is that even something quite definitely tangible, like a falling body, is not regarded by a physicist as one would expect. He sees a motion picture of such a falling body, and it interests him as a curiosity, and may even elicit from him surprising remarks, such as how interesting an art form it provides; but he has long ago found a quite different and very powerful method of thinking about the object in the moving picture, and he holds to that method when he wants to under-stand what is happening, rather than studying the direct vision.

Degrees of abstraction vary and deepen as each sharp advance is made in physical science as can be seen by the approach of three men—Brahe, Kepler, and Newton—to the problem of the motion of the planets. Brahe, a wealthy man who built an elaborate observatory at Copenhagen in the latter part of the sixteenth century, spent his scientific lifetime recording the positions of stars and planets at definite times, with considerable accuracy. His life was devoted to the first stage of abstraction, the replace-ment of the observation by the eye of where a planet or star appears by a number, or set of numbers, in a catalogue. One can think of Tycho Brahe almost as a collector, seeking to add to the volumes of precise data about stars, and having something of the satisfaction of the philatelist who sees his albums grow and takes delight in the order in them and the completeness of his collection. Even though they may seem to be rather away from the primary purpose of discovery about the stars, such cata-logues do represent a valuable advance, and they are often the first step in something much more simple and penetrating. While we are on this subject we should mention that such catalogues of the wavelengths of light emitted by many things, and of the apparent dimensions, called "cross sections," of atomic nuclei, are of the greatest value in our time. The wavelengths tables have yielded to better methods of thinking, but the atomic nuclei are still "holding out" on our theoretical skill. Today the Atomic Energy Commission spends millions of dollars annually on almost the same type of collecting process that we associate with Tycho Brahe and the positions of the planets.

This type of collecting process does not, at first glance, seem to be a very great abstraction. And, in fact, our modern culture has made us familiar with the process, which has strongly invaded the financial pages of newspapers and is a factor in the world of a well-addicted baseball fan. In reality, quite a step has been taken, intellectually, in bringing under comprehension a whole set of athletic events in terms of sets of numbers in tables, and it is our tendency to take such a way of analysis for granted. We must nevertheless remember that knowing that so-and-so bats .300, while very informative, is not really a substitute for seeing the actual muscles possessed by so-and-so and watching him swing his bat. The pitcher who has to pitch to him probably wants to know quite a bit more about him than just his cumulative average. In the same way, the number which describes the angle of elevation of a star, or a planet, cannot really substitute for the actual sight of it, and our feeling for the way we have to bend our head back to see where it is. The reason the substitution is of great importance to the physicist is that he really wants to do much more than look at a star. He may want to predict where it can be found in a week's time; or he may want to use the motion of the star to tell him something else—for example, to test a theory of gravitation. So, to him, as perhaps to the baseball coach, the number is actually more important than the sight of the thing itself.

We can see a complete difference in the description of the planets given by Kepler. Kepler, who worked in Brahe's observatory, not only helped to compile the data about planets but kept steadily trying to make some sort of analysis of them and to reduce them to a simple system. He had for guidance a very old theory of planetary motion, known as the Ptolemaic theory, and the newer and revolutionary (and heretical) theory of Copernicus, by which the planets were supposed to move in circles around the sun. Kepler deduced quite simple mathematical statements which accurately covered the behavior of the planets as seen and recorded by Brahe. His statements were to the effect that the planets move in paths described by a geometric figure, the ellipse, that the sun is one focus of these ellipses, that the line from the sun to the planet "sweeps out" equal areas in equal times, and that there is a relation between the time it takes a planet to complete its orbit and the distance of the planet, on the average, from the sun. These mathematical statements represented a very simple and very new method of describing the position of a planet, and they made the compilations of Brahe seem quite cumbersome. More important, they seem to point irresistibly to something very regular and orderly in the scheme of the Universe, something which seems also to have some sort of relationship to mathematics and, in particular, to geometry and algebra, the sciences of form and of number. Once one turns from the actual vision of the planet, and starts to substitute the ideas of ellipses, foci, areas swept out, times, and distances, one becomes involved in really considerable abstraction. One has to imagine the motion of the planet in a controlled and definite way; but all the same in a way that is purely imaginative. This imaginative faculty, which is seen in the description given by Kepler, is something which has come to dominate science, or, at any event, to dominate physical science. It is our belief that it will soon dominate biological science.

There is still one more stage that we can look at. While it is very exciting and strongly suggestive to discover these geometric relationships about the motion of planets, it is even more exciting if the regularity they show can be found to be part of a regularity which *everything in the universe* shows. Newton made such a suggestion, in the latter part of the seventeenth century, and in doing so he reached a far greater depth of abstraction than Brahe or Kepler. At this depth of abstraction one has to suppose that the motion of the planets is subject to a *cause,* a *force,* which is due to a universal process. The exact nature of what is meant by the word *force* must be known, and the exact consequence which will result from the action of a force must be known. The force must be accurately described, in character and in size, over a wide range (the whole solar system). Almost all these ideas are truly *abstract,* and the whole triumph of Newton's scheme of mechanics and his Law of Universal Gravitation lies not only in its great generality and simplicity, but just as much in the property of *accurate imagination* (which we have called "abstract thinking") which it contains. Later we will have to cover all this ground more carefully. For now, we have just summarized one of the great areas of scientific advance. We can perhaps add that Einstein moved the use of accurate imagination one stage further by suggesting that space and time form a four-dimensional space and that Newton's gravitational force is due to a curvature of space-time, which automatically produces the force. We can see that this process of abstract thinking, in accurate terms, is one of the major weapons, or techniques, if you prefer the term, of science. So we have to pay careful attention to it, and this we are now about to do.

NUMBERS

Dantzig has written a very informative and readable book which quickly summarizes a great deal in the title: *Number: the Language of Science.* Kelvin, one of the scientific giants of the nineteenth century, made an often quoted statement, much liked by physical scientists:

. . . when you can measure what you are speaking about, and express it in numbers, you know something about it; but when you cannot express it in numbers, your knowledge is of a meager and unsatisfactory kind; it may be the beginning of knowledge, but you have scarcely, in your thoughts, advanced to the stage of Science, whatever the matter may be.

In physical science we use numbers as a means of description of some attribute, such as length or time. But such description is only a small fraction of our use of numbers. We have found that there are some very simple ways of combining numbers, such as adding them or subtracting them, and while we, as scientists, may insist that these combinations are concerned with the numbers of eggs or elephants, the truth is

that there is a lot of interest simply in the way the combinations of numbers themselves happen, and how they develop if you use quite a few
combinations in an orderly way. The subject which describes the behavior
and relationships of numbers is algebra. Algebra is quite basic to all
science, and therefore, for a little while, we will look at algebra, not so
much to learn it, for we already know it, or at some time claimed to know
it, but to see what its content is and how it can possibly be related to
science.

Algebra

THE OPERATIONS OF ALGEBRA

All mathematics, and in fact all developments of thought, are somehow
related to ourselves and our experience. However, because we are great
developers and elaborators, it is not always easy to see how a subject like
numbers, and hence algebra, grew to be the way it is. Think for a
moment about music. Music is based upon a pattern in *time* (a fact
pointed out to us by Hindemith). There are many aspects of this pattern.
A bongo drum player stresses one aspect, the rhythmic beat. A singer
produces a note that has a pitch, which is really the same as the rhythmic
beat but occurs so rapidly that it sounds as one whole note. The pitch
of the note depends on the number of vibrations per second. Musicians—
probably thousands of years ago—developed a set of interesting notes,
based on *integer numbers* 1, 2, 3, 4 etc., and very simple fractions, which
become part of a *scale,* and from there on a tremendous elaboration became possible. This elaboration took place over several centuries and
finally produced music as we know it. Most listeners are not aware of
this long development, or of the stages of psychological adjustment
which men needed to make as each change in the elaboration brought
new sounds and patterns. But musicians are keenly aware of it and
interested in it, and the listener who learns of it usually finds a greater
sense of enjoyment of music and a broadening of his acceptance of composition.

Just the same process has gone on with regard to numbers. Consider a
set of apples. Two apples clearly differ from one apple. "How many
apples?" is a very necessary question, and the number is often interesting,
and in a family, most important. So it is easy to see how *integers* came
into being, to tell us the number of recognizable objects. It is interesting
that animals can probably not count beyond 3. We can do better.

Now apples can be grouped. Some apples can be on the left—say three of them—and some on the right—say two of them. Then *all* the apples, the *sum,* is $3 + 2$, or 5. This process of addition is simple and soon understood. Clearly it can be extended. If we have 5 apples on the right and move 2 to the left, we have 3 remaining, which we call the difference. We write the process, which is subtraction, $5 - 2 = 3$.

So far, there is not very much abstract thinking.

However, suppose we have five children and we have promised them each an apple, but the market has only sent us three. Now we have two lacking. If we like, we can say that the market owes us two. We can write this statement as $3 - 5 = - 2$.

This is quite abstract. We now embody a quality in the number: it is owed; it is *negative.*

For many people this is the crucial moment in the development of mathematics, this first abstraction, this first superposition of a quality to a description, originally developed for the description of touchables and now expressing the concept of lack as well. Most of us can remember tastes which seemed strange at first but which became quite palatable. Something of the same process of assimilation of something a little strange, but necessary, is called for here.

The scientist doesn't mind negative numbers. For one thing, he has to add some quality to numbers anyway, or he can't even start. To him the number is a necessary attribute of something which is actual and physical; and since, for example, he will have to find a way of describing forward and backward (to pick one example out of many), he welcomes this elaboration. So he says, let's associate a direction with these "qualities." Let's call forward "plus" and backward "minus." Then he would say that, for example, $3 - 5 = - 2$ could mean that he has taken three steps forward and five backward, and so has arrived at a place two steps behind. It makes sense, is convenient and easy.

Enter negative numbers.

We can keep going. Suppose each of three people bring in two apples. Then we get two apples three times. We of course, have six apples, and we write the mathematical process, which is multiplication, as $2 \times 3 = 6$. Here is no problem, no abstract thought.

Let us now have six apples and three children. How many apples each? Well, if we can make three equal groupings, that will be it. Six divided by three equals two. So we can see that there is a process which we have called division. But a moment's thought shows that we have been altogether too glib about the nature of the process, because we might have five apples and two children, and then we could never make two equal groupings out of the five apples. In other words, for this kind of process, with this kind of number it can't be done. In the system of integer numbers $5/2$ is meaningless. Our "operation" of division has brought an insecurity with it. Only some numbers will divide. To return to music, there was a long stage when all intervals on our present scale were liked and tolerated except one—the interval from C to F♯, called the augmented fourth. Musicians banned the use of the interval. Then a few courageous souls began to use it, to place it in a progression, and to replace the harsh sound by one pleasing which followed. Today one of the most common chords heard is the dominant seventh, which contains an augmented fourth, that once banned interval—and we all love to hear it. So with numbers. Some courageous souls said, why not include *fractions?* After all, a knife will cut an apple, and if we cut the apple equally, we have two halves, so that 5/2 becomes 2½ and we can make two equal groupings and keep peace between the children. If we keep these numbers, and allow all sorts of fractions, always of *integers,* we have a new system—the *rational number system.*

With this system we have four operations: addition, subtraction, multiplication, and division.

Now we add another. Suppose we multiply a number by itself, $2 \times 2 = 2^2$, or do so more than once: $2 \times 2 \times 2 = 2^3$. This is not very special in the system of integers, but it is rather interesting to look at. Consider this. $2 \times 2 \times 2 \times 2 \times 2$. It is 2^5. By drawing a line we can see that:

$$2 \times 2 \mid \times 2 \times 2 \times 2 = 2^5, \text{also} = 2^2 \times 2^3.$$

So we see that when we multiply the separate "squared" and "cubed" together to make 2^5, we add the *indices.*

This process, which we call "raising to a power," a special confined kind of multiplication, where we only multiply by ourselves, so to speak, might seem to be rather useless as a general idea. It proves otherwise, and in fact, even if mathematicians were quite uninterested in this sort of process, scientists would have had to study it themselves. One illustration can be used to show this. One very important aspect of Nature is the crystalline condition. Salt, sugar, and many other substances crystallize into very regular shapes. Now these regular shapes are derived from simple geometrical regulations. For example, the crystalline shape of salt is governed by the fact that the distance between the sodium atoms and chlorine atoms is always monotonously the same. The result is that the form of the salt crystal is that of a geometric cube. This means that if we know the distance between any pair of atoms, and we want to know the area of the square made by four of them we will have to consider the distance squared; and if we want to know the volume of a little cube of eight atoms, we have to consider the cube of the distance. (It is not only in physical science that these powers are important. In psychology it is recognized that the relative sensation of a stimulus goes as the power.

Thus a stimulus which is increased 100 times may be felt as only ten times more.) Thus we are most interested when the mathematician begins to inquire into the behavior of numbers when they are multiplied by themselves, and we want to know what rules he develops—for we, as scientists, want to see if we can use what he produces.

We remind the reader that the little number at the upper right, which tells us the number of times the number is multiplied by itself, is the *power* to which the number is "raised," and is also called more compactly the index (plural—indices). Now we said above that when we multiplied two such numbers together we added the indices, $2^2 \times 2^3 = 2^5$. Suppose we divide. Then

$$\frac{2 \times 2 \times 2}{2 \times 2} = \frac{2^3}{2^2} = 2^1$$

This means that we subtract the indices. What happens if we have 2^{-1}, a negative index? Well, it would be the same as $2^2/2^3$, or $\frac{1}{2}$. So a fraction, always involving the one number which is being multiplied by itself, can be made of these indices. Incidentally, as a small precaution, we can examine whether we can start with a fraction as the number which is multiplied by itself. Will it work? Yes it will. $\frac{1}{2} \times \frac{1}{2}$ makes sense; it is $(\frac{1}{2})^2$. No problem.

Before we push ahead to the one remaining operation which completes the scheme of algebra, we are faced with a very great problem. This problem will come all the way through this book. It does not arise from the material we are going to present, because that is, all of it, easy. The problem arises because we can not guarantee that the reader actually reads what we write. We do intend, without resorting to risqué pictures or off-color jokes, to keep the necessary attention, but the truth is that we do have to pile development upon development, at least some of the time. When we do, there is only one thing to do: read with attention and, indeed, go back over the material several times. Actually, teachers of science have devised a much hated backdoor method of forcing attention on the reader. They provide a textbook with a horrendous number of problems at the end of each chapter, and assign the problems with a kind of sadistic vigor. The student finds that he can get some slight help from the text and reads it in desperation. Now we don't propose to use this subterfuge, and we want the reader to give us credit to the extent that he will actually go back and read over the last two paragraphs and decide that, while they may seem pretty grotesque in any relation to actuality, yet, in this curiously specialized context, it is true that they are not very profound—at least with regard to ideas.

With this preparation, we are ready to ask the final question about numbers which, when answered, gives us the whole basis of algebra. Can we think of a number which when multiplied by itself makes a given number? Such a number is the *square root*. Once again, as in the case of division, we see that there are "easy" numbers and a lot of hopeless ones. Numbers like 4, 9, 16, and so on, are simple, and with them the answer to our question is easy—namely, 2, 3, 4, etc. But even for a simple number like 2, the answer is hopeless. There is not a fractional number *at all* which when multiplied by itself will yield 2. And this raises the formidable question whether something which cannot even be represented by the integers which we used to tell us how many apples we had, can be considered to be a number at all. It is actually a tough problem. On the one hand, we don't have any doubt that whatever we might want to describe by a number will exist, if it is such a square root. Thus, if we tell an architect that we must have a room which is square and which has an area of 200 square feet, he isn't going to be held back by any of our philosophical doubts, about the square root of 2. He will very quickly decide what length the side has to be and won't even bother us any more. And the mathematician will agree that his solution to the problem is satisfactory. The mathematician will, however, retire to his study and complain to himself a bit because he doesn't yet have a way to admit these obviously "good" numbers into his scheme.

The solution to the dilemma between the practical and the theoretical came with what is known as the Dedekind "cut." Dedekind supposed that one can divide numbers into two classes, so that all the numbers in one class are less than any number in the other class. He then supposed, or rather, asserted, that there is a number such that all the numbers less than it belong to the lesser class, and all the numbers greater than it belong to the greater class. This number, which belongs to what is called the "real number system," can be used to describe square roots of *any* number, and it conforms to the rules for all the operations of algebra. So, in the real number system, it is possible to add, subtract, multiply, divide, raise to a power, and "extract" a root. The subject which describes what happens when all these operations can take place on real numbers is algebra.

It very often comes as a considerable surprise to be told that the definition of a number is actually complicated and subtle—after all, numbers are used casually by every educated person for many purposes. It would seem that there might be some reason to accept the idea that fractions represent a stage beyond the primitive notion of numbers which needs some thought, and more, that fractions should be capable of being used to describe all that we can ever need in our consideration of Nature. We are not going to pretend that in a few sentences we can clarify the concept of the Dedekind cut, a matter of some concern to first-rate mathematicians, but the simple diagram of Figure 2.1 may help some readers. We have drawn a line, supposedly one unit long, and marked on it a few fractional numbers. Each mark represents a number, and it can be seen that they appear with a kind of regularity, but that they do not fill the whole line. For a moment suppose that the marks we have made were all the numbers that we could have—a rather limiting supposition, but nevertheless, not absurd if we should happen to want to think about a logical extreme. Then we could not go from 0 to 1 in a continuous fashion, but instead would have to go from 0 to 1/5 *or not go at all*. Somehow this violates a very profound physical intuition: we *should* be able to use numbers to describe something which is quite steadily advancing. With fractions we cannot do so. The Dedekind cut asserts that *all* the infinity of points on the line are numbers, so that we can think of quite uniform progression from 0 to 1 without the succession of jumps imposed by the fractional system. The differential and integral calculus, used so much in physical thinking, cannot be developed in their present form without the use of the Dedekind cut and the real number system.

This problem, of defining a number, is one of the hardest that the mathematician has had to face, and even now one might say that he is uneasy about the definition. To the physicist there is no such uneasiness —for two reasons. In the first place, the physicist is well aware that he can never measure anything and so represent it by a number with total accuracy, so that to him a little sloppiness about numbers is inevitable. In the second place, the idea of a "cut" is very sensible to him, for in almost any process he considers, for example one involving time or distance, he feels free, at least in his imagination, to divide time or distance anywhere he chooses; and he thinks that when he has done so he ought to be able to represent what results by a number. We tend to take the attitude of the physicist, but we have enough respect for mathematicians to know that when they are uneasy there may be trouble ahead for us ordinary mortals.

Fig. 2.1. The division of a line into fractional parts. With only these as numbers it is not possible to think of proceeding uniformly from 0 to 1. The Dedekind cut and the real number system make every point on the line a number.

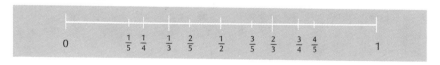

The reader simply will not believe us if we assert that there is no more
to algebra than the use of the six operations we have described on numbers in the real number system. He has had enough, and often bitter,
experience with it to be quite convinced otherwise. So we have to make
some comforting remarks.

In science, the aspect of algebra which we find most useful is that part
which expresses a relationship between two or more things in terms of
numbers. Thus, there is a relationship between the population of the
United States and time. At present, the population is increasing as time
goes on. The mathematical physicist would love to express this relationship in a very abstract way, which is most dear to his heart. First, he
would like to represent the number of people in the United States by a
symbol. Most of us need to have a little security about this representation
and would like to use P as the symbol—P standing for either people or
population. The mathematical physicist is probably just as happy to
represent it by some symbol which has no relationship to the word for
population, but which doesn't bother him any more than it bothers a
woman to refer to a color as "tan" or "beige." Oddly enough, we find he
has a prejudice about the symbol for time; he usually insists on being t,
which we all find agreeable. If we adopt our own prejudice, then the way
the physicist would like to refer to the relationship between the population of the United States and time is

$$P = f(t)*$$

Now we do have to discuss this kind of algebra a little bit. Mathematically it is dignified by a name which is higher in the categories of
prestige: it is called "analysis." It contains two ideas. The first is contained in the equals sign, and this means that whenever we make ourselves put in exactly the right numbers, the number we put for P will be
the same number we put for $f(t)$. We picked a rather hard illustration
(but one not obviously involved with physical science); we can take a
much easier one. The area, which we will represent by A, of a room is
related to the length of the side of the room. If the room is square, and
we represent the length of the side by s, we have

$$A = s^2.$$

If the room is 10 feet long, the right-hand side of the equation is 100.
Now if we measure the area of the room directly, by putting down tiles,

---

* Whenever the letter f precedes something in parentheses the meaning is understood to
be "function of" and not to be "algebraically multiplied by." We will discuss this
whole process at length on pp. 23–25. We read the above as "P is a function of t."

each of area one square foot, we will find that we can cover the floor with exactly 100 of them. Thus the two numbers are equal, and they must be if the equals sign is there. Notice that the physicist and the algebra teacher have rather different attitudes toward that equals sign. The teacher goes ahead and puts it in. The physicist is quite tense about it, and he will consider that if you can put an equals between two things which are represented by numbers, then you must know a great deal about what goes on and must under no circumstances treat it casually. To him, an equation is not a rather trivial relationship, but it borders on an intimate knowledge of the character of Nature, for which he has great respect.

The second idea in the equation between population and time is the notation $f(t)$. It means that for any time you care to mention, the knowledge of that time guarantees that you also know the population. If you have been given the mathematical form for the relationship expressed by $f(t)$, then all you have to do to find out the value of the population in 1888 or 2100 is to obey the rules of the mathematical form. This idea, that once you have measured something and expressed it as a number, you are also able to see if that number is related to something else expressed as a number, is the basic idea of theoretical science. It is so basic to a scientist that he finds it hard to realize that it may be a new idea to non-scientists. And yet this method of describing Nature *is* really new: it is scarcely 300 years old, and it really did not have any great success until the latter part of the nineteenth century. In a strange sequence of discovery, this successful development was followed shortly by a need to renounce the very use of the method in order to make any advance. This requirement of atomic physics will be part of what we discuss later. For now, we call attention to the fact that we believe that natural phenomena show relationships, and that many of them can be expressed mathematically.

It would be much too detached from normal concepts if we left the matter just there. The reader must be wondering what that $f(t)$ business is. It is, in truth, not a hard idea, but it can be greatly confused by the symbolism of mathematics and the fact that explanations are almost bound to be dull and hence hard to pay attention to, so that many people tend to give up and not think about it. To do so, as far as we are concerned, would be fatal, so we must get some concept of what is meant by a "function." Let us first try to describe it in a very particular way. In the table below we give figures for the population of the United States, starting in 1790. We have elected to measure time from 1790, so that for that year we call the value of t, our symbol for time, zero; and we add progressively to make 1800 a value of 10 and so on. In the last column of the table we give a set of values of something involving a very little algebra. We have chosen $3,900,000 + 5,900t^2$ as a mathematical relation which will also represent the population of the United States. No great care was taken to make this relation the very best we could find, because, almost certainly, we would have found that to get a perfect fit we would have needed something quite complicated.

Year	Time (t)	Population (P)	$3,900,000 + 5,900t^2$
1790	0	3,900,000	3,900,000
1800	10	5,300,000	4,500,000
1810	20	7,200,000	6,300,000
1820	30	9,600,000	9,200,000
1830	40	12,900,000	13,300,000
1840	50	17,100,000	18,600,000
1850	60	23,200,000	25,100,000
1860	70	31,400,000	32,700,000
1870	80	39,800,000	41,600,000
1880	90	50,200,000	51,500,000
1890	100	62,900,000	62,900,000
.	.	.	.
.	.		.
.	.	.	
1960	170	178,400,000	175,000,000

What the last column signifies is that if the elapsed time after 1790 is multiplied by itself, and that number is then multiplied by 5,900 and added to the population at the start, which is 3,900,000, we find a number which is rather close to the actual population of the United States. Actually, if we realize that the number 5,900 was obtained from the first 100 years, and then see what it predicts for 1960, the prediction is not at all bad. So, as armchair demographers, the name for population experts, we feel that if you wish to say that the population is a function of time then we have found a mathematical expression which is rather close to that function—and it is $3,900,000 + 5,900t^2$.

Notice two important things about what we have just said. The first is that the mathematical expression is not perfect; it does not tell us the exact truth about the population. This is very common in the early stages of seeking to find how something natural can be described mathematically. For example, Copernicus suggested, at first, that the earth and the other planets move in circles around the sun. His description of where they were to be seen at any time, which resulted from this mathematical representation of their motion, was not perfectly accurate: as we already know, the paths of the planets are ellipses, not circles. Nevertheless, the first suggestion is often very full of meaning, even though it may need to be improved later. Our simple analysis shows that the factors at work in determining the population are the number of people there to start with: 3,900,000, the fact that the number seems to depend on the square of the time, which needs some thought, and the actual factor of increase, which is 5,900. The reader will promptly see one missing factor, which is the rate of death, which ought to bring in a negative term. If he is so minded, it would not be too hard for him to improve on our "function" by modifying it to have such a negative term.

The second important thing about our function is that it is indeed true that for every value of the time there is a corresponding value of the population it expresses. This is the prime requirement of a function.

There is a completely different way of describing this property of relationship, and it is highly prized by physicists. This is by the means of a line, whose form, or shape, shows the nature of the relationship. The line is part of a "graph," and the plotting of graphs is one of the most respectable activities of a physical scientist. In a rather small department of this University, the Biophysics Department, the research workers consume about 50 sheets of graph paper daily. Most of the graphs plotted seem to mean something—though by no means all, which is one of the hazards of research.

The trick used in plotting out a relationship is to represent one of the factors by a line drawn vertically, and the other factor by a line drawn horizontally. We often refer to the vertical line as being the "y axis," or more esoterically, the "ordinate," and the horizontal line as the "x-axis," or the "abscissa." The axes are not very important: they are primarily starting places and guidance lines. What has to be done in plotting the relationship is to mark a point in which *both* the factors have been allowed to have their values, and to do this many times at different points until a line appears.

Now we are well aware that the above paragraph is obscure. This is with deliberate intent, because the reader is about to see how very simple it is once the picture and not the words make impact on his mind. In the meantime, we have introduced some very impressive words, which he can, if he wishes, let drop in the presence of experts in physical science and perhaps produce a slight impression. (Actually even hardened physical scientists are often quite insecure about which is the "ordinate" and which the "abscissa," and we only introduce them here so that they will be found in the index. The experts can consult them surreptitiously, to remind them which is which, like the Admiral who carried around the sheet of paper with "starboard—right" on it.)

If the reader will glance at Figure 2.2, he can see the figures for population plotted in the way described above. (Because this process of plot-

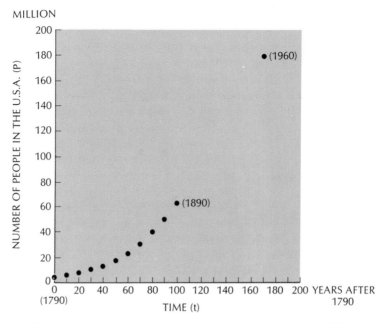

Fig. 2.2. Dots representing population of the United States at different times.

ting one thing in relation to another is so very important, we have included an account in Chapter 14 which goes into the process much more
than we do here, and in which some opportunity is given for practice in
this technique of plotting.) In Figure 2.2 we have measured off a length
which bears a direct proportion to the number of people in the United
States, and set this length up on the graph at the place corresponding to
the appropriate year. The result is a series of dots, which obviously go
in a rather definite progression. We have intentionally left out the years
from 1880 to 1960 and have included the one dot for 1960 at the upper
right. To a physical scientist, these dots are much more than an array of
marks on a page. The first thing he sees is that they are regular, with a
uniformly sweeping rise. The next thing he does is to inquire whether
there is any reason why there should not be quite equivalent information
between the dots. If he is told that the population was increasing steadily
during the year, then he immediately wants to draw a line through the
dots, as has been done in Figure 2.3. Now he says that with this line, as
properly plotted, he can tell you the population of the United States at
any time you may say, so long as it is not too much prior to 1780 or too
far beyond 1960. In other words, to him the line represents the function,
just as the mathematical relation did previously. To the physicist, the

first thing to do with almost any information of this kind (which he calls data) is to plot it to see if there is a significant relationship to be found. If he decides that there is, the second thing to do is to see if he can find a mathematical relation which will be the same as the line which he has drawn. Almost half of all physical reseach follows this pattern.

While we are about it, we can get two more words into the index. If the population is to be deduced from the line for times *within* the dates of measurement it is called "interpolation." If it is to be deduced *beyond* these dates, for example, for 1980 or 1770, it is called "extrapolation." Interpolation is respectable but a bit banal. Extrapolation is daring, but often very interesting, as can be seen by extrapolating to 2200 A.D. (1,000,000,000).

To complete this brief discussion, or rather, to move away from it, as we have said all we need to say, we point out that when we say that one thing is a function of another, we mean that the two are quantitatively interdependent and that we expect to be able to represent the interdependence either by a mathematical expression or by a line on a graph.

The reader who has been exposed to some algebra (and who has not?)

Fig. 2.3. Line joining dots representing population of the United States. The line suggests that there is a functional relation between time and population.

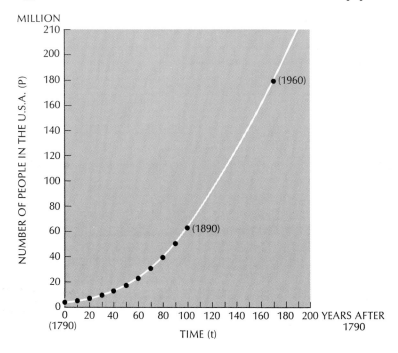

will be wondering when we are going to say something about equations
and the strange manipulations that seem to make sense out of them. The
manipulations are not strange, but like so many mathematical operations,
are simply further glimpses of the obvious. Thus it is clear that if we have
some things equal and we add the same thing to both the resulting complex is still mutually equal. The same holds for subtraction, multiplication, division, etc. This is all that is involved in the manipulation of
equations. We are much more interested in trying to say something about
why one should manipulate at all. Probably, if we had really good
mathematically adapted minds, we would think all the manipulation a
great waste of time because we would see the conclusion from the start
directly. However, because we don't we have to learn to apply some
simple rules to make the conclusion become apparent. This is called
"solving" an equation. Suppose we have the statement that the width of
a room plus a five-foot hallway is 30 feet. In mathematics, this would be
expressed by an equation as follows. If w is the width of the room, then

$$w + 5 = 30.$$

The authors are in the position of being skilled in mathematics, and they
can easily form a picture of the width of the room. But one not so skilled
might easily find the above equation to be very obscure. The mathematician then suggests that if there is trouble, why not simply take 5
away from both sides of the equation?

$$w + 5 - 5 = 30 - 5$$

or $$w = 25$$

It is now clear that the room is 25 feet wide. In some measure this always
the purpose of manipulating algebraic statements. In reality there is no
such thing as the "solution" of an equation. The equation automatically
carries the fact of the solution in it, and it is only to bring to our biologi-
cally evolved brains the simple meaning of the mathematics that we are
concerned with solution at all. Obviously our brains do need help, but at
the same time it is quite true that there is no magic nor any mystery in
the manipulations which bring this help. And though the reader needs
no magic, he emphatically needs a kind of low cunning. We want to
assure him that the lack of this property does not mean that he has missed
out on some vital genetic endowment: it almost certainly means that he
didn't get much fun out of mathematics when he first tried it, and lost
interest before long. We don't intend to do more than arouse a faint
spark of interest, because it isn't necessary, but we do want the reader
to know why the things said in equations are not always left alone, and
what the processes of manipulating them really are.

THE NATURE OF MATHEMATICAL EXPRESSIONS

To understand physical science, and to have any love for it, requires some understanding of the meaning of mathematical expressions. This is often a great stumbling block, and is the first point at which many quite well educated people give up. Just as a non-artist may recoil from the requirements of color sense or composition put on him by an art instructor, or the non-musician recoil from the word "tonic," so the non-scientist recoils from formulas. It is natural: nobody likes to commit a great deal of intensive effort to something which may well result in an abortive attempt to gain a skill, and reluctance is to be expected. It is our job to show that, unlike the art and musical analogues, the effort required for the necessary understanding of mathematical expressions is not great and the acquisition of the skill is certain.

The above statement would not be true if all civilized educated systems did not include quite a bit of training in arithmetic. Whether we liked it or not, we had this training and we do not expect to be able to live without using it some of the time. We might as well take advantage of it to develop the ability to tell the difference between mathematical formulas. Actually, using our training in the way we are going to suggest is about the one pleasant use of arithmetic to anyone (other than an accountant) and it may conceivably remove a bit of the dullness from that subject. In any event, we must try to get the reader to go along with us for the next few paragraphs or so.

Here are four relationships. We write them as equations, to make them look like the expressions which will show up later.

$$y = s + t; \quad y = st; \quad y = \frac{s}{t}; \quad y = st^2.$$

We don't believe in being unnecessarily vague about these formulas, so we are going to say that by s we mean a distance, and by t we mean a time. Some of our readers may be able to look at these formulas and see that they are all completely different: to those happy mortals we may have little to say. On the other hand, experience with very good students has taught us that nearly half of them look at all four of these as though they are *just the same*. They aren't and it is one of the properties of numbers that the differences are vast. We can remind the reader of Mr. Micawber's famous remark: "Annual income twenty pounds, annual expenditure nineteen, nineteen six, result happiness. Annual expenditure twenty pounds ought and six, result misery. The blossom is blighted, the leaf is withered, the God of day goes down upon the dreary scene, and— and in short you are forever floored." Mr. Micawber is really discussing a relatively trivial difference, that between "y" being positive or negative, even though in small amount, and the result goes all the way from happiness to misery. So these four formulas are *not* all the same. Let us look at them in a very simple but quite legal way. Suppose s to be 4 and t to be 2. For the moment we will forget that both these have units, like feet or seconds. Now the first will require that $y = 4 + 2$, or 6; the second that $y = 4 \times 2$, or 8; the third that $y = 4/2$, or 2; and the fourth that $y = 4 \times 2 \times 2$, or 16. If these were to be our annual salary in thousands of dollars, the difference in the results would not seem trivial at all: clearly the difference between happiness and misery is there.

However, it won't do to conclude that the fourth formula is the one to give big numbers. Suppose we change things a bit, just by making $t = 1/10$. We can keep s the same. Now we have to face the only difficult piece of arithmetic we need in this whole book: we have to remind ourselves what happens when we divide by something less than one. It isn't simple, but we can figure it out. Let us take the third formula;

$$y = \frac{4}{\frac{1}{10}}$$

It looks queer. However we do remember from the long-ago days that when we multiply the top and bottom of a fraction by the same number we do not change the fraction. Let us do this, and let us be bright about it. Let us multiply by 10, top and bottom. Then we get

$$y = \frac{4 \times 10}{10 \times \frac{1}{10}}$$

and if we look at the bottom, we see that $10 \times 1/10$ is 1, so that we have eliminated the wretched thing that we didn't know what to do with. We thus wind up with the simple result that $y = 40$. What we see is that division by a number smaller than one gives us a bigger number, a surprise, but that is what the rules of arithmetic, which are also the rules of algebra, require.

Now we see that the four results for y are

$$y = 4 + \tfrac{1}{10} = 4\tfrac{1}{10}$$

$$y = 4 \times \tfrac{1}{10} = \tfrac{4}{10}$$

$$y = 4 \div \tfrac{1}{10} = 40$$

$$y = 4 \times \tfrac{1}{10} \times \tfrac{1}{10} = \tfrac{4}{100}$$

Once again, they are all different, and this time the fourth gave us the least, and the third the most. Sharpening it emotionally by relating it to our annual salary, the difference is quite big.

Perhaps now we have convinced the reader that the four formulas are different, but in doing so we can hardly have added to his or her mental security. Oddly enough, as teachers we prefer it that way, just as a musician will feel happier if his pupil at least knows that a violin and a viola aren't the same, even if he can't tell them apart, because he can at least *talk* about them and make sense. But we don't intend to leave it there. Each of these four expressions has a certain character: let us see if we can deduce it, or if we do not like that seemingly precise word "deduce," simply "observe" it. The first is very simple: we just take the two numbers and total them. The y will just grow with the numbers. In the second, third, and fourth, one number imposes a sort of quality on the other, and for that reason they are really quite different. In the second t imposes its own nature on s. If t is small, then it makes y smaller than it might have been. If t is large, then it magnifies the effect of s. In the third, t imposes a kind of opposite of itself on s. If t is small, then it makes the result bigger, as we say above; if it is big then the result is smaller. We often speak of this as "reciprocal to," or "inversely proportional to." The fourth imposes an intensified character of t on the result. If t is big, then t^2 is huge and the value of y is huge; or if t is tiny, then its square is minute and the result is liable to be minute.

The crucial skill here is that added or subtracted things are really separate, while multiplied or divided things impose on each other. Really knowing just that, and being a little patient with any one formula, is all that is necessary as far as our material will be concerned. The whole of physical science requires more, but not really twice more.

Whether we have made good on our claim that "the acquisition of the skill is certain," may be questioned, but we would like to challenge the reader at this point. Is not the very certainty of acquisition of that skill the factor which induces the daydreaming as the page is read? Is it not really true that putting in numbers and finding y can be done by anybody?

Now we have two more remarks to make, and they are related. First, what we really ask the reader to do is to get some idea in his mind of the way these expressions will work—not in actual numbers, but in what we have to call "behavior." A formula with a square or a cube in it will be "lively" with regard to that thing. A formula with distance squared on the bottom will be terribly lively about distance if the distances are tiny, as they are in atoms. (To help the reader with this kind of so-called "intuitive" feeling for formulas, we have included material in Chapter 14). Second, the numbers have units—an item we agreed to forget at the start. Because the numbers have units, so will y have units, and the units will differ for each expression. We are going to go heavily for concept and not for calculation, so we play down this feature of mathematical relations. We do want to remind the reader that it can be most important. Later on we will have a considerable discussion of units, and of calculations in general.

Calculus

Physical science has turned out to be dominated by the study of *changing things*. The reader must have thought, when we were looking at the statistics of population, that we were being very aloof and formal about it, for it is obvious that the essence of a population is birth and death, both of which are dramatic change, and yet we showed only a formula (clearly not the best) and a line on a graph. The algebra we have so far discussed is tantalizing, for while it is most convenient and informative, and can be used, with some subterfuge, to describe change, it really lacks the very essentials necessary to include a study of change. There are two additions to the scheme of algebra which permit it to be extended to include such change, and when they are included they provide a thinking technique of great power which has made a huge difference to physical science. The two additions are really part of one idea, but we will treat them separately. They are called the Differential Calculus and the Integral Calculus, and the idea they have in common is known as the idea of a Limit.

Suppose we think about a definite case. We shall shortly find we have to go through the history of the emergence of this study, so we will anticipate a little. Suppose we have to know the speed at an instant, to see if it is dependent on something else. In our minds there is no trouble about this, because we know that we measure speed in miles per hour. Even with the precision of these physicists, all we have to do is to measure how far the object has gone, and how long it took. Then, we suppose, you divide the distance gone by the time, and that ought to satisfy anyone. This is correct, but it has a catch. If the speed is changing very considerably, as it does with a jet at a takeoff, or a falling body, it is going to be necessary to measure the distance gone in very short times, or it will be meaningless to our study. We can do it, and when we do we find that we have to divide a very small number, the distance gone, by a very small time. This is quite legal, but there comes a time when we ask the question, what is the speed at an instant? An instant which is no time at all? Watching the jet take off, we know that there is meaning to the speed at an instant, for the jet certainly doesn't proceed in a series of sudden jerks. So we turn to our mathematics and find to our dismay that the very useful structure of algebra cannot handle this case. To divide by zero invites disaster. Try even getting close to it. Divide 10 by 1: you get 10. Divide by 0.1: you get 100. Divide by 0.01: you get 1,000 and this isn't even close to zero. Dividing by zero would give a meaninglessly large number. Don't divide by zero.

This doesn't bother a mathematician. He makes the rules, so he obeys them. But it is very frustrating for a physicist. We have already said that we know that a car, or a jet, which has a changing speed, must have a speed at any instant, and so the process of dividing by something very close to zero itself must be able to tell us something definite. Yet the mathematician starts to look worried if we say that we can find a speed at any one time, and not over an interval near that time, because the dread forbidden operation of division by zero seems to be involved and this is OUT.

The calculus—more correctly for this problem the differential calculus —overcomes this problem. It adds one more operation to algebra: the idea of a limit. These seven operations—addition, subtraction, multiplication, division, raising to a power, extracting a root, and the limit— comprise the scheme of mathematics which has been basic in science from the time of Newton to the present.

THE IDEA OF A LIMIT

In the example we just used, a fixed number, 10, was divided by smaller and smaller numbers and the result became bigger and bigger. In this case, only one number was controlled. The other, 10, was fixed. But suppose both were controlled, as would be the case of the jet taking off, or a car accelerating or the population of the United States increasing. Taking the example of measuring the speed of a jet, we can suppose that we arrange to take pictures of the jet at shorter and shorter intervals and to measure how far it has gone between pictures. As the time between pictures gets less, the distance the jet has moved on the runway also gets less, so that both are controlled.

The idea of a limit expresses the fact that the ratio of two numbers is somehow controlled by circumstances so that it stays the same, regardless of how small both of them become. The words "controlled by circumstances" can easily be seen to be intimately concerned with whether the two numbers are related or not. If there is no relation between them —as for example, if one number were the temperature in New York and the other the number of cattle moving west in Montana—it would not be expected that the ratio of a small change in temperature in New York divided by a small change in the cattle moving west would have any sort of fixed value. But if they *were* related—for example, as the temperature in New York and the shortness of temper of New York taxicab drivers are—this could easily be expected to yield a fixed value to the ratio.

It is possible that this idea may present no problem to the reader. There is all the difference in the world between dividing a fixed number by a progressively smaller number and dividing two progressively smaller numbers one by the other. We hope that this aspect strikes the reader and he relaxes. If not, we will go into it much more in the Appendix. Here we will give one simple example and then go on with physical science.

In Figure 2.4 we show a graph of the temperature in University Park, Pennsylvania. It is an averaged graph, for the weather is quite variable there, but it is still useful. It is rather interesting, showing the steep rise in spring and the steep drop in fall. Now suppose we want to know the change in temperature per month. We can find this quite easily. In April, for example, it is $54° - 38°$, or $16°$, and in June it is $74° - 66°$, or $8°$. Now someone might ask, what is the daily change in average temperature? To find this one might divide by 30 (both months have 30 days) and get 16/30 for April and 8/30 for June. But our inquiring friend might then look at the graph and say that toward the end of June the temperature hardly changes, while at the start it is changing almost like April. He will not like the answer we gave. So now we ask him to specify the particular day he is interested in. Now we look carefully at the graph and pick a day or two before and a day or two after, read off the temperature difference and divide by the number of days. Suppose he said June 28. Here is a table of the figures we might get.

Fig. 2.4. The average temperature in University Park, Pennsylvania, plotted against the time of year. The derivative of temperature with respect to time is required for June 28.

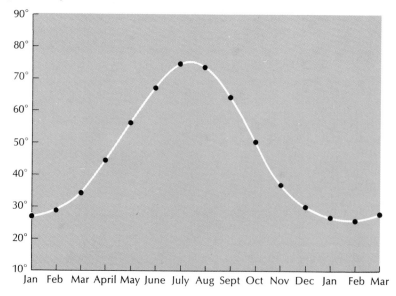

Whole Month   June 20-July 6   June 26-June 30   June 27-June 29

30 days   16 days   4 days   2 days
8/30, or 0.265°F.   2/16, or 0.125°F.   0.45/4, or 0.112°F.   0.22/2, or 0.110°F.

What we see is that reducing the time interval to bracket the date gives numbers which get closer to the one we believe. We notice that the division involves two numbers:

$$\frac{8}{30} \; ; \; \frac{2}{16} \; ; \; \frac{0.45}{4} \; ; \; \frac{0.22}{2}$$

and that the ratio comes down progressively to 0.110. What we assert is that even though we make the time interval (and hence the temperature interval) as short as we like, *this ratio will not alter,* except in a trivial way (0.112 to 0.110, for example). When this happens, we call the figure which does not alter the *limit.*

The differential calculus establishes the rules for working with such limits. The name for the limit of a ratio taken like this is the *derivative.* We propose to return to this topic more than once; next, however, we will discuss Galileo's work on falling bodies.

Suggestions for Further Thought

1. The following list defines Roman numerals in terms of the familiar Hindu-Arabic notation:

Hindu-Arabic	1	5	10	50	100	500	1000
Roman numerals	I	V	X	L	C	D	M

   a. Add MDCLXIV to CCCXXXVI.
   b. Subtract CCLXLVI from DCCLXXXIII.
   c. How would you do division using Roman numerals?
   d. How would you express fractional parts in Roman numerals?
   e. How would you express zeros in Roman numerals?

2. In the physical sciences a method frequently used to discover relationships between experimental variables (cause and effect) is the graphical method. Expressing experimental data in the form of a graph gives a pictorial view of the results and makes it possible to interpret the data more quickly. The following set of numbers is a table of experimental data where x represents the independent variable (cause) and y the dependent variable (effect).

x	0.1	0.2	0.5	1	2	3
y	10	5	2	1	0.5	0.33

a. Plot y along the ordinate (vertically) against x along the abscissa (horizontally). What is the form of the resulting graph? Can you really determine the relation between x and y from this graph?

b. Plot y along the ordinate against $1/x$ along the abscissa. What is the form of the resulting graph? What is the relation between x and y? Is plotting y against $1/x$ more advantageous in this example than plotting y against x?

3. For each of the following lists of data plot y against x. Then try to obtain a straight line graph by plotting y against some function of x. For each case express the relation between y and x.

a.

x	0.1	0.2	0.5	1	2	
y	100	25	4	1	0.25	

b.

x	100	49	25	4	1	0.25
y	10	7	5	2	1	0.5

c.

x	1	2	3	4		
y	1	4	9	16		

4. The results of a particular experiment show that the relation between x and y has the following form:

$$y = ax + b$$

where a and b are constants.

a. Set b equal to zero and plot graphs of y against x for a equals 1, a equals 2, a equals 4, a equals -1, and a equals -2.

b. Set a equal to 1 and plot graphs of y against x for the case b equals -2, b equals 0, b equals 2, and b equals 3.

Is the form of the graph altered by varying a? By varying b? What effect does a have? What effect does b have?

5. Scatter ten toothpicks (or matchsticks) at random over a large piece of paper on which parallel lines have been ruled just one toothpick length apart. Count the number of toothpicks that cross lines on the paper. Calculate the ratio of 2 times the total number of toothpicks to the number of toothpicks crossing lines. Repeat the operation for 20 toothpicks, 40 toothpicks, 80 toothpicks, 100 toothpicks. Statistical theory predicts that the most probable value of this ratio is π and only by tossing larger numbers of toothpicks does the ratio approach π. Describe how this exercise illustrates the concept of a limit.

References

T. Dantzig (ed.), *Number, the Language of Science,* (Garden City, N. Y.: Doubleday & Co., 1956).

Godfrey H. Hardy, *A Mathematician's Apology,* rev. ed. (New York: Cambridge University Press, 1967).

L. Hogben, *Mathematics for the Million,* 3rd ed. (New York: W. W. Norton & Co., 1951).

3
Falling Bodies

The most developed, best understood, most used, and most respected branch of physical science is mechanics. It was developed by many, notably Aristotle, Galileo, Newton, Lagrange, D'Alembert, Hamilton, and Einstein. In its modern form, when it began to become of real use, it began with the study of falling bodies by *Galileo*.

Galileo himself, as a person, seems of a familiar type to anyone who knows contemporary scientists. One can somehow imagine Enrico Fermi,* a quiet, skeptical, intensely alive, clear thinking, accurately imaginative person, who was associated with the first successful man-made nuclear chain reaction, as being rather like Galileo. Galileo was one of the first human beings to experience the pleasure of performing consistently repeated experiments that revealed a uniform behavior. That he wanted to share his pleasure with others is obvious from his writings; that he could enjoy that pleasure only while also arousing controversy with others must have been one of his sorrows.

To understand the world in which Galileo began his work it is important to make some remarks about Aristotle. To make any kind of assessment of Aristotle as a scientist is very hard. He lived twenty-three centuries ago. He combined great and influential intellectual power in the areas of physics, of biology, and of literary criticism, all of which he can fairly be said to have originated, at least in a form related to their present form. In addition, he was the tutor of Alexander the Great. Aristotle can be said to have conceived the idea of the University. It is not surprising that he should have had great and lasting influence, though the authors suspect that some of this influence was of a kind he would not have desired. Aristotle, in setting up the fields of study, and

---

* A biography by Laura Fermi, *Atoms in the Family,* makes delightful reading.

in writing on them himself, clearly wanted the study to go deeper: he did not want his writings to become a kind of philosophical dogma. It seems impossible to believe that Aristotle would have been more than normally skeptical if he had been presented with Galileo's studies: It is much easier to believe that he would have enthusiastically adopted all of Galileo's ideas. Yet Aristotle's writings *did* become dogma. Because he wrote of Nature in a way which seemed rational, with no superficial surprises, and because he was clearly an individual who combined the arts and sciences in one, his ideas were extended and adopted by medieval philosophers, and formed the core of the influential school of thought known as *Scholasticism*. To the Scholastics, Aristotle was "the philosopher." The teachings of the Scholastics were held to reconcile philosophy and medieval, dogmatic religion, and there was then no question about the underlying authoritarianism of their teachings. It is interesting that almost no more solid evidence of the essential eclipse of science during this period could be found than the long existence of this authoritarian approach. Science does, indeed, have very influential figures, and their opinions are respected to the extent of delaying acceptance of some change, but in modern times the delays have been measured in years, at most, not centuries, and today, when science is intensely active, the delay introduced by the opposition of some eminent man usually lasts no longer than weeks. Even then, the net effect of this kind of challenge by opposition is usually to spur skeptics to reason or experiment, and generally there is no delay at all. The authors can remember more than one episode in which the plan and execution of an experiment were undertaken to show someone was "wrong." As Galileo started his work, none of this prevailed. To challenge teaching in any but minor ways was to invite reprimand and correction. It is true that by 1550 the climate was changing, and that it did not need science, per se, to start the change, but still enough rigidity remained to make it hard for Galileo to be himself and be secure. Also, how can we know the extent to which Galileo himself was motivated by the desire to prove someone wrong?

Galileo (1564-1642) was educated by the Scholastics at the University of Pisa. Automatically he was taught Aristotle's approach. Aristotle's scheme of Nature, as made of earth, water, air, and fire, gave a qualitative description of many events: thus fire rose to the top, then air, then water, and then earth. The heavier a body, the more earth in it and the more rapidly it sank, i.e. fell. During the time it took a body of ten pounds' weight to fall a certain distance (said Aristotle) a body of one pound's weight would only fall one-tenth as far. People tried it on occasion, and Aristotle was obviously wrong, but nobody seriously challenged the scheme to the extent that Aristotle's teachings were questioned and invalidated. It fell to Galileo to do the questioning and prove the error. He was not popular.

The whole essence of the controversy lay in the rejection of accurate description. Living in the fourth century B.C., Aristotle probably despaired of ever producing a complete philosophical scheme which would fit everything with exactness. In view of the fact that we still don't have it twenty-four centuries later, he can be considered to be justified. In contrast, inherent in Galileo's thought was the idea that to begin accurate description was well worth while, even if many others would have to carry it on and correct it before it came to anything like a comprehensive science. The two men were thus quite different—as were the times in which each lived. Certainly many minds like Galileo's had existed before Galileo, but at the time Galileo worked, humanity was beginning an enormous intellectual advance, and for that reason, as well as because of Galileo's lucid writing, his influence was felt as a permanent effect. Others who were earlier are mostly lost to us.

The Measurement of Time

One may well ask why it took so long to challenge Aristotle. A part of the answer lies in the measurement of short times. Crude clocks existed before Galileo, in which the oscillations of various mechanical systems were used to keep time during the absence of the sun. Galileo had himself noticed that a pendulum (in this case a swinging lantern) swings regularly, and that as the swings grow less in extent, the time for each swing remains the same. He measured the time of oscillation by counting his own pulse—but this is still not of much help in measuring the way in which a body falls freely. We can do it today with relative ease. All we need to have is a good-sized ball bearing, a movie projector, and a camera. The motor and shutter of the movie projector provide a rather accurate series of short illuminations at equal, and short intervals, about $\frac{1}{15}$ second. If we take a photograph of this in the dark, leaving the camera's shutter open while the ball bearing is dropped and is illuminated by the regular flickering of the movie projector, we find that the bright spot made by the reflection of light from the ball bearing appears many times as the ball falls, and the distance gone in the $\frac{1}{15}$ second interval can be seen with great ease. Such a picture is shown in Figure 3.1, and it tells at a glance the kind of motion involved.

Galileo would have given a great deal to have been able to produce a trace like this, which can be obtained in a few minutes at the present time. But because Galileo did not have photographic film, and a bright light that could be accurately flashed at very short intervals of time, he

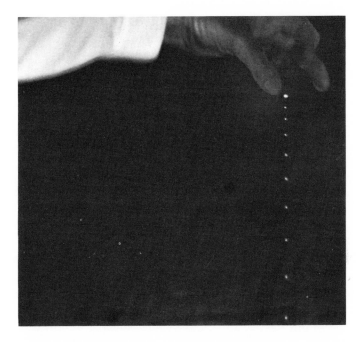

Fig. 3.1. The appearance of a multiple-exposure picture of a falling ball bearing. The ball is illuminated by rapidly occurring bright flashes of light. The ball bearing is going faster as it falls and covers more distance between flashes. We thank Mrs. Bridget Stemberger for technical assistance with this picture.

could not get such a trace. So he had to do what every pioneer experimenter has to do—settle for something much less, and fill in the missing part with hours of careful work, much use of his imagination, and also of his reason. When he had finished, Galileo was perfectly able to construct a drawing of the way an object would appear while falling freely, if observed at intervals of $\frac{1}{15}$ second. Such a drawing would only differ from the picture we show in being rather more accurate, so that the careful experiments he did actually took the place of the modern technique, and perhaps gave him even more insight. Obviously we need to look carefully at what Galileo did, and how he started an experimental study of motion which has led directly to our most respected subject of mechanics.

Galileo's work on falling bodies, and on uniformly accelerated motion, occupied many years of his life. He showed an early interest in mechanics, but this seems to have been secondary to his interest in astronomy, and, as he improved on the telescopes of his time, this is easy to understand.

His telescopic observation led him to believe strongly in the Copernican idea that the sun and not the earth is the center of planetary motion, and he made the mistake of presenting these ideas rather clearly and provocatively in the first of his two major books, *Dialogue on the Two Great World Systems.* This work ran counter to official Church doctrine, and was put on the index of prohibited books; Galileo himself was forced to retract his views on his knees. This brush with authority removed some of Galileo's freedom to work actively in astronomy, and he turned his attention to mechanics, which was less dangerous. In 1638, six years after the publication of his first *Dialogue,* and four years before his death, Galileo published the second of his major works, *Dialogue on Two New Sciences,* which contained both the account of his experiments on falling bodies and the reasoning and conclusions which led to the firm start which he gave to the science of mechanics.

We can pick out, from all Galileo's years of effort, the work most significant for us. These are experiments in which Galileo rolled a very smooth, hard, bronze ball down a long sloping plank, in a shallow groove lined with parchment so as to be smooth. (See Figure 3.2.) In order to measure the time the ball took to go different distances, Galileo used a large vessel full of water, with a narrow pipe soldered to it at the bottom, and he measured the amount of water that flowed while the ball was rolling by collecting it and weighing it.

Fig. 3.2. Representation of Galileo's experiment measuring the time taken for a bronze ball to roll down a groove in a sloping plank. Time was measured by weighing the amount of water that flowed while the bronze ball rolled.

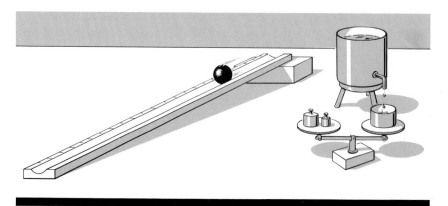

Notice that as we start, with Galileo, to study motion with accuracy, that motion involves both distance and time. To measure time, one must have a usable unit of time, and to have such a unit, either a clock or a stream of water, one must rely on motion (about to be studied) in some form. Thus there is a kind of closed circle which must be broken into, after which it is possible to move forward. One of the perennial problems of scientific study is breaking into such circles. For instance, one major problem which faces us today is to understand how the living cell works, to reduce its behavior to known processes, which we can hopefully duplicate in the laboratory one day. But to study its structure, we have to destroy it in some way. This is a modern closed circle and somehow we must break into it.

One way of breaking into it is to try a hypothesis and see if it works. Galileo evidently spent much effort on the problem of measuring time. We know that he used his pulse as a timing device to show that a lantern swinging in church kept the same time for each swing as the extent of its movement diminished. This suggested the pendulum to him as a method of measuring the steady passage of time, and we use it today. But to measure the time the rolling ball took to travel a certain distance he used another technique. Galileo supposed that the flow of water from a large tank through a small opening was uniform and steady. In these experiments, as Galileo observed the behavior of the rolling ball he found that his supposition led him to a consistent description of the motion of the ball; and then to freely falling bodies, and other uniformly accelerated motion (such as projectiles); as the consistencies multiplied, his faith in the supposition developed. Of interest is the undoubted fact that Galileo would have respected a skeptic regarding his time measurement, though he would have insisted that the results he found by his water-flow timing were suggestive of a regular uniform behavior. They pointed toward a sensible and simple description of motion and he would say that such a suggestion should be followed.

Falling Bodies: Galileo's Experiment

With the crude timing devices available, Galileo did not attempt to measure accurately how a body fell freely. Instead, as we have already mentioned, he chose to examine how a bronze ball rolled down a very smooth groove in a sloping wooden plank. The sort of experiment he completed (in his own words, hundreds of times) would be represented by the table below:

Time (Arbitrary Units)	Distance (Cubits)
0	0
1	2
2	8
3	18
4	32
5	50
6	72

A glance at the table shows a regular behavior. Galileo examined it. If we make (as he did) a new table giving the distance the ball has gone in each second, we get:

Unit	Cubits
1st	$2 = 2 \times 1$
2nd	$6 = 2 \times 3$
3rd	$10 = 2 \times 5$
4th	$14 = 2 \times 7$
5th	$18 = 2 \times 9$
6th	$22 = 2 \times 11$

Thus the distance gone in each second is related to the successive odd numbers. This regularity delighted Galileo. It is not surprising that he repeated the experiment hundreds of times.

The above is by no means the only way to analyze Galileo's data. In fact, one of the features of scientific study is the process of subjecting data to various methods of analysis. If the observations are really indicative of some true order which is part of Nature, there will be more than one way in which this order can become apparent. One should be suspicious when anyone claims that there is only one way to examine and interpret observations about natural behavior. Another way to analyze Galileo's figure is as follows: try dividing the distance gone by the square of the time. Then we get the results shown in the following table:

Time	Time ^{2}	Distance	Distance/Time ^{2}
0	0	0	–
1	1	2	2
2	4	8	2
3	9	18	2
4	16	32	2
5	25	50	2
6	36	72	2

The number in the last column is always 2; it is constant. So Galileo would say, for this experiment, that

$$\text{Distance}/\text{Time}^2 = 2.$$

Since we have stressed the value of the use of abstract thinking in science, we shall use one symbol for distance and another for time. Call distance s and time t. Then we get

$$s/t^2 = 2.$$

We can reduce the above statement to a very simple form:

$$s = 2t^2.\text{*}$$

We now need to follow Galileo farther. He carefully established the relation for one angle of tilt of the parchment-lined groove. Next he changed the angle. Suppose it to be greater. Then the following figures could result:

Time	Time ^{2}	Distance	Distance/Time ^{2}
0	0	0	3.6
1	1	3.6	3.6
2	4	14.4	3.6
3	9	32.4	3.6
4	16	57.6	3.6
5	25	90.0	3.6
6	36	129.6	3.6

---

* If we multiply both sides by t^2, which is a perfectly respectable number, and since multiplying equals by equals does not disturb the fact that the original relationship was an equality, we get:

$$(s/t^2) \times t^2 = 2t^2, \quad \text{and because } \frac{t^2}{t^2} = 1, \quad s = 2t^2.$$

For this case the equation is

$$s = 3.6t^2.$$

The greater angle has not changed the form of the motion: it has changed the rapidity with which it expresses itself. Galileo tried many angles and he found the same result to be true for them all—that the form of the motion is the same though the rapidity may alter.

We cannot resist an aside at this stage. Many of our readers will be able to perform the little mathematical manipulation above without trouble. Others will stop focusing their eyes on the page as they read. Some will see the purpose of mathematics in physics illustrated in this very simple example. Once one mathematical relationship is derived by a careful study of some natural event, then a scrupulously careful use of mathematics can be used to deduce many relationships, all of which will be true. There is thus a great deal of economy of effort in this use of mathematics, and for this reason no physical scientist can possibly afford to be without some mathematical skill and, more particularly, a respect for those with such skill. Because this is so we introduce mathematics in our treatment, both for its own sake, and for the chance the reader gets to see how it operates.

Another way to analyze the data we have is to plot a graph. We do this in Figure 3.3(a). Let us put distance vertically (the ordinate) and time horizontally (the abscissa). The result is a nice regular curve. In fact, it is part of a parabola. Or we can plot distance versus (time)². This is shown in Figure 3.3(b). The result is a straight line, the simplest form of a graph, and one which has great significance to a physicist. If he can devise any way to present his data in such a way as to give a straight line plot, he feels a great sense of accomplishment, for he knows that he has not only found something very regular, which delights him, just as it did Galileo, but he also feels that he is close to being able to understand the regularity, and perhaps even explain it.

All these methods and even many more are useful. Today we have a tradition of understanding about such ways of making tables and plotting graphs; and would quickly move to the next stage. It took Galileo longer, but he did it.

Velocity and Acceleration

Galileo could see that the rolling ball behaved in a regular way. The distance gone didn't seem to him to be the simplest feature of the motion, however. He began to wonder if measuring speed wouldn't show up something even simpler than the regular motion which he seemed to

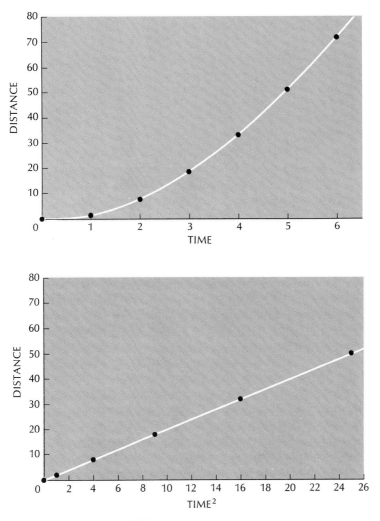

Fig. 3.3. A plot of data in a rolling ball experiment. In (a) distance versus time is shown, a regular but curved graph. In (b) the time is squared, which stretches the points so as to produce a straight line.

have found. To find the speed (or velocity, which is almost the same thing in the early stages of thought) it is necessary to consider distance gone divided by time. We can rush headlong into this very easily. Take the figures already given in the second table above and plot a graph relating distance gone in any second versus the starting time of that second. The graph is shown in Figure 3.4(a), (b), and (c). The result is very

Fig. 3.4. The distance gone in one second plotted against time. It is a straight line, but it cannot start at zero because the time of measurement is too long. By dividing the time into many short intervals, as seen in 3.4(b), and plotting the distance gone in one third of a second divided by the time, the initial starting point is closer to zero. Finer division reduces the discrepancy even more.

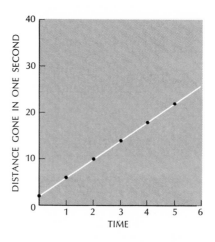

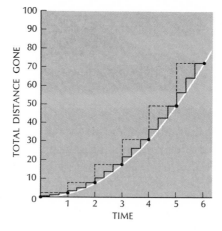

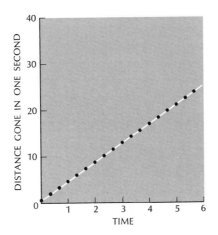

Continued Fig. 3.4 (c).

nice—the distance per second increases very regularly with the time. The ball is going steadily faster. This relationship is certainly significant and obviously our intuition that speed rather than distance was the item about motion to think about is good.

There is something a bit disquieting to worry us before we can relax, something very small at first glance, but since it contains an absurdity we have to think about it. This trouble is the way our graph is plotted at zero time. We know that the ball starts with no speed, and yet on our graph we have treated it as having some speed, namely 2 units of distance per unit of time. The result is nice, but too nice. We could, perhaps, remove the absurdity by picking the halfway point in each interval, but to do so is still something which limits us. We want to be able to look at velocity and time in an untrammeled way.

To see how to remove this discrepancy, let's draw Figure 3.3(a) a little differently, as in 3.4(b). We have taken the time at each second and drawn a series of steps as well as the smooth graph. Our way of finding the distance gone in each unit of time, which we call the speed, has been to take the height of each step and divide it by the width of the step. The resulting number went into the graph of Figure 3.4(a). Perhaps our regular graph, based on these steps (which certainly don't represent the actual behavior of the ball) was a bit lucky and perhaps we should be surprised that an absurdity shows up only near the start. Now we *can* do better. Suppose we made the number of steps 18 instead of six and suppose we again divide the height of each (now shorter) step by the (now smaller) time. We shall find we have 18 points and the discrepancy at the start is much less, as in 3.4(c). We are encouraged to go to still smaller intervals of time, always plotting the ratio distance/time versus time. After a while we realize that we can make this little initial error as small as we like by making the time intervals (and, of course, the distances) as short as we please. When we do this, we find that the graph is a straight line, starting at zero and going up uniformly.

Now this ratio, distance gone/time taken, for very short distances and times, we call velocity. We propose to use the symbol v for it. The straight line graph between v and t tells us that the ratio of v to t, or if the reader prefers it, v divided by t, for this kind of rolling ball is fixed. This means that we write a mathematical relation:

$$\frac{v}{t} = a$$

where a does not change in any one experiment on any fixed sloping ramp. Galileo called a the *acceleration*. He was struck by the very simple nature of the motion, looked at in this way.

In thinking about what we have just written above we perceive a difficulty in communication. This is the well-known difficulty of the person steeped in some particular field of knowledge seeking to convey his feeling for the subject to someone encountering it for the first time. To us, the little relation above is a beautiful thing. And beauty is the right word. But to the reader it may seem to be just something contrived and quite artificial. After all, quite a lot of "juggling" was needed to produce it, and several new terms had to come in before we could even talk about it. The physical scientist brushes aside the suggestion of contrivance, for he sees that all the reasoning and manipulation are done with facts observed about something *natural*. Galileo could not *invent* the figures describing the way the ball rolls. These had to be accepted by him with absolute fidelity and honesty. The physicist does not question the right of an experimenter to examine and analyze his findings, including the mathematical "juggling," so long as there is no interference with the original observations. And if there is found, in the process, something which can be put in a very simple mathematical form, and which works better the more carefully the observations are made, he is truly impressed. Also, because the simple mathematical form does indeed describe something natural, and since we all share Nature, this simple result seems to the physicist to be something not only very beautiful, but also something *given to him* personally. He can use it as a parlor amusement, or to calculate how a meteor falls. Perhaps the one major objective of this book will be lost if none of the sense of beauty in such a simple relation is felt by the reader. He must forgive us if we hammer on the same idea whenever it turns up.

Free Fall

Galileo's findings were made on experiments with sloping planes. He found that as he made the slope steeper the acceleration increased, but for each slope was the same. He then argued that if the slope was increased until it was vertical, the ball would still fall with a fixed acceleration. He thus asserted that freely falling bodies are uniformly accelerated and that the acceleration does not depend on the weight.

Philosophy about Falling Bodies

The analysis of the work of Galileo which we have just presented has a twofold purpose. In the first place, it serves as an example of how a physical problem has been studied and reduced to the minimum effective description. In the second place, the solution of the problem of uniformly accelerated motion, or rather the discovery of the significance of such motion, led to much more penetrating ways of looking at motion. We propose to look at those ways shortly. In the meantime we want to point out to the reader that to follow exactly all the processes of experimentation and of subsequent thought is not nearly as important as seeing the kind of thing that can be done and the kind of "payoff" which results. Galileo thought it exciting and interesting and must have felt surprise that everyone else did not think it so. So must many a painter, writer and musician have felt excitement at their creative work, and also must have felt surprise that everyone else did not always share that excitement. It is a shock to realize that Mozart was considered to be harsh and unmelodious by many in his own time. One of the delightful schools of painting is that of the impressionists. Today they are familiar everywhere and we (most of us) like them and go to see them when we can. Yet when their first exhibition was held in 1867 one critic remarked that their work was the equivalent of a monkey tipping the paintbox. These painters had the advantage of being a group and of having strong loyalties among each other. Galileo, while not having such a group, moved among friends and had associates who would today be classed as "students." His two major publications, *Dialogue on the Two Great World Systems* and *Dialogue on Two New Sciences*, were well received when they were first published, but the established order set out to force the rejection of the work and insisted that Galileo be punished for even thinking about such new ideas. Galileo probably should have known better.

Suggestions for Further Thought

1. Why was the study of falling bodies so important? Indicate what talents Galileo brought to this study, how he went about it, and what major contributions he made.

2. The following graphs illustrate the "history" of motion for a particle traveling in a straight line. State for each graph whether the velocity is positive, negative, or zero and whether the acceleration is positive, negative, or zero in the intervals OA, AB, and AC.

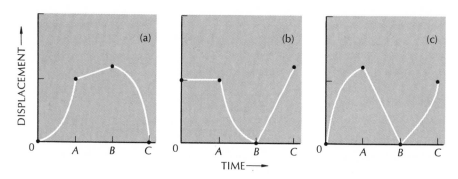

3. The operator of an automobile traveling at 60 m.p.h. (88 ft./sec.) applies the brakes and brings his vehicle to a stop in 4 seconds. Assume that the deceleration was uniform throughout the braking action. Calculate (a) the deceleration and (b) the distance the automobile travels during braking.

4. A stone is thrown horizontally from a cliff 64 ft. high. The initial velocity is 10 ft./sec. How long does it take the stone to strike the ground? How far from the base of the cliff does the stone strike the ground? Explain your solution.

5. Galileo's experiments to measure the time taken for a bronze ball to roll down a groove in a sloping plank are repeated on the planet HT A located in the galaxy A.

   Part of the data are reproduced below. Using these data obtain a straight line graph of displacement x as a function of time t. What is the relation between displacement and the time on the planet HT A? Is the motion uniformly accelerated motion?

x	0	46	65	80	92	103	112
y	0	1	2	3	4	5	6

References

Laura Fermi and Gilberto Bernardini, *Galileo and the Scientific Revolution* (New York: Basic Books, 1961).

Galileo Galilei, *Dialogues Concerning Two New Sciences,* trans. by Henry Crew and Alfonso de Salvio (Evanston, Ill.: Northwestern University Press, 1952).

Galileo Galilei, *The Sidereal Messenger,* trans. by E. S. Carlos (London: Dawsons of Pall Mall, 1960).

Guy C. Omer, Jr., H. L. Knowles, B. L. Mundy, and W. H. Yoho, *Physical Science: Men and Concepts* (Boston: D. C. Heath, 1962).

From "The Sidereal Messenger," by Galileo Galilei, 1610

The Telescope.—About ten months ago a report reached my ears that a Dutchman had constructed a telescope, by the aid of which visible objects, although at a great distance from the eye of the observer, were seen distinctly as if near; and some proofs of its most wonderful performances were reported, which some gave credence to, but others contradicted. A few days after, I received confirmation of the report in a letter written from Paris by a noble Frenchmen, Jacques Badovere, which finally determined me to give myself up first to inquire into the principle of the telescope, and then to consider the means by which I might compass the invention of a similar instrument, which after a little while I succeeded in doing, through deep study of the theory of Refraction; and I prepared a tube, at first of lead, in the ends of which I fitted two glass lenses, both plane on one side, but on the other side one spherically convex, and the other concave. Then bringing my eye to the concave lens I saw objects satisfactorily large and near, for they appeared one-third of the distance off and nine times larger than when they are seen with the natural eye alone. I shortly afterwards constructed another telescope with more nicety, which magnified objects more than sixty times. At length, by sparing neither labour nor expense, I succeeded in constructing for myself an instrument so superior that objects seen through it appear magnified nearly a thousand times, and more than thirty times nearer than if viewed by the natural powers of sight alone.

Discovery of Jupiter's Satellites

—I have now finished my brief account of the observations which I have thus far made with regard to the Moon, the Fixed Stars, and the Galaxy. There remains the matter, which seems to me to deserve to be considered

the most important in this work, namely, that I should disclose and publish to the world the occasion of discovering and observing four Planets,
never seen from the very beginning of the world up to our own times,
their positions, and the observations made during the last two months
about their movements and their changes of magnitude; and I summon
all astronomers to apply themselves to examine and determine their
periodic times, which it has not been permitted me to achieve up to this
day, owing to the restriction of my time. I give them warning, however,
again, so that they may not approach such an inquiry to no purpose,
that they will want a very accurate telescope, and such as I have described
in the beginning of this account.

On the 7th day of January in the present year, 1610, in the first hour
of the following night, when I was viewing the constellations of the
heavens through a telescope, the planet Jupiter presented itself to my
view, and as I had prepared for myself a very excellent instrument, I
noticed a circumstance which I had never been able to notice before,
owing to want of power in my other telescope, namely, that three little
stars, small but very bright, were near the planet; and although I believed
them to belong to the number of the fixed stars, yet they made me somewhat wonder, because they seemed to be arranged exactly in a straight
line, parallel to the ecliptic, and to be brighter than the rest of the
stars, equal to them in magnitude. The position of them with reference
to one another to Jupiter was as follows:

Ori.   *   *   0   *   Occ.

On the east side there were two stars, and a single one towards the
west. The star which was furthest towards the east, and the western
star, appeared rather larger than the third.

I scarcely troubled at all about the distance between them and
Jupiter, for, as I have already said, at first I believed them to be fixed
stars; but when on January 8th, led by some fatality, I turned again
to look at the same part of the heavens, I found a very different state of
things, for there were three little stars all west of Jupiter, and nearer
together than on the previous night, and they were separated from one
another by equal intervals, as the accompanying figure shows.

Ori.   0   *   *   *   Occ.

At this point, although I had not turned my thoughts at all upon the
approximation of the stars to one another, yet my surprise began to be
excited, how Jupiter could one day be found to the east of all the afore-
said fixed stars when the day before it had been west of two of them;
and forthwith I became afraid lest the planet might have moved differently
from the calculation of astronomers, and so had passed those stars by
its own proper motion. I, therefore, waited for the next night with the

most intense longing, but I was disappointed of my hope, for the sky
was covered with clouds in every direction.

But on January 10th the stars appeared in the following position with
regard to Jupiter, the third, as I thought, being hidden by the planet.

Ori.   *   *   0   Occ.

They were situated just as before, exactly in the same straight line with
Jupiter, and along the Zodiac. . . .

When I had seen these phenomena, as I knew that corresponding
changes of position could not by any means belong to Jupiter, and as,
moreover, I perceived that the stars which I saw had always been the
same, for there were no others either in front or behind, within a great
distance, along the Zodiac—at length, changing from doubt into surprise,
I discovered that the interchange of position which I saw belonged not
to Jupiter, but to the stars to which my attention had been drawn, and
I thought therefore that they ought to be observed henceforward with
more attention and precision.

Accordingly, on January 11th I saw an arrangement of the following
kind:

Ori.   *   *   0   Occ.

namely, only two stars to the east of Jupiter, the nearer of which was
distant from Jupiter three times as far as from the star further to the
east; and the star furthest to the east was nearly twice as large as the
other one; whereas on the previous night they had appeared nearly of
of equal magnitude. I, therefore, concluded, and decided unhesitatingly,
that there are three stars in the heavens moving about Jupiter, as Venus
and Mercury round the Sun; which at length was established as clear as
daylight by numerous other subsequent observations. These observations
also established that there are not only three, but four, erratic sidereal
bodies performing their revolutions round Jupiter. . . .

These are my observations upon the four Medicean planets, recently
discovered for the first time by me; and although it is not yet permitted
me to deduce by calculation from these observations the orbits of these
bodies, yet I may be allowed to make some statements, based upon them,
well worthy of attention.

Orbits and Periods of Jupiter's Satellites

—And, in the first place, since they are sometimes behind, sometimes
before Jupiter, at like distances, and withdraw from this planet towards
the east and towards the west only within very narrow limits of diver-
gence, and since they accompany this planet alike when its motion is

retrograde and direct, it can be a matter of doubt to no one that they perform their revolutions about this planet, while at the same time they all accomplish together orbits of twelve years' length about the centre of the world. Moreover, they revolve in unequal circles, which is evidently the conclusion to be drawn from the fact that I have never been permitted to see two satellites in conjunction when their distance from Jupiter was great, whereas near Jupiter two, three, and sometimes all four, have been found closely packed together. Moreover, it may be detected that the revolutions of the satellites which describe the smallest circles round Jupiter are the most rapid, for the satellites nearest to Jupiter are often to be seen in the east, when the day before they have appeared in the west, and contrariwise. Also, the satellite moving in the greatest orbit seems to me, after carefully weighing the occasions of its returning to positions previously noticed, to have a periodic time of half a month. Besides, we have a notable and splendid argument to remove the scruples of those who can tolerate the revolution of the planets round the Sun in the Copernican system, yet are so disturbed by the motion of one Moon around the Earth, while both accomplish an orbit of a year's length about the Sun, that they consider that this theory of the universe must be upset as impossible: for now we have not one planet only revolving about another, while both traverse a vast orbit about the Sun, but our sense of sight presents to us four satellites circling about Jupiter, like the Moon about the Earth, while the whole system travels over a mighty orbit about the Sun in the space of twelve years.

Science and Its Relation to Society

On the surface, societies all over the world impose no restriction on science. Nearly every nation encourages scientific research and in every nation a scientist is accorded respect. But a little below the surface some very strong influences become apparent. That such influences are to be expected should be no surprise because society actually cut off science almost completely for many hundreds of years and really there have only been three hundred years in which freedom of inquiry has been permitted at all. In Oxford, in the Middle Ages, one had to pay a fine (the equivalent of $20) for each statement one made that disagreed with the teachings of Aristotle. These problems of freedom of thought do arise when the scientist finds he has to say things which are not accepted by his society. As recent examples we can quote the removal of security clearance from Oppenheimer and the requirement of recantation imposed on Schrödinger when the Nazis took over Austria.

Thus it is true that unless science and society march together very real problems develop.

In this essay some of the aspects of scientific revolutions and their effects upon society will be considered. These are by no means the only revolutions, nor do they include the intellectual aspect of the revolutions introduced by science: rather they are the more dramatic and striking developments in science which are clearly related to changes in society. The theme of this essay is the coercive aspect of scientific change, change which could nearly always be helpful but which occurs in such a way that it seems to force an adaption. This coercive aspect only results from lag in understanding: people who are eagerly awaiting an advance know how to use it. It is the people who find the advance already upon them, who are unwilling to see change, that recoil into a hostile and conservative attitude. In most cases, but, as we shall see, not all, the advance has come without being awaited and the characteristic resistance has been clearly seen. Such resistance could, one day, be very dangerous and perhaps the truth of this statement may become apparent as we write.

THE REVOLUTION IN ENERGY SOURCES AND THE CONTROL OF ENERGY

Everyone is aware of the Industrial Revolution. With the use of coal for heating, the need for cheap operation of mines developed. The first steam engine, used to keep the mines pumped out, resulted. From the invention of the first crude engine to the creation of a powerful, effective source of power an evolutionary period of only fifty years was needed. To take advantage of this new use of power a whole set of machines now became worth thinking about: steel was needed and made for the ships, railroads, and bridges which were built on an increasing scale. In the United States the Revolutionary War almost preceded this era (1770-1850), and our use of the new technology was relatively smooth and unrelated to any great human struggle for justice and the right to live adequately. Not so in Europe.

In Europe there was no developing frontier, no simple relationship between working on farms and having enough to eat. And so the Industrial Revolution in Europe coincided with vast social change, with political revolution upon revolution. Take England, a relatively mild example, mitigated by an expanding empire. Here the growth of factories for the cotton industry, for ship building, for making all the products of the developing sweep of technology, resulted in a great migration off the farm and into the cities. Cities grew rapidly and cruelly: slums were there almost from the day the rows of houses were completed. Sickness spread and was uncontrolled: for example, the chance of death of the mother after childbirth in city hospitals reached *one in four*.

Water supplies and sewage became severe problems. Uncertainty and misery became widespread. The work of almost every sensitive English writer in the mid nineteenth century reflects this human turmoil, for example, Mrs. Gaskell's *Mary Barton* and, somewhat differently, Dickens' *Hard Times*. The result was that instead of the "golden age" which should have resulted from man's first conquest of the natural sources of power there was poverty and hunger and considerable political agitation of a sharp and desperate nature. This was the great period of parliamentary reform in Great Britain, starting with the Reform Bill of 1832 and progressing steadily throughout the century. In place of the religious skepticism which is usually ascribed to scientific advance there was a strong element of religious revival. Only slowly was there a gain in the standard of living. Thus something which one would confidently say was of the utmost benefit to society—the control of energy to take back-breaking drudgery from mankind—did introduce strong differences in the way of living, but it did *not* introduce a relaxation of social tension and a bettering of life all around.

Why did it go wrong like this? The Manchester School in England believed the social upheaval was caused by the lack of international free trade, and forced the acceptance of this doctrine in Britain until the early twentieth century. Marx believed it was inherent in capitalism and the profit motive. Though we do not pretend to know ourselves what caused these dislocations of society, we can point to the improvement which came as the educational system in England became competent and humane. No misery is worse than misery which follows expected comfort and happiness, and education at least taught people what to expect from technology.

THE REVOLUTION IN MEDICINE: A CONTRAST

The revolution in medicine, still very much in progress, began rather later than the revolution in energy. We can quote a few major features: the introduction of vaccination in 1820, the use of anesthetics in 1846, the work of Pasteur and Koch on communicable diseases, the development of vaccines for virus infection, and, in much more recent years, the development of antibiotics. Some of this is beautifully set out in Zinnsser's *Rats, Lice, and History*.

In commenting on these remarkable advances one can really say that they are all essentially positive: society has had nothing but benefit from them. The attitude toward physicians is interesting in this whole time. In Fielding and Smollett they do not fare so well. In 1850, with Trollope's *Dr. Thorne,* one sees an early use of a physician as a hero. He is presented as a very wise, kindly, and shrewd individual with considerable courage, and it is quite clear that this is also a part of his practice. Today the physician is almost universally a hero. At the same time there is the beginning of an undercurrent of discontent. It is felt that the availability of medical services to people has become something which is not always straightforward. So that even in a revolution which is essentially completely beneficial one is aware of the interaction between the performer and the population. It is an interaction not always without strain.

THE REVOLUTION IN COMMUNICATION

May 24, 1844, "What hath God wrought," the first message by "magnetic telegraph," was transmitted from Baltimore to Washington. By 1851, 50 lines crossed wide areas of the United States; by 1861, there was the same degree of penetration of the telegraph into Europe. In less than twenty years the time for urgent communication had gone from weeks to minutes and the happenings of the whole world could be brought to any intelligent reader with no delay. This development is quite vivid to the author, who spent some of his childhood in a remote part of China. To travel to Europe took six weeks, yet the lone wire of the telegraph brought the news of World War I within the day.

Communication is not just "news": all the impressions of a face, a scene, a sequence are part of communication. It is good to receive a telegram: better to hear a voice on the phone, and startling to see a face on the screen and hear the voice at the same time. The wrinkles around the eyes, and the way the whole face changes as it meets challenge, the whole impression of the way a man is managing himself, all these can now be seen, all over the world by millions at once. Because this is so, it is just as well to remind ourselves that all the results are not yet in on this revolution. Some say that hearing the strange timbre of Hitler's voice as he spoke to the crowds in Nazi Germany influenced many in the United States against him, and that this solidified our position in the days before World War II. Some say that the television debates influenced the marginal victory of Kennedy over Nixon. But no one really knows what the effect of continuous exposure to TV for information and amusement will be on the whole of the people of the world. Do we know whether the immediate mass impression of an event is the best way to produce the wisdom necessary to guide us in the future. Isn't reflection and thought also necessary? What happens if two nations choose radically different ways of using mass communications? Are they bound to move toward conflict?

None of these ideas are very fresh or novel, in fact they are well worn.

But they cannot be swept aside. What *should* society do about cheap and attractive mass communication?

Perhaps we can pose another aspect of the problem. Radio waves travel through space freely and economically. The means to generate radio waves and send signals with them can be put into smaller and smaller volume. Are we facing an era when every room will be "bugged" and all conversations recorded? Are we going to tolerate this, and if not, how are we going to prevent it? Clearly we shall not prevent it by taking no action *as a society*. So the challenge to society of scientific advance in communication is clear on two counts at least, and once again we begin to sense the coercion of scientific advance.

THE REVOLUTION IN WARFARE

Perhaps the most drastic of all revolutions is that in warfare, and yet it is grimly true that its effects can only be assessed when wars occur and demonstrate the changes that have taken place.

There is an honorably held opinion that one reason Hitler lost World War II was that he did not mobilize his scientists, including his university scientists, while the Allies did. The result of the scientific mobilization of the Allies was a variety of quickly produced and very effective weapons, ranging all the way from counter-mine measures and anti-submarine measures to the celebrated atomic bomb.

The degree to which scientists were used by the Allies is perhaps not realized by everyone. Some of the largest laboratories that ever existed were brought into being in a very short time. The scientists at the MIT radiation laboratory, which worked on microwave radar, a very narrow branch of the war effort, numbered 5,000 at the end of the war. The various atomic energy laboratories taken together must have exceeded that number. Laboratories existed for infra-red detection, countermeasures, radio, proximity fuses, and a whole number of scientific aids to warfare. In addition, a wholly new facet of war was developed, called "operations research." In these "laboratories" the methods of using weapons and, indeed, of using military forces in general, were studied *just as means,* not for the sole purpose of design of new weapons. These are still seen today—witness the RAND Corporation.

One result of all this applied science is that the cost of destruction has dropped sharply. The cost of a hydrogen bomb which can cause the destruction of a whole city is less than half a million dollars. In the 1966 accident over Spain involving an aircraft carrying hydrogen bombs over Spain, there were *four* bombs lost. Thus these bombs cannot really be very expensive. Yet their effect is devastating. The result of this sharp dimunition in the cost of destruction means that the amount of destruction to be faced in a future war is so great that it is almost certain we will never fight an all-out war in the future at all. The speed of the first exchange of weapons when missiles are used is so great that it is probable that the first catastrophe will last only a matter of minutes. Very probably humanity has no means to contain such an attack. As a result of this revolution in warfare we are surely going to see new methods of facing it. For the first time it looks likely that nuclear disarmament is something that will genuinely benefit all the people that will take part in it. When, and only when, this is true, is there any possibility of disarmament. So disarmament which benefits *all* may possibly be something which we shall see in the future. This will, indeed, be with very little precedent in human history.

THE REVOLUTION IN COMPUTING

A computer revolution is now in its beginning stages, and it is certainly going to continue for some time to come. The use of computers to decide quite intricate questions, such as how best to use telephone lines and cables and pipelines and as a means both of keeping records and of "information retrieval," is already vigorously in process. The first effects of this type of computation are likely to be what we shall call "beneficial." We may, in fact, find ourselves able to comprehend complex subjects like economics and possibly social science to a degree beyond our present expectations. At the same time we must face the possibility that this type of rapid electronic computation may easily start to supplant the human features of life to the point that human beings may not be able to bear the kind of living they will then face. Already where computers are an important part of society there are more restrictions and "strait jacketing" than many people like—for example, in a university where computer records are kept, changes cannot be made because they will not readily adapt to the computer.

We do not know how society will be able to handle this new revolution. Once again we see the coercive aspect of scientific development, rather than the hoped-for advance with relief at its attainment.

THE REVOLUTION IN BIOLOGY

A revolution in biology is just beginning. Until the last few years advances in medicine have been made without much understanding of how living things work. From the medical point of view, the majority of the philosophy of cure has been to "remove the cause and wait," because the human body has enormous recuperative powers. If the cause of illness has been the invasion of the body by a bacterium or a virus, then medical science has been able to remove the cause—in most cases—very effectively, so that these diseases are no longer feared very much, and incidentally our life-span has greatly lengthened. We have also learned something about nutrition as related to the development of the individual, and this has also benefited society considerably.

We are now on the threshold of something much greater. We are learning how the whole basis of life operates. We are learning that the operation is very much the same in practically all living things to the extent that we can say that the similarities exceed the differences. We have not yet begun to be inventive with regard to controlling the features of living things except in a shadowy way, but it does lie just around the corner. One starts to see indications of the problems that may arise when we start to use more powerful drugs and more incisive technical advances. Experimentation with such drugs as LSD indicates a new dimension in study: questions are being posed whether the knowledge of the functioning of the human mind can be related to the use of drugs to alter it or "improve it" in some way; there will always be pressure for either doing this or outlawing it. Thus society is going to see a succession of sharp questions with regard to the use of drugs and some answers may have to come much quicker than some societies are prepared to make them. We can see the sorts of things that may occur illustrated in the case of thalidomide. When pregnant women took this apparently useful tranquilizer it was discovered to cause severe damage to the unborn children. There was one celebrated trial in Belgium in which a number of people, including a physician, admitted the destruction of a badly malformed baby. The jury acquitted these confessed killers of the crime of murder. It is unlikely that there is any precedent to this in history, and it is quite clear that the basis of the acquittal lay in the fact that the use of a scientifically developed drug with side effects that were unknown at the time of its use had given the mother and parents a problem which essentially was not capable of being handled. The solution chosen was a solution which, while not acceptable, was not deemed to be punishable.

ACCELERATION OF TEMPO

There is no question that in describing these revolutions the reader can see that they have been coming faster and faster. We see almost a century for the completion of the revolution in energy sources and perhaps a century in the revolution in communication. The great revolution in warfare has taken place since World War II and the revolution in computing has taken place in the time subsequent to World War II, the revolution in biology has not yet happened but everyone feels it is upon us, so that we are really under the impact of three revolutions, any one of which would be a considerable shock to any society. This increasing tempo means that we must face more and more problems posed by science. The problems are not necessarily sharper, but there are more of them, and to face them we should act as an educated society and not as a group of people who are doing what they are told without knowledge. Obviously, this is a valid reason to want scientific understanding by a wide group of people and not just a narrow few. It is strongly related to the content of this book. Only with this understanding can people make scientific discoveries lose their semblance of coercion and bring them to wise and intelligent use.

ERNEST C. POLLARD, 1965

References

Jacob Bronowski, *Science and Human Values*, rev. ed. (New York: Harper & Row, Torchbooks, 1965).

René Jules Dubos, *The Dreams of Reason; Science and Utopias* (New York: Columbia University Press, 1961).

E. J. Hobsbawm, *The Age of Revolution* (Cleveland: World Publishing Co., 1962).

Ralph E. Lapp, *Atoms and People* (New York: Harper & Row, 1956).

A. P. Rowe, *One Story of Radar* (New York: Cambridge University Press, 1948).

Smyth Report (Princeton, N.J.: Princeton University Press, 1946).

C. P. Snow, *Science and Goverment* (Cambridge, Mass.: Harvard University Press, 1961).

Hans Zinnsser, *Rats, Lice and History* (New York: Bantam Books, 1960).

4
Newton and the Laws of Motion

Looking out of the window on a warm summer's afternoon, it is hard to see why the understanding of motion is so important. The trees and bushes sway a little in the breeze, but the bricks and ivy of the house opposite are still, and so is almost everything in the room in which the writing is going on. It is not really surprising that most philosophers who wished to understand their environment have considered the moving things as secondary. It has proved to be otherwise. We look at our universe today and find that it is anything but an extension and amplification of what we can readily perceive; indeed, it is often totally at variance with the plain evidence of our senses. For example, the sun does *not* revolve about the earth, at least not in the rational scheme we now adopt. And we have found that, inside the swaying bushes, the living cells of the plant kingdom are changing and modifying themselves in a way which demands intense motion of varied kinds—from the flow of sap to the molecular motion which is the very basis of the molecular chemistry that sustains the life of the plant. Even the bricks are not really still, not in the inmost motion of the atoms which make the bricks. So we have to ask the reader to believe us when we assert that the most valuable scientific knowledge acquired by man is comprised in the laws of motion.

These laws were first stated in a satisfactory and complete form by Newton, although Galileo was aware of two of Newton's famous three laws, and Newton made it plain that this was so.

First let us recall Galileo's findings about falling bodies. He found that they represented a simple form of motion in which, to summarize his conclusions:

$$\frac{\text{Velocity}}{\text{Time}} = \text{Constant}.$$

For the case of falling bodies the "constant" in the above relation measured the acceleration, which, for a falling body, is always the same. His great contribution lay in calling attention to acceleration, and in showing how it could be measured.

Now the absolutely fundamental question arises: what causes motion? First, we have to look into something which goes against our direct experience: we have to ask whether there is any kind of motion that has no cause at all. Even to ask this question seems stupid. If we first commented that the world around us seems to be mostly still, and we did at the beginning of this chapter, then we have to admit that anything moving is unusual, and it would seem to be stupid to say that something unusual was without cause. This feeling, that the idea of motion without active cause is foolish, is one of the "intuitive" feelings which have kept mankind back for thousands of years. It was adopted by Aristotle, twenty-three centuries ago. The first inkling that it was a grand illusion, not a reality in Nature, came from Galileo's experiments.

Out of the ideas contained in these experiments, and out of ideas suggested by the nature of the motion of planets, Newton drew a bold and sweeping generalization. He asserted that there are two kinds of motion for which no cause need be supposed: the obvious case where there is no motion at all, i.e. the condition of rest, and the case where the motion, *no matter how fast,* is quite uniform and in a straight line. Every other condition, said Newton, has to have a cause, and he called that cause a *force.* Thus Newton asserted that force causes motion, but the motion so caused must have some changing character about it, a statement which clearly fits in with Galileo's discovery of the importance of acceleration, which is definitely a motion of changing character.

Newton's First Law of Motion, which in a sense is *the* big step, is this:

EVERY BODY CONTINUES IN A STATE OF REST OR OF UNIFORM MOTION IN A STRAIGHT LINE UNLESS COMPELLED TO DO OTHERWISE BY AN IMPRESSED FORCE.

This first law we must examine carefully. First of all, what do we mean by "force"? It will soon be seen that in spite of the cogency and generality of Newton's statement, the meaning is by no means clear. And the reason for this lack of clarity is, again, the necessity of "breaking into a circle," that we mentioned before. Newton said a force is that which causes motion, yet clearly we often observe force without motion, and Newton himself said that there can be motion without force. This deadlock kept humanity from making a proper start on the study of mechanics for centuries; Newton broke it. To see what he did, we have to realize that even Newton wasn't entirely clear. If you stand still on a cement floor, after a while your feet will ache. If you

lie down for an equivalent time, they won't. The difference is that you
feel that you have been pressing down on the floor to hold yourself up,
and though you have not been going anywhere or moving at all, the
pressure tires you. So some "force" has been involved, Newton or no
Newton. Also, if you put on roller skates (which the author has found
to be a serious error), and skate on a smooth rink, things are moderately
under control until you wish to stop. Again, the discovery is made, often
painfully, that stopping is not feasible, and the adventure ends in a thud.
In attempting to stop, the essence of frustration is that no force can
apparently be exerted. Yet experience confirms that the skater is only
too surely *going*. There is no force present, but there is no doubt about
the motion. How did Newton get around these two opposing facts, of
motionless force and forceless motion?

He stated a "Third" Law of Motion:

TO EVERY ACTION THERE IS AN EQUAL AND OPPOSITE REACTION.

If this idea is brought into the scheme of things it becomes possible to
understand the phenomenon of tired feet on the cement floor. Feet
become tired because the action of standing upright, which means pressing on the floor, also requires that the floor press up on your feet. The
force which tires your feet is not a fiction: it is real, but there are two
forces, one exerted *by* you, and one exerted *on* you. Your exertion also
causes your fatigue. (Some effect is also produced in the cement, but this
usually takes some years to show.) The Third Law of Motion says that
forces are in pairs, mutually opposite to each other and equal in size.

As the first feeling for the great beauty and generality and power of
Newton's approach begins to show, it is also necessary to realize that
Newton failed to make clear two important qualifications to both these
laws. In the First Law he should have said that there is no motion unless
an unbalanced or net or excess force acts on the body, and in the Third
Law he should have said that, if there is no acceleration, then to every
action there is an equal and opposite reaction. These two Newtonian
imperfections have cost much intellectual hardship to students. In
justice to Newton it must be remembered that he presented these laws in
a work of tremendous stature, *The Mathematical Principles of Natural
Philosophy*, always known as *The Principia* from its Latin title. If one
follows out the reasoning in this work, which includes many applications
of the principles, it is quite clear what Newton meant. It is only today,
when we want these principles to contain as much as they can in their
statement, that we begin to criticize. As students, we would like everything to be as explicit as possible. Let us simply remember the two
qualifications, and remind ourselves that we do not really wish to criti-

cize the active origin of an idea in terms of wisdom acquired over hundreds of subsequent years.

To return to force. In his First Law, Newton said quite clearly that force produces motion: objects at rest must either have a whole set of balanced forces acting on them or else no force. But he also said—and in so doing he introduced a tremendous innovation, which brought with it a considerable shock to many—that a body moving in a straight line, with uniform speed, no matter how fast it is going, also has no force on it. Thus, force acts to change either a resting condition or a condition of uniform motion in a straight line.

Again we notice the necessary character of hypothesis (sometimes called an educated guess). Newton knew that muscular effort produced a force which sometimes did and sometimes didn't move things. He knew that the earth pulls down with force: and that it, too, sometimes does and sometimes doesn't move things. So he supposed that whenever a force obviously acts and no motion takes place, two forces act—one to disturb and one to resist. Only when one of the two wins out does motion occur.

While these two laws represent a great advance, there remain the questions of how much and what kind of motion a force produces. These two questions are answered in Newton's "Second" Law of Motion. This states:

RATE OF CHANGE OF MOTION IS PROPORTIONAL TO THE IMPRESSED FORCE AND TAKES PLACE IN THE DIRECTION OF THAT FORCE.

Once again, this statement is partly masterly and partly obscure. "Motion" is a very vague term, and only by reading further in Newton's discourse does it become clear. By "motion," Newton meant to include two quite distinct ideas, both quite abstract, and both highly significant. The first idea concerned a description of how *massive* the thing which moves is found to be. If we have to push a truck on the level, it will matter whether it is fully loaded or not, when we actually face the problem of "getting it started," which is a colloquial way of describing the process that scientists would call the "initial acceleration." So one of the terms in Newton's "motion" is *mass,* a measure of the amount of material in the thing to be moved—or, if the reader prefers the term, a measure of the "inertia." This concept of massiveness is one aspect. The other is the velocity, or colloquially (and in a sense, as we shall see, incorrectly), the speed.

Thus Newton knew that the whole complex he wanted to describe by motion was made up of the two ideas of massiveness and speed (or velocity). Now how do we actually assemble these two ideas to make one thing, which we call "motion"? We can imagine several ways of doing it; we will examine two. The first, and most obvious is to say we will add the "mass" of the body and the velocity of the body. Let us become mathematical and introduce the symbol m for mass and v for velocity. Then

$$\text{Motion} = m + v.$$

Let us look at what this means. It is helpful in one sense because there is no doubt that a fast-moving and massive body will have lots of "motion." Let us be more definite about what we mean. Suppose we had something of mass 10 units and speed 10 miles per hour. The thing we are calling "motion" then is $10 + 10$ and is 20. Now suppose that we had two of these going along together. The mass is now 2×10, or 20 and the speed is 10 as before, so that we get for the total motion, $20 + 10 = 30$. This is a bit depressing, for we would have liked to think that if we saw two ten-ton trucks doing ten miles per hour, they would have exactly twice the "motion" of one of them alone, and yet we don't say this, for 30 is not twice 20. So perhaps we should not have simply added the two conceptual parts of "motion." Suppose we try something a little different. Suppose we multiply the mass and the velocity together. Now for the case above, the first one will be $10 \times 10 = 100$ for the "motion" and the second will be $20 \times 10 = 200$. This is better, for it tells us what we seem to know intuitively, without either experiment or actual proof—that two of the same things taken together are twice one alone. We could try other combinations, and we suggest that the reader try the result of dividing the mass by the velocity, both for the case of one object and then two, and for the case of one object which at one time has a velocity of 10 units and then gets to be going twice as fast, in which case there should result twice the "motion."

All these "elementary" ideas must have passed through Newton's mind. They are the ideas which the reader must be asking himself; and they are not "elementary" at all. Anyone with any thought for the philosophical basis of science will see that, even beyond the principles which we are going to present, there are ideas of basic reason or "common sense" which we invoke in the starting process. One of the reasons why many students develop an aversion to science is that many years ago they asked some of these "elementary" questions, and found that they were subjected to a certain amount of bland patronizing, coupled with a thinly veiled suggestion that they were stupid. We are not going to pretend that we are much better about this. We are, unquestionably, scientists, and human, and so we are not always going to be able to know when something which we have accepted for years is really an obscure idea or not. However, when our sins are pointed out to us, we will try to reform. The reader should ask the "elementary" questions without inhibition. If we stand on our dignity, we admit that we should be punished.

To return to Newton. Suppose we say that the idea he wished to convey by "motion" is the mass multiplied by the velocity, or, as mathematicians write it: Motion $= m \times v$. With this supposition, we can look back at Newton's Second Law of Motion. He speaks of "rate of change of motion." We have no difficulty at all about the rate of change of velocity, for Galileo has taught us that this is the acceleration, and his masterly study of falling bodies, which developed this idea, is still fresh in our minds. But we must also remember that presumably the amount of motion can change if only the mass changes. We can actually see something like this if we watch a chain slide off a flat table. As the chain goes over the edge, the part which has already started down is pulling the part still on the table and as the chain slides this gets less, so that, in a certain sense, the mass is changing. Such an analogy is rather contrived; actually, for a very large number of cases we can suppose that the inherent massiveness of something does not change. This so often true that we commonly write Newton's Second Law in the mathematical form:

$$\text{Force} = \text{Mass} \times \text{Acceleration}.$$

To go a little farther with this matter, we can point out that Einstein, who examined the fundamental basis of the method of measuring motion, also suggested that mass depends on velocity, becoming greater as the velocity approaches the velocity of light. In Einstein's scheme, known as "relativity," the mass can change. Newton would have pointed out, doubtless complacently, that his Second Law of Motion had already made provision for that sort of thing.

Universal Gravitation

With the Three Laws of Motion, we have a full scheme for mechanics capable of much elaboration. At this stage we could invent a whole lot of ways in which forces might act on bodies and we could show how the laws of motion work out. If we prefer to stick to reality, however, we soon notice that, so far, no mention of a single actual cause for force has been made. So our forces must be invented. Now that we have injected the small beginnings of a philosophical note, we can go a little further and point out that there are really only four actual causes for force, or kinds of force, if you wish: gravitational, electrical, two kinds of nuclear. Four is a very small number, so small that it is hard to resist the thought that all four are somehow connected and there is really only one cause. A great deal of effort—much of it by Einstein in the so-called "unified field theory"—has gone into an attempt to reduce these four to one, but the work has been so abstract and the success so qualified that we prefer to keep asserting that there are four causes.

One of these—the weakest in a certain sense—is described by the Law of Universal Gravitation, which is another of the giant contributions made by Newton. This law is easy to state and it has an all-inclusive application:

> EVERY BODY ATTRACTS EVERY OTHER BODY WITH A FORCE PROPORTIONAL TO THEIR TWO MASSES, DIRECTED TOWARD EACH OTHER AND ALSO PROPORTIONAL TO THE INVERSE SQUARE OF THEIR DISTANCE APART.

Figure 4.1 helps to show what this means. The larger object on the left is a mass of size M, and the smaller object on the right is a smaller mass m. We measure the distance between the centers of the two masses, and call it R. Newton's Law of Universal Gravitation says that on each mass a force, F, will occur. That on the left pulls to the right; that on the right pulls to the left. Both forces are equal in size, as required by the Third Law of Motion. (Notice one convention. A force is represented by a line with an arrowhead. This symbol is so commonly used that most physicists have forgotten that it needs to be explained.)

Also, we have used the words "proportional" and "inverse." The first means that as one thing changes, to become greater or less, so does the other change. The two are then called proportional to one another. The

Fig. 4.1. Representation of the force on each of two masses M and m produced by gravitational attraction. The formula for the F is

$$F = \frac{GMm}{R^2}$$

G is a constant. Its value depends on the units of measurement, but if they are consistent then G is the same for all bodies throughout the universe, at least as far as is now known.

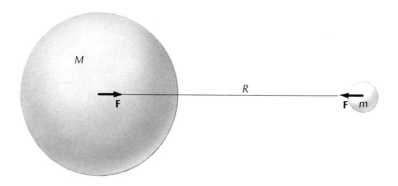

word occurs often in physics because it is one stage less precise than "equals": this lack of precision is a great help to the physicist, who very often cannot control the way in which things are measured. Thus he may find a measurement in feet per second or miles per hour and they could both be of the same object. Yet they will be different numbers— for example, 60 m.p.h. is 88 feet per second. If the physicist wants to talk about a relation, he may not be able to find out enough about it to call it a relation between equal things and yet he wants to talk about what he has found. So he will say that "A is proportional to B." When this is true, it is also true that

$$A = (C)B$$

where we represent by (C) some unchanging number—unchanging once it is found. Thus, for a car, if s is the speed in miles per hour and S the speed in feet per second,

$$S = \frac{44s}{30}$$

and the number $\frac{44}{30}$ would be represented by (C), the unchanging number or "Constant."

The word "inverse" means that it is on the denominator of a fraction. We divide by it; the bigger it is, the less is something else dependent upon it.

We express Newton's Law of Universal Gravitation in symbols:

$$F = G\frac{Mm}{R^2}$$

G is the unchanging number—the constant of gravitation. The rest can be seen from Figure 4.1.

We are going to discuss this law later, along with similar electrical and magnetic laws. For now, let us accept it as stated, and work out a simple problem: that of a falling body.

Suppose the mass of the earth to be M. Suppose its radius is R and that this radius is very big, indeed, huge compared to the height of the body we propose to let fall. Then we can call the distance from the center of the earth to the center of the body also R.

The body we are about to drop, a baseball, has a mass we can call m. If it is at a distance R from the center of the earth, then the Law of Universal Gravitation tells us that the earth exerts a force on it which is

$$\frac{GMm}{R^2}$$

If we let the baseball go, this force is the force which makes it fall, and the motion will be, as found by Galileo, and required by Newton, to be an acceleration which we can denote by a. The Second Law of Motion then states that for any force causing an acceleration there is the quantitative

$$\text{Force} = \text{Mass} \times \text{Acceleration}$$

So for our case, in symbols,

$$\frac{GMm}{R^2} = ma$$

and by dividing both sides of the equation by the equal, m, we find a definite relation for the acceleration; it is $a = \dfrac{GM}{R^2}$.

One of the abilities of the mathematical physicist is that he can look at such a relation and see the significance in it. He first asks, what does the acceleration depend upon? Well, clearly, it depends upon the mass of the earth. It also depends upon the distance to the center of the earth. It depends on G, the constant of gravitation. But it does not depend on m, the mass of the baseball. So the unexpected item of significance is found in the omission of m. If the acceleration does not depend on the mass of the baseball, this will be true of anything we let fall. The acceleration will only depend on the mass of the earth (the same for all things we let fall), the distance to the center (also the same for all things we let fall in the same place), and the constant of gravitation—the same always. So all bodies fall at the same acceleration regardless of their mass.

With no trouble at all we can calculate the acceleration of the earth as it comes up to meet the baseball. Call the acceleration of the earth A. The force on the earth, by the Law of Universal Gravitation is

$$\frac{GmM}{R^2}$$

and this must equal the mass times acceleration of the earth. Thus we find

$$\frac{GmM}{R^2} = MA$$

and, as before, we can obtain a definite expression for A, which is,

$$A = \frac{Gm}{R^2}$$

Looking at this we see that it doesn't contain the mass of the earth. It *does* contain the mass of the baseball. The lesson of this kind of gravity-induced motion is that the acceleration depends on the other body. Incidentally, the mass of the earth is about 2×10^{25} (meaning 2 followed by 25 zeroes) times the mass of the baseball. The acceleration of the earth is thus much less than that of the baseball. It is not surprising that we never notice it.

Before we conclude this chapter it is worth a moment to consider the nature of the pairs of forces which are involved in the law of action and reaction. In a sense we are writing this paragraph more for the teacher than for the student, and yet no harm can be done in saying what follows to both. What starts as a philosophical question ends in a rather sharp scientific conclusion, and forms the basis for a sweeping principle: the principle of conservation of momentum. The question is whether it is possible to produce a force without also producing an equal and opposite force somewhere. We have not answered this in the paragraphs above, and perhaps have suggested that it could be done in some cases. We can go a little further into this by looking at Figure 4.2. The figure introduces two ideas which are necessary to complete our understanding. The first is the idea of *adjustable forces*. There is a whole class of forces which might be called *adjustable:* we show one example here. Let us consider an elastic rod, made of something firm yet springy, like a thick piece of rubber about of the diameter of a baseball bat. If we stand it on its end, we can proceed to balance carefully a good-sized weight on the upper end. When we do this the rubber will give, that is, compress, and the molecular structure inside the rubber will come under strain, which in turn will call forth forces from the molecular strain. These forces permeate the whole interior of the rubber rod, all of which is under strain, but at the two ends the forces cause an outward push on the weight at the top and the earth at the bottom. If the weight is smaller, the distortion is less, the strain is less, and the force is less. If larger, all are greater.

We now see the second important idea, the idea of equilibrium. With the presence of adjustable forces, it is quite possible to balance our weight on top of the rod: when we have done so, we find that the upward thrust of the elastic force exactly equals the downward force of the earth's gravity. This is not an automatic event, though to a point it is. If the weight is too great, the rod will be crushed and there will be no equilibrium, but often, as we all know from looking at things on tables and hanging from beams, equilibrium *can* be achieved.

With these ideas in mind, we can look further at the *paired nature* of forces. Looking at the bottom of the rod and at the earth, we see that the thrust of the elastic force of the rod is now downward. To produce equilibrium there must be an upward force to balance it. The nature of this force is simple in one sense and quite elaborate in another: it is simple in that the earth itself now acts like the rubber rod, being pinched between the upward force of gravity acting from the weight on the earth, and the elastic force of the rod, so the earth develops an elastic force exactly to balance the force downward of the rod. It is elaborate in that all the force factors are distributed majestically throughout the earth,

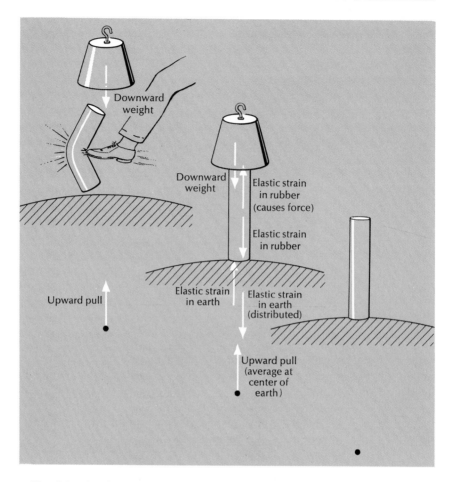

Fig. 4.2. Showing the paired forces which develop when a weight is put onto a support which can become compressed to just the right amount. The support gives, which means that it shortens and the molecular forces inside it grow bigger. At the weight and at the surface of the earth, these molecular forces press outward as shown. Thus there are two sets of paired forces: the gravitational forces and the forces due to the strain of the support. Both sets obey the law of action and reaction. If we suddenly remove the support by a sharp blow then the elastic forces disappear, the weight falls, and the earth rises. The accelerations of the weight and the earth must be calculated from the single forces on each.

and are by no means so easy to calculate. Newton spent much time worrying about this spread, and actually never did clearly and in one sentence state the law of gravitation, because he was occupied with how gravity would work in a large body like the earth.

To return to the simple part: we see that the essential pair of forces at the lower end can be thought of as the elastic force down and the upward gravity force on the earth. What emerges from all this is that forces are *always* paired: there is no way to create one force without the mate to it.

Why, then, have we said some of the things in the earlier paragraphs? The quickest way to answer this question is to imagine the rubber rod kicked out of the way, creating the situation in the left-hand figure. Now we see that there are still paired forces, though only two of them, one on the weight and one on the earth. The earth and the weight will move, *and to calculate how they move* we must take the single force on each, and relate it to the mass times the acceleration. Thus, in the situation where we are, conceptually, in the middle of the pair, watching one or both of them move, we must treat the single force on each and the acceleration of each. This situation arises often, and because it is related to the change of something, which is usually revealing, it is of great importance. The overwhelming majority of forces are locked in equilibrium, where pairs of pairs balance each other. When the exception occurs, and the balance is lost, then to find the acceleration we treat each unit alone with the individual force on it. Thus, to start the concepts going, we have taken the approach in the text.

We want to make one more remark here. Forces are never *consumed*. They are inherent: forces like elastic forces can become large or small as demanded by the strain of the material, but they do not become used up as they act. There is a valid concept of consumption, and it is related to forces, but this must be deferred for the moment. It is *energy* which can be consumed, or rather, changed in use, not force.

Frames of Reference

In this section there is one final important aspect of these laws of motion which we cannot omit. Motion must be measured relative to something, and that "something" is given the special term "frame of reference." We have made light of the idea that just the act of measurement in a particular frame of reference could introduce a force. Newton did not make light of this, nor should we. In the early stages of thinking about this problem it is not hard to convince oneself that two frames of reference which differ from each other only in that one is moving with uniform speed relative to the other do not introduce the appearance of forces when measurement is transferred from one to the other. Thus although the earth travels in its orbit at 6300 m.p.h., we do not notice any difference in walking at different seasons of the year. This statement is true for normal massive bodies, such as we have discussed in this chapter. On the other hand, if we use one frame of reference which is *rotating* relative to another, we find that the basis of measurement *does* introduce something suspiciously like a force. We can see this by watching a massive pendulum swing: the rotation of the earth affects a slow change in the direction of swing of the pendulum, and yet no visible object exerts a force on the bob to push it to one side. Newton's First Law of Motion is true for many frames of reference, and what should be said is that frames can be selected in which it is true. Such frames of reference are called *inertial frames.* For most purposes the rotation of the earth is not sufficient to be noticed, so that there is usually no problem.

It is of interest that, for light, problems arise which require a new approach to the nature of frames of reference that differ in speed. These problems formed the origin of the theory of relativity, to be discussed later.

Suggestions for Further Thought

1. State and discuss the significant features of Newton's laws of motion. What do you understand by the concept of a force?
2. Write an essay on Newton's life. Contrast the social climate in which Galileo worked to that of Newton.
3. Using the Law of Universal Gravitation and Newton's Second Law of Motion, show that bodies fall with the same acceleration regardless of their mass. What assumption have you made?
4. If G has a numerical value of 6.7×10^{-8} dyne cm.^{2}/gm.^{2} and the radius of the earth is $6.4 \times 10^{+8}$ cm., calculate the mass of the earth.
5. Make an estimate of the force exerted on your back with respect to the force exerted on your seat at takeoff in a jet airplane. Use this to make a "guestimate" of the acceleration of the airplane. How long with it take the airplane to reach 300 miles per hour? (60 m.p.h. = 88 ft./sec. and the acceleration of gravity = 32 ft./sec.).

References

George Gamow, *Biography of Physics* (New York: Harper & Row, Torchbooks, 1964).

Julien A. Ripley, Jr., *The Elements and Structure of the Physical Sciences* (New York: John Wiley & Sons, 1964).

Sir Isaac Newton

Since this chapter is Newton's chapter, we should add something about him as a man and about the impact that he had on his age. There is no doubt that it was great. Alexander Pope wrote:

> Nature and Nature's Laws lay hid in night
> God said "Let Newton be" and all was light.*

Instead of writing this appraisal ourselves, we include two essays on Newton, one by Humphrey Newton, who was Newton's laboratory assistant, and the other by John Maynard Keynes, the eminent economist. Together they show great insight into his character.

Sir Isaac Newton

BY HUMPHREY NEWTON

His carriage was very meek, sedate and humble, never seemingly angry, of profound thought, his countenance mild, pleasant and comely. I cannot say I ever saw him laugh but once, which put me in mind of the Ephesian philosopher, who laughed only once in his lifetime, to see an ass eating thistles when plenty of grass was by. He always kept close to his studies, very rarely went visiting and had few visitors. I never knew him to take any recreation or pastime either in riding out to take the air, walking, bowling, or any other exercise whatever, thinking all hours lost that were not spent in his studies, to which he kept so close that he seldom left his chamber except at term time, when he read in the schools as Lucasianus Professor, where so few went to hear him, and fewer that understood him, that ofttimes he did in a manner, for want of hearers read to the walls. Foreigners he received with a great deal of freedom, candour, and respect. When invited to a treat, which was very seldom, he used to return it very handsomely, and with much satisfaction to himself. So intent, so serious upon his studies, that he ate very sparingly, nay, ofttimes he has forgot to eat at all, so that, going into his chamber, I have found his mess untouched, of which, when I have reminded him, he would reply—"Have I?" and then making to the table would eat a bite or two standing, for I cannot say I ever saw him sit at table by himself. He very rarely went to bed till two or three of the clock, sometimes not until five or six, lying about four or five hours, especially at spring

---

* It did not last, the Devil howling "Ho
Let Einstein be!" restored the status quo.

J. C. Squire

and fall of the leaf, at which times he used to employ about six weeks in his elaboratory, the fires scarcely going out either night or day; he sitting up one night and I another till he had finished his chemical experiments, in the performance of which he was the most accurate, strict, exact. What his aim might be I was not able to penetrate into, but his pains, his diligence at these set times made me think he aimed at something beyond the reach of human art and industry. I cannot say I ever saw him drink either wine, ale or beer, excepting at meals and then but very sparingly. He very rarely went to dine in the hall, except on some public days, and then if he has not been minded, would go very carelessly, with shoes down at heels, stockings untied, surplice on, and his head scarcely combed.

His elaboratory was well furnished with chemical materials, as bodies, receivers, heads, crucibles, etc. which was made very little use of, the crucibles excepted, in which he fused his metals; he would sometimes, tho' very seldom, look into an old mouldy book which lay in his elaboratory, I think it was titled Agricola de Metallis, the transmuting of metals being his chief design, for which purpose antimony was a great ingredient. He has sometimes taken a turn or two, has made a sudden stand, turn'd himself about, run up the stairs like another Archimedes, with an Eureka fall to write on his desk standing without giving himself the leisure to draw a chair to sit down on. He would with great acuteness answer a question, but would very seldom start one. Dr. Boerhave, in some of his writings, speaking of Sir Isaac: "That man," says he, "comprehends as much as all mankind besides."

Newton, The Man

Read by Mr. Geoffrey Keynes at the Newton Tercentenary Celebrations at Trinity College, Cambridge, on 17 July 1946, and therefore not revised by the author who had written it some years earlier.

It is with some diffidence that I try to speak to you in his own home of Newton *as he was himself.* I have long been a student of the records and had the intention to put my impressions into writing to be ready for Christmas Day 1942, the tercentenary of his birth. The war has deprived me both of leisure to treat adequately so great a theme and of opportunity to consult my library and my papers and to verify my impressions. So if the brief study which I shall lay before you to-day is more perfunctory than it should be, I hope you will excuse me.

One other preliminary matter. I believe that Newton was different from the conventional picture of him. But I do not believe he was less great. He was less ordinary, more extraordinary, than the nineteenth century cared to make him out. Geniuses *are* very peculiar. Let no one here suppose that my object to-day is to lessen, by describing, Cambridge's greatest son. I am trying rather to see him as his own friends and contemporaries saw him. And they without exception regarded him as one of the greatest of men.

In the eighteenth century and since, Newton came to be thought of as the first and greatest of the modern age of scientists, a rationalist, one who taught us to think on the lines of cold and untinctured reason.

I do not see him in this light. I do not think that any one who has pored over the contents of that box which he packed up when he finally left Cambridge in 1696 and which, though partly dispersed, have come down to us, can see him like that. Newton was not the first of the age of reason. He was the last of the magicians, the last of the Babylonians and Sumerians, the last great mind which looked out on the visible and intellectual world with the same eyes as those who began to build our intellectual inheritance rather less than 10,000 years ago. Isaac Newton, a posthumous child born with no father on Christmas Day, 1642, was the last wonder-child to whom the Magi could do sincere and appropriate homage.

Had there been time, I should have liked to read to you the contemporary record of the child Newton. For, though it is well known to his biographers, it has never been published *in extenso*, without comment, just as it stands. Here, indeed, is the makings of a legend of the young magician, a most joyous picture of the opening mind of genius free from the uneasiness, the melancholy and nervous agitation of the young man and student.

For in vulgar modern terms Newton was profoundly neurotic of a not unfamiliar type, but—I should say from the records—a most extreme example. His deepest instincts were occult, esoteric, semantic—with profound shrinking from the world, a paralyzing fear of exposing his thoughts, his beliefs, his discoveries in all nakedness to the inspection and criticism of the world. "Of the most fearful, cautious and suspicious temper that I ever knew," said Whiston, his successor in the Lucasian Chair. The too well-known conflicts and ignoble quarrels with Hooke, Flamsteed, Leibnitz are only too clear an evidence of this. Like all his type he was wholly aloof from women. He parted with and published nothing except under the extreme pressure of friends. Until the second phase of his life, he was a wrapt, consecrated solitary, pursuing his studies by intense introspection with a mental endurance perhaps never equalled.

I believe that the clue to his mind is to be found in his unusual powers of continuous concentrated introspection. A case can be made out, as it also can with Descartes, for regarding him as an accomplished experimentalist. Nothing can be more charming than the tales of his mechanical contrivances when he was a boy. There are his telescopes and his optical experiments. These were essential accomplishments, part of his unequalled all-round technique, but not, I am sure, his *peculiar* gift, especially amongst his contemporaries. His peculiar gift was the power of holding continuously in his mind a purely mental problem until he had seen straight through it. I fancy his pre-eminence is due to his muscles of intuition being the strongest and most enduring with which a man has ever been gifted. Anyone who has ever attempted pure scientific or philosophical thought knows how one can hold a problem momentarily in one's mind and apply all one's powers of concentration to piercing through it, and how it will dissolve and escape and you find that what you are surveying is a blank. I believe that Newton could hold a problem in his mind for hours and days and weeks until it surrendered to him its secret. Then being a supreme mathematical technician he could dress it up, how you will, for purposes of exposition, but it was his intuition which was pre-eminently extraordinary—"so happy in his conjectures," said de Morgan, "as to seem to know more than he could possibly have any means of proving." The proofs, for what they are worth, were, as I have said, dressed up afterwards—they were not the instrument of discovery.

There is the story of how he informed Halley of one of his most fundamental discoveries of planetary motion. "Yes," replied Halley, "but how do you know that? Have you proved it?" Newton was taken aback—"Why, I've known it for years," he replied. "If you'll give me a few days, I'll certainly find you a proof of it"—as in due course he did.

Again, there is some evidence that Newton in preparing the *Principia* was held up almost to the last moment by lack of proof that you could treat a solid sphere as though all its mass was concentrated at the centre, and only hit on the proof a year before publication. But this was a truth which he had known for certain and had always assumed for many years.

Certainly there can be no doubt that the peculiar geometrical form in which the exposition of the *Principia* is dressed up bears no resemblance at all to the mental processes by which Newton actually arrived at his conclusions.

His experiments were always, I suspect, a means, not of discovery, but always of verifying what he knew already.

Why do I call him a magician? Because he looked on the whole universe and all that is in it *as a riddle,* as a secret which could be read by applying pure thought to certain evidence, certain mystic clues which God had laid about the world to allow a sort of philosopher's treasure hunt to the esoteric brotherhood. He believed that these clues were to be found partly in the evidence of the heavens and in the constitution of elements (and that is what gives the false suggestion of his being an experimental natural philosopher), but also partly in certain papers and traditions handed down by the brethren in an unbroken chain back to the original cryptic revelation in Babylonia. He regarded the universe as a cryptogram set by the Almighty—just as he himself wrapt the discovery of the calculus in a cryptogram when he communicated with Leibnitz. By pure thought, by concentration of mind, the riddle, he believed, would be revealed to the initiate.

He *did* read the riddle of the heavens. And he believed that by the same powers of his introspective imagination he would read the riddle of the Godhead, the riddle of past and future events divinely fore-ordained, the riddle of the elements and their constitution from an original undifferentiated first matter, the riddle of health and of immortality. All would be revealed to him if only he could persevere to the end, un-interrupted, by himself, no one coming into the room, reading, copying, testing—all by himself, no interruption for God's sake, no disclosure, no discordant breakings in or criticism, with fear and shrinking as he assailed these half-ordained, half-forbidden things, creeping back into the bosom of the Godhead as into his mother's womb. "Voyaging through strange seas of thought *alone,*" not as Charles Lamb "a fellow who believed nothing unless it was as clear as the three sides of a triangle."

And so he continued for some twenty-five years. In 1687, when he was forty-five years old, the *Principia* was published.

Here in Trinity it is right that I should give you an account of how he lived amongst you during these years of his greatest achievement. The east end of the Chapel projects farther eastwards than the Great Gate. In the second half of the seventeenth century there was a walled garden in the free space between Trinity Street and the building which joins the Great Gate to the Chapel. The south wall ran out from the turret of the Gate to a distance overlapping the Chapel by at least the width of the present pavement. Thus the garden was of modest but reasonable size, as is well shown in Loggan's print of the College in 1690. This was Newton's garden. He had the Fellow's set of rooms between the Porter's Lodge and the Chapel—that, I suppose, now occupied by Professor Broad. The garden was reached by a stairway which was attached to a veranda raised on wooden pillars projecting into the garden from the range of buildings. At the top of this stairway stood his telescope—not to be confused with the observatory erected on the top of the Great Gate during Newton's lifetime (but after he had left Cambridge) for the use of Roger Cotes and Newton's successor, Whiston. This wooden erection was, I think, demolished by Whewell in 1856 and replaced by the stone bay of Professor Broad's bedroom. At the Chapel end of the garden was a small two-storied building, also of wood, which was his laboratory. When he decided to prepare the *Principia* for publication he engaged a young kinsman, Humphrey Newton, to act as his amanuensis (the MS. of the *Principia,* as it went to the press, is clearly in the hand of Humphrey).

Humphrey remained with him for five years—from 1684 to 1689. When Newton died his nephew-in-law Conduitt wrote to Humphrey for his reminiscences, and among the papers I have is Humphrey's reply.

During these twenty-five years of intense study mathematics and astronomy were only a part, and perhaps not the most absorbing, of his occupations. Our record of these is almost wholly confined to the papers which he kept and put in his box when he left Trinity for London.

Let me give some brief indications of their subject. They are enormously voluminous—I should say that upwards of 1,000,000 words in his handwriting still survive. They have, beyond doubt, no substantial value whatever except as a fascinating sidelight on the mind of our greatest genius.

Let me not exaggerate through reaction against the other Newton myth which has been so sedulously created for the last two hundred years. There was extreme method in his madness. All his unpublished works on esoteric and theological matters are marked by careful learning, accurate method and extreme sobriety of statement. They are just as *sane* as the *Principia,* if their whole matter and purpose were not magical. They were nearly all composed during the same twenty-five years of his mathematical studies. They fall into several groups.

Very early in life Newton abandoned orthodox belief in the Trinity. At this time the Socinians were an important Arian sect amongst intellectual circles. It may be that Newton fell under Socinian influences, but I think not. He was rather a Judaic monotheist of the school of Maimonides. He arrived at this conclusion, not on so-to-speak rational or sceptical grounds, but entirely on the interpretation of ancient authority. He was persuaded that the revealed documents give no support to the Trinitarian doctrines which were due to late falsifications. The revealed God was one God.

But this was a dreadful secret which Newton was at desperate pains to conceal all his life. It was the reason why he refused Holy Orders, and therefore had to obtain a special dispensation to hold his Fellowship and Lucasian Chair and could not be Master of Trinity. Even the Toleration Act of 1689 excepted anti-Trinitarians. Some rumours there were, but not at the dangerous dates when he was a young Fellow of Trinity. In the main the secret died with him. But it was revealed in many writings in his big box. After his death Bishop Horsley was asked to inspect the box with a view to publication. He saw the contents with horror and slammed the lid. A hundred years later Sir David Brewster looked into the box. He covered up the traces with carefully selected extracts and some straight fibbing. His latest biographer, Mr. More, has been more candid. Newton's extensive anti-Trinitarian pamphlets are, in my judgement, the most interesting of his unpublished papers. Apart from his

more serious affirmation of belief, I have a completed pamphlet showing up what Newton thought of the extreme dishonesty and falsification
of records for which St. Athanasius was responsible, in particular for his
putting about the false calumny that Arius died in a privy. The victory
of the Trinitarians in England in the latter half of the seventeenth century was not only as complete, but also as extraordinary, as St. Athanasius's original triumph. There is good reason for thinking that Locke
was a Unitarian. I have seen it argued that Milton was. It is a blot on
Newton's record that he did not murmur a word when Whiston, his
successor in the Lucasian Chair, was thrown out of his professorship and
out of the University for publicly avowing opinions which Newton himself had secretly held for upwards of fifty years past.

That he held this heresy was a further aggravation of his silence and
secrecy and inwardness of disposition.

Another large section is concerned with all branches of apocalyptic
writings from which he sought to deduce the secret truths of the Universe
—the measurements of Solomon's Temple, the Book of Daniel, the Book
of Revelations, an enormous volume of work of which some part was
published in his later days. Along with this are hundreds of pages of
Church History and the like, designed to discover the truth of tradition.

A large section, judging by the handwriting amongst the earliest, relates to alchemy—transmutation, the philosopher's stone, the elixir of
life. The scope and character of these papers have been hushed up, or
at least minimized, by nearly all those who have inspected them. About
1650 there was a considerable group in London, round the publisher
Cooper, who during the next twenty years revived interest not only in the
English alchemists of the fifteenth century, but also in translations of the
medieval and post-medieval alchemists.

There is an unusual number of manuscripts of the early English
alchemists in the libraries of Cambridge. It may be that there was some
continuous esoteric tradition within the University which sprang into
activity again in the twenty years from 1650 to 1670. At any rate, Newton
was clearly an unbridled addict. It is this with which he was occupied
"about 6 weeks at spring and 6 at the fall when the fire in the elaboratory
scarcely went out" at the very years when he was composing the *Principia*
—and about this he told Humphrey Newton not a word. Moreover, he
was almost entirely concerned, not in serious experiment, but in trying
to read the riddle of tradition, to find meaning in cryptic verses, to
imitate the alleged but largely imaginary experiments of the initiates of
past centuries. Newton has left behind him a vast mass of records of these
studies. I believe that the greater part are translations and copies made
by him of existing books and manuscripts. But there are also extensive
records of experiments. I have glanced through a great quantity of this

—at least 100,000 words, I should say. It is utterly impossible to deny that it is wholly magical and wholly devoid of scientific value; and also impossible not to admit that Newton devoted years of work to it. Some time it might be interesting, but not useful, for some student better equipped and more idle than I to work out Newton's exact relationship to the tradition and MSS. of his time.

In these mixed and extraordinary studies, with one foot in the Middle Ages and one foot treading a path for modern science, Newton spent the first phase of his life, the period of life in Trinity when he did all his real work. Now let me pass to the second phase.

After the publication of the *Principia* there is a complete change in his habit and way of life. I believe that his friends, above all Halifax, came to the conclusion that he must be rooted out of the life he was leading at Trinity which must soon lead to decay of mind and health. Broadly speaking, of his own motion or under persuasion, he abandons his studies. He takes up University business, represents the University in Parliament; his friends are busy trying to get a dignified and remunerative job for him —the Provostship of King's, the Mastership of Charterhouse, the Controllership of the Mint.

Newton could not be Master of Trinity because he was a Unitarian and so not in Holy Orders. He was rejected as Provost of King's for the more prosaic reason that he was not an Etonian. Newton took this rejection very ill and prepared a long legalistic brief, which I possess, giving reasons why it was not unlawful for him to be accepted as Provost. But, as ill-luck had it, Newton's nomination for the Provostship came at the moment when King's had decided to fight against the right of Crown nomination, a struggle in which the College was successful.

Newton was well qualified for any of these offices. It must not be inferred from his introspection, his absentmindedness, his secrecy and his solitude that he lacked aptitude for affairs when he chose to exercise it. There are many records to prove his very great capacity. Read, for example, his correspondence with Dr. Covell, the Vice-Chancellor, when, as the University's representative in Parliament, he had to deal with the delicate question of the oaths after the revolution of 1688. With Pepys and Lowndes he became one of the greatest and most efficient of our civil servants. He was a very successful investor of funds, surmounting the crisis of the South Sea Bubble, and died a rich man. He possessed in exceptional degree almost every kind of intellectual aptitude—lawyer, historian, theologian, not less than mathematician, physicist, astronomer.

And when the turn of his life came and he put his books of magic back into the box, it was easy for him to drop the seventeenth century behind him and to evolve into the eighteenth-century figure which is the traditional Newton.

Nevertheless, the move on the part of his friends to change his life came almost too late. In 1689 his mother, to whom he was deeply attached, died. Somewhere about his fiftieth birthday on Christmas Day 1692, he suffered what we should now term a severe nervous breakdown. Melancholia, sleeplessness, fears of persecution—he writes to Pepys and and to Locke and no doubt to others letters which lead them to think that his mind is deranged. He lost, in his own words, the "former consistency of his mind." He never again concentrated after the old fashion or did any fresh work. The breakdown probably lasted nearly two years, and from it emerged, slightly "gaga," but still, no doubt, with one of the most powerful minds of England, the Sir Isaac Newton of tradition.

In 1696 his friends were finally successful in digging him out of Cambridge, and for more than another twenty years he reigned in London as the most famous man of his age, of Europe, and—as his powers gradually waned and his affability increased—perhaps of all time, so it seemed to his contemporaries.

He set up house with his niece Catharine Barton, who was beyond reasonable doubt the mistress of his old and loyal friend Charles Montague, Earl of Halifax and Chancellor of the Exchequer, who had been one of Newton's intimate friends when he was an undergraduate at Trinity. Catharine was reputed to be one of the most brilliant and charming women in the London of Congreve, Swift and Pope. She is celebrated not least for the broadness of her stories, in Swift's *Journal to Stella*. Newton puts on rather too much weight for his moderate height. "When he rode in his coach one arm would be out of his coach on one side and the other on the other." His pink face, beneath a mass of snow-white hair, which "when his peruke was off was a venerable sight," is increasingly both benevolent and majestic. One night in Trinity after Hall he is knighted by Queen Anne. For nearly twenty-four years he reigns as President of the Royal Society. He becomes one of the principal sights of London for all visiting intellectual foreigners, whom he entertains handsomely. He liked to have clever young men about him to edit new editions of the *Principia*—and sometimes merely plausible ones as in the case of Fatio de Duillier.

Magic was quite forgotten. He has become the Sage and Monarch of the Age of Reason. The Sir Isaac Newton of orthodox tradition—the eighteenth-century Sir Isaac, so remote from the child magician born in the first half of the seventeenth century—was being built up. Voltaire returning from his trip to London was able to report of Sir Isaac—" 'twas his peculiar felicity, not only to be born in a country of liberty, but in an Age when all scholastic impertinences were banished from the World. Reason alone was cultivated and Mankind cou'd only be his Pupil, not his Enemy." Newton, whose secret heresies and scholastic superstitions it had been the study of a lifetime to conceal.

But he never concentrated, never recovered "the former consistency of his mind." "He spoke very little in company." "He had something rather languid in his look and manner."

And he looked very seldom, I expect, into the chest where, when he left Cambridge, he had packed all the evidences of what had occupied and so absorbed his intense and flaming spirit in his rooms and his garden and his elaboratory between the Great Gate and Chapel.

But he did not destroy them. They remained in the box to shock profoundly any eighteenth- or nineteenth-century prying eyes. They became the possession of Catharine Barton and then of her daughter, Lady Lymington. So Newton's chest, with many hundreds of thousands of words of his unpublished writings, came to contain the "Portsmouth Papers."

In 1888 the mathematical portion was given to the University Library at Cambridge. They have been indexed, but they have never been edited. The rest, a very large collection, were dispersed in the auction room in 1936 by Catharine Barton's descendant, the present Lord Lymington. Disturbed by this impiety, I managed gradually to reassemble about half of them, including nearly the whole of the biographical portion, that is, the "Conduitt Papers," in order to bring them to Cambridge which I hope they will never leave. The greater part of the rest were snatched out of my reach by a syndicate which hoped to sell them at a high price, probably in America, on the occasion of the recent tercentenary.

As one broods over these queer collections, it seems easier to understand —with an understanding which is not, I hope, distorted in the other direction—this strange spirit, who was tempted by the Devil to believe, at the time when within these walls he was solving so much, that he could reach *all* the secrets of God and Nature by the pure power of mind— Copernicus and Faustus in one.

5

Discovery: Electricity and Magnetism

We have stated that almost all the basis of explanation of Nature which is accepted today is quite different from what would be naturally accepted. In the Preface we used the words "unseen real world"; the implication is that the scientist sees things altogether differently from the way they *appear* to be. Thus we stressed the importance of motion even in the cells of plants and the molecules in bricks, motion which is not seen by even a most careful surface study of both. The reader should realize that this book does have a theme. It is that there really is a new way to look at Nature, a way revealed by scientific study, and that when this way of looking is used Nature loses none of her beauty, but rather gains.

Perhaps the greatest surprise of all, in the way in which we now need to look at Nature, is the importance of electricity. All the origins of our discovery of electricity are strange and more like freaks than solid manifestations of reality: the rubbing of amber and the twitching of muscles from frogs, for example. So it is quite strange to realize that the agency which exerts tight control over the intimate form of atomic structure, of the way in which atoms combine to form molecular patterns, is electricity. It is worth a moment to compare gravity, the major force of which we are all aware, with electricity. Gravity is quite apparent to us; it obviously causes form on the large scale: planets, mountains, trees, even animals. Yet it is precisely because the scale is large that gravity produces its effect. To anticipate later knowledge in this book for a moment, we can work out the force between all the positive charge in a small teaspoonful of water and all the negative charge placed about one little finger's breadth away from it. The force is truly gigantic: it could move the whole earth. The gravitational attraction between a proton and an electron in a hydrogen atom is so small that no effect on the behavior of the

87

atom could possibly result, in contrast with the electrical force, which
gives the atom its whole form.

When we think of this seeming paradox, something else about electricity strikes us—its double feature of attraction and repulsion. Because
of this, two equal charges which are close together produce very little
effect outside their own locale. Thus we shall find it hard to detect pairs
of electrical charges, and since the force between them is great, we shall
find it hard to separate the charges so as to know that electricity is there.
We also find something else, which should not surprise us: when we start
to deal with a potent agent of Nature, such as electricity, we find that it
has more than one property. Thus still (or static) electricity is one thing,
and moving electricity is another; accelerated electricity is something
even more. So far we have not found it easy to discover the added properties of gravity; this is not to say that they are not there, but that in a
weak force they may prove hard to find.

Four natural manifestations of electricity have been known for so
long that it is very difficult to write any historical account of them. They
are:

Lightning. Rubbing of amber to attract light objects. The discharge of
the electric eel. "St. Elmo's fire," a brush of light seen near pointed objects in storms.

No relationship was seen between these four, even between the first
and the last (which is really rather surprising), and they were all considered to be quite separate phenomena. In the ages when experimentation was essentially unknown and observation was not very acute and
was strongly tinged with superstition, there was really no likelihood that
the nature of electricity would be uncovered. The first important steps
in the "uncovering' process were made in the late sixteenth century by
Gilbert. He was interested in both electricity and magnetism, and, unlike the majority of his predecessors, he designed a series of skilled experiments to study these natural phenomena. In his experiments he used
the idea of a specially designed, though very simple, test instrument.
This was very much like the compass needle; it consisted of a light rod of
dry wood balanced at its center on a sharp point and so free to turn.
He measured the effects of electrification by seeing if he could make the
rod turn. For example, if he rubbed a piece of amber and brought it
near the rod, there was an obvious effect. If he put a piece of rubbed
amber on one end of the rod and brought another rubbed piece near, the
effect was still greater. Gilbert found that many other rubbed substances,
including glass, would produce an effect. He described, rather carefully,
what we today call frictional electricity. He classified it into two kinds,
"vitreous" (made by rubbing glass) and "resinous" (made by rubbing

amber) and showed that electrification is a general property which can be produced in many substances.

One does have to wonder at how long it took to make the basic discoveries about frictional electricity. At the same time, it must be realized that the character of such electricity is such that it does not lend itself to many kinds of experiment: it is produced sparingly and is altogether lost if the air is damp.

The property of electrical conduction was discovered much later, in 1731, by Gray. Gray worked with this kind of electricity and he found that many things can transmit (or conduct) electrification. With frictional electricity a damp surface appears to conduct almost like a metal, so his work was done under great difficulty. However, as he pursued his experiments, he began to realize that substances such as glass, silk, and amber are what we today call "insulators," that is, they do not conduct, while brass, and all metals, are excellent conductors. In Gray's day, insulators were called "electrics."

Coulomb's Law

In 1785 Coulomb made a quantitative study of the force between electric charges. As a measure of force, he used an improvement in Gilberts' instrument. Instead of relying on the motion of a dry piece of wood, Coulomb carefully suspended a light, insulating rod which had a metal ball at each end. The suspension was by means of a fine thread; at the top, where the thread ended, he put a support which he could turn and a simple means to measure the amount of turn. Today we call this device a "torsion balance." How it works can perhaps be best understood by looking at Figure 5.1. When an electric charge is introduced on to the metal ball attached to one end of the rod, it becomes subject to the influence of any other electric charge, let us say of the same sign, on another metal ball. Suppose we produce such a second charge and bring it close to the first—as we show in the figure. When this is done, the two charges repel each other and this will cause the metal ball on the rod to move away. Because it is attached to the thread, the thread must twist, and it is now possible to twist the thread back by turning it at the top until the two charged objects are once more at their original distance apart. The force of repulsion is thus overcome ultimately by twisting the thread, and the amount of twist is a measure of the force of the repulsion.

Let us look at a table of data which might result from this kind of experiment. Such a table is much like Galileo's observations on the rolling ball, and it is interesting to compare the analysis. The support, which is free to turn, can twist many times, and we have measured the angle of

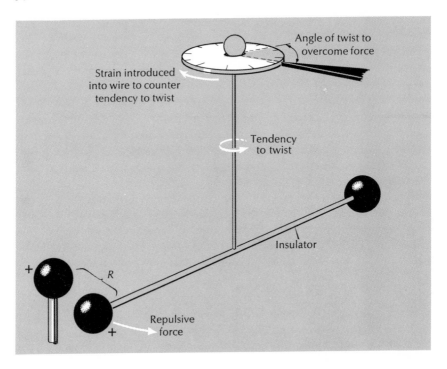

Fig. 5.1. Illustration of how the repulsion between two like positive charges was measured by Coulomb. The suspending wire was twisted to counteract the repulsive force and bring the charged metal ball back to its original position.

twist in degrees, which are familiar to many. One feature appears at once: as the distance R gets less, the angle of twist needed to bring back the charged ball to where it started, and hold it there, gets much greater. We are clearly dealing with an inverse relation, much as with gravity. If we try to relate this inverse relation with $1/R$, the feature of increase as R gets less is observed, but it does so weakly. Thus $1/R$ only increases by a factor of 20, from $\frac{1}{10}$ to 2, while the number of degrees goes from 2 to 800. We find that the use of $1/R^2$, the inverse square, does excellently: the way the degrees march up is exactly matched by the way the value of $1/R^2$ marches up. Coulomb could thus directly tell that electric charges repel in the same way that gravity attracts. If the kind of electricity on the ball which can swing is made into the opposite kind, "resinous" instead of "vitreous," then the balls have to be kept apart by twisting: this means that unlike charges attract. The behavior as regards distance is unchanged. The direction of the force is altered from *away*

TABLE 5.1

Distance between centers of charged objects (R)	1/R	1/R²	Angle of twist (Degrees)
10 inches	1/10	1/100	2.0
7 inches	1/7	1/49	4.1
5 inches	1/5	1/25	8.0
3 inches	1/3	1/9	22.2
2 inches	1/2	1/4	50.0
1 inch	1	1	200.0
1/2 inch	2	4	800.0

from each other to *toward* each other as the change from like to unlike is made.

So far this is a direct and satisfying study. But there is a harder problem, which is related to the very interesting property that the harder we rub to make electric charge, the greater the force. How, then, do we decide what the quantitative relation for the force is in terms of the electrification, in analogy with the effect of mass for gravity? This is another of the examples of what we have termed "breaking into a circle." We do not know what the magnitude of the electrification is until we have some relation which it obeys, and we can not find this relation until we know what electrification does. Coulomb broke into this closed circle by supposing that if he "charged" one brass ball and then touched it to another exactly similar ball, the "charge" would be shared equally and then he could study the effect of half the original "charge." (This trick can be worked for three, four and so on.) The conclusion he reached was that the force depends on the amount of electrification of each body in just the same way as it does with gravity.

By this method of study, Coulomb was able to show that the force between two charges depends on two factors. The first is that the force depends on the amount of electrification of either object. This "amount of electrification" we call the "electric charge," or more simply, the *charge*. The second factor is the distance apart. If the reader will allow us to draw a diagram and introduce a mathematical formula, we will attempt to repay him by making the formula clear. Suppose, as in Figure 5.2, the two electric charges are set a certain distance apart and suppose that the magnitude of the charges are q_1 on the left and q_2 on the right. Then the force F on each (equal and opposite, incidentally), shown by the dotted arrows, will obey the equation:

$$F = \frac{q_1 \times q_2}{R^2}$$

This is Coulomb's Law.

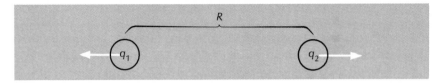

Fig. 5.2. Representation of two charges q_1 and q_2 a distance R apart. The force F between them is

$$F = \frac{q_1 \times q_2}{R^2}$$

This is Coulomb's law.

The $1/R^2$ part is no surprise: the more obscure part concerns the two charges. What are they? And how are they measured? It is interesting that today, after some centuries of obscurity, these questions can be given a satisfactory answer. The components of an electric charge are either protons, which are positive and relatively massive, or electrons, which are negative and so light as to seem to be "pure' electricity. As nearly as anything in the description of the physical world is exact, the numbers of protons and electrons are exactly equal. This perfection of matching is the reason why electricity, while so important in Nature, can be hidden so effectively. When amber is rubbed we perceive that something electrical has developed—but there are actually far less than one in a million electrons in excess of the protons which are also present. It is not surprising that even this very slight excess should be rather an oddity: it would seem to be much more normal to have no excess at all, which means things are, for the vastly greater part, electrically neutral.

While we sense insight for a moment about electrons and protons—of which we have heard at some time or another—it will not do to ignore the problem, faced by Coulomb and the early experts on electricity, of deciding what to do about measuring q_1 and q_2. The resolutions of this problem, like that of almost all measurement, can be seen in the evolution of clarity both in ideas and in techniques. Coulomb had to rely on the methods we described for getting charges which were even approximately of known size. However, this was by no means the only method by which Coulomb's Law, the law of force between electric charges, has been established. A very important indirect method is the most significant. This is the development of electrical theory. It is worth a few moments to consider this theory and the reasons why it is significant.

By and large electrical theory rests on three ideas. The first is purely geometrical and involves the fact that a relation such as $1/R^2$ and the area of a sphere (which is $4\pi R^2$) have a complementary aspect. See Figure 5.3.

If the force exerted by a charge at a radius R is multiplied by the area of the sphere of the same radius then a number which does not change is the result. This proves to be a trick of symmetry, or better, of geometry, which is most useful to the theorist. The second idea is that in a conductor the movement of any electrification is so easy that it can be supposed to happen for any small cause, so long as there is a cause. The third is that the positive and the negative charge are equal. With these ideas it is possible to construct a fairly elaborate theory of what is called "electrostatics." Among the early developers of this theory was Gauss.

When such a theory takes form it suggests that there are consequences which are interesting, and sometimes capable of test. The odd geometic relation between the law of electrostatic force (Coulomb's Law) and the sphere requires that it be impossible to put an electric charge on the inside of a good conductor: all the charge is always on the outside. This is capable of test, and the test was made first by Cavendish and then Maxwell. It proved to be right and so Coulomb's Law took on an added authority.

One of the hardest problems of communication between the scientist and the layman concerns just what we have described. The layman very much wants the scientist to tell him that so and so is true *because.* . . . Now that "because," if the scientist is honest and a good scientist, is practically never simple and practically never something short. A moment's reflection will show why this is. If it were true that any area of science had a simple "reason why," so simple that it could be explained

Fig. 5.3. The complementary relation between $\dfrac{1}{R^2}$ and the area of a sphere of radius R.

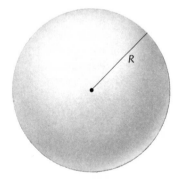

Big sphere, area $4\pi R^2$

$$4\pi R^2 \times \frac{1}{R^2} = 4\pi$$

Little sphere, area $4\pi r^2$

$$4\pi r^2 \times \frac{1}{r^2} = 4\pi$$

correctly to a child, then long ago that area would have been understood and accepted and really be a part of what we consider everyday affairs. The strange truth is that none, not one single aspect, of natural behavior comes in this class. The authors have been trying to devise examples, but there are none. So we have to accept the idea that the elegance and simplicity of science is *not* to be found in common sense and everyday concepts, but rather in developed and constructed abstractions. This may seem to be rather unattractive to a new student, and in one sense it is. But any person who has developed an intellectual interest in any area knows that he will encounter the same feature of developed abstraction no matter what the area.

Consider painting, for example. Try to paint so that it is worth looking at. It doesn't take long to realize that worthwhile painting involves a great deal of understanding of technique as well as a realization of the work of past artists. We have never subscribed to the school of thought which says the colors flung by whim at a canvas constitute art worth looking at. And we find that our artist friends agree with us. So the painter finds himself separated from the layman. He, too, cannot simply say "do this and you will have a fine painting." Rather, in such art, the reverse is true: It is harder to convey the ability to perform in art than it is in a science.

To return to Coulomb's Law. The two electrical charges which we have called q_1 and q_2* are not too easy to measure, but it can be done. One early way to "define' a unit charge was to say that if we put two equal unit charges at unit distance from one another, then they would produce a unit force. This system of definition, which we only give to provide the reader with an inkling of the way in which a scheme of electricity can be created, is called "the electrostatic system" of units. For now, all we ask is that Coulomb's Law be accepted as something both fundamental and of wide importance.

The reader may feel that because we have not stated very clearly what Coulomb meant by electric charge and how he measured it, that we are in a way "putting something over on him." In fact, the process of "breaking in" a new measurement is always difficult and arduous. We are all familiar with length and its measurement, but even there a long history of improvement took place before it settled down. Even now, better ways of measuring length are being devised. And the same is true

---

* It is a common practice to use subscripts to designate symbols. These subscripts are useful in that they can convey some sense of order—thus the charge on the metal ball 1 is called q_1. Subscripts must not be confused with the symbolism of "squares" and "cubes," which are written above, not below the line. Since subscripts are often used by theorists, we shall use them.

of measuring time. Now electric charge is really quite a new thought. The idea that electrification is quantitative introduces a new need and a new method of measurement, and it is necessary to use a certain amount of a pioneering attitude, to adopt imperfect measurements temporarily and to continue a process of refinement and modification until good, sound measurements can be made. These have been made, particularly in terms of other properties of electricity, and today the accurate measurement of electric charge is commonplace and simple.

Magnetism

The knowledge of magnetism is very old. It is so old that the origins of this knowledge are involved with legend, as that of a Cretan shepherd having his iron-tipped crook attracted to the ground and digging for, and finding, the lodestone ore which caused the attraction. A compass needle, constructed by fastening a piece of lodestone to a piece of wood and floating the assembly on water, was certainly known in the twelfth century. In the days of the Greek philosophers it was known that iron rubbed with lodestone became magnetic. In the middle of the thirteenth century, Peregrinus, one of the first experimenters, established the character of the poles of magnets and showed that they always occurred in pairs, and that like poles repel. Three hundred years later Gilbert followed the same kind of method, and deduced that the earth itself is a magnet. Two hundred years later still, Michel, and, independently, Coulomb, showed that the poles of magnets attracted or repelled according to the inverse square law, just as found for gravity or electricity. In the early part of the nineteenth century the subject of magnetism was made mathematically quantitative by Poisson.

All this discovery has played an important part in our knowledge of electricity, but not in the primary way in which it might have been expected. A seemingly small but highly significant difference between electricity and magnetism was observed by Gilbert and Peregrinus: in magnetism no north pole is ever found alone; there is always an accompanying south pole. This is traced ultimately to the nature of magnetism: it is a property of electricity *in motion* and is most notably due to the spinning of an electron or a proton about an axis, a process which we find to be inevitable and omnipresent.

We intend to return to the inherent nature of magnetism later. At the moment, we want to note that magnetism exists and that its presence can be shown with a compass needle. This will suffice until after we have described one of the most remarkable experiments in the whole of scientific study.

Galvani and Current Electricity

Galvani was a physiologist who worked just before the start of the nine-teenth century. He was interested in the action of nerve and muscle, and had observed that static electricity, developed by friction using one of the machines then in existence for producing electricity, would cause muscles in freshly killed frogs to contract. On one occasion he observed that such frogs, in which a brass wire was forced through the spinal column, showed muscular contraction when the wire touched both an iron plate and the legs of the frog in some way.

This extraordinary experiment, a combination of circumstances which nobody would suspect would have significance, started two large areas of discovery. One, of course, was the start of electrophysiology, the reali-zation that electrical action could cause muscular change. The other consequence was the realization that some kind of "current" could pass in a metal wire and that it was caused by two damp, dissimilar metals (iron and copper). It became worthwhile to make more of a study of this "galvanic" current, and an area of work, never before thought of, suddenly became of keen interest. Galvani himself discovered that the current could be made much more obvious by the right choice of metals. At almost the same time, Volta developed the "voltaic pile," a primitive battery consisting of a series of copper and zinc discs arranged alternately, with pads moistened with acid in between. A stack such as this, with twenty or so pairs, produces quite dramatic and obvious effects. Wires connected to the two opposite plates, when touched on the tongue, pro-duce a sharp effect, not to say a shock. A wire connected across the oppo-site plates becomes hot, as indeed do the plates themselves.

With this development of the battery, the new phenomenon became readily available for study, and it is not surprising that a series of dis-coveries followed. One of the most important was made by Oersted.

Magnetic Effect of a Current: Oersted's Experiment

The beginnings of discovery in a new area of knowledge are of a remarka-ble character. One has only to realize that the possession of a good voltaic battery should have been sufficient to discover magnetic effects, the production of light by heating a wire, and the chemical breakdown of solutions, known as electrolysis—all striking new effects. Yet these discoveries were not made within a few days by the first possessor of such potential power.

Volta's description of the voltaic pile was published in 1800. Some twenty years later, Oersted, a Danish professor, was allegedly setting out to show a class that there was no relation between current electricity and the compass needle, when he performed the experiment illustrated in Figure 5.4. A wire, which he could connect to a battery and thus cause a current to flow in it, was held above a compass needle. On connecting the wire to the battery Oersted observed that the compass needle swung around, and to his surprise, the needle seemed to want to point perpendicularly to the wire. After class he followed up the experiment (again, so the story goes) and made certain he really had found something he could repeat and which was a new relationship. For example, he showed that the needle, when placed *above* the wire, moved in the opposite direction, and also that reversing the direction of the electric current reversed the direction of the needle.

It was perfectly definite that the wire produced a magnetic effect, but the effect was in some way *around* the wire, and not particularly *along* the wire. It didn't seem to make too much sense to invent magnetic poles which came into existence with the current. Oersted's experiment can be made dramatic, and, indeed, obvious, by putting the needle inside a coil of wire of many turns. The upper part of the turns urges the magnet one way and the lower part in the same way, so that the magnet revolves, as can be seen from Figure 5.5. Thus, just as Volta was able to magnify the effect of his battery by many pairs of plates, so it is possible to increase the effect of a current on a compass needle by many turns of wire.

Almost as soon as the news of this discovery reached Paris, Ampère, a French physicist, began to make a thorough study of it. He showed that two electric currents would attract each other if they were flowing in the right direction and repel each other in the reverse direction. He had

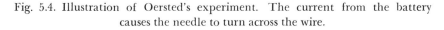

Fig. 5.4. Illustration of Oersted's experiment. The current from the battery causes the needle to turn across the wire.

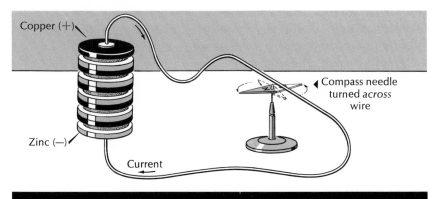

Copper (+)

Zinc (−)

Current

Compass needle turned *across* wire

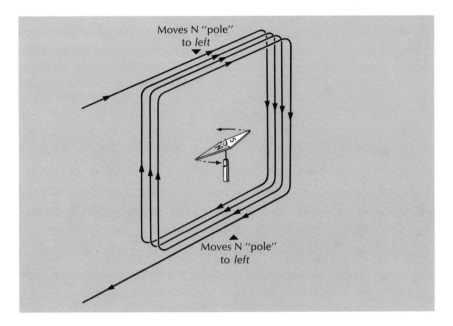

Fig. 5.5. The use of many turns of wire to magnify the effect of a current on a magnetic needle. The upper part of the turns all move the N "pole" to the left and the S "pole" to the right, and the lower turns, where the current is opposite, are now *below* the needle and also produce the same motion. Thus a small current can produce a big effect.

considerable talent for formal analysis and devised a theory by which he showed that the effect of an electric current was like a rather strange notion—a magnetic shell, which was, in Ampère's mind, a thin shell of many north poles on one side and many south poles on the other, rather a hard thing to make as an actual object, but in Ampère's imagination the means by which he could formulate the way in which the electric current caused its magnetic effects. His studies were so acute and his theory so effective that the unit of electric current has been named after him.

Thus two seemingly unrelated things, magnetism and current electricity, were found to be linked together. One of the strong characteristics of the later development of science has been the repeated discovery of such relationships, so that today it is possible to speak of the subject of chemistry being the same as that of atomic and molecular physics without being frivolous. We have already said that the ways in which science has found it necessary to explain the working of Nature are not exactly what one would characterize as simple or obvious. Indeed, the means by which the scientist looks at Nature do include vast ranges of phenomena. This link between electricity and magnetism is one of the earliest examples of the power of interpretation which has proved to result from accurate observation and description. Since then we have found it possible to link this combined subject of "electromagnetism" with that of light—a truly startling interpretation. This pattern of relationship seems to be inherent in Nature, so much so, that physicists are always alert for even wider relations—and they may yet be found.

The Formation of Scientific Societies

Since the time of Galileo and Newton there has been an acceleration in the tempo of discovery. When we consider the nineteenth century it becomes apparent that science itself picked up speed and moved forward sharply. The factors which contributed to the forward surge are many, but one which must be reckoned of importance is the growth of scientific societies. The earliest of these, hardly "scientific" in the present-day meaning of the word, was the Accademia dei Lincei, founded in 1603, which had a short early life just before and during the time of Galileo. Galileo was a member, and it is certain that the support, encouragement (and sometimes moderation) of Galileo by this small group of influential, courageous, and sharply inquiring individuals, was a factor in his productivity. Like some societies today, this Academy had a limited life, and the real growth of scientific societies became apparent with the formation of the Royal Society in England, in 1660.

The Royal Society began as an "invisible college" composed of a small group of scientists and intellectuals, including Wren, the architect, and Boyle. In 1660, after they had met informally for a number of years, they made the decision to form a society, with a membership limited to fifty-five. In the following year King Charles II indicated a desire to be a member, by which he meant much more than that simple fact; he felt the Society was doing something worthy of his support. From that time it has been "The Royal Society of London for Improving Natural Knowledge," always shortened to "The Royal Society." Almost at once the Society began publishing scientific discoveries and investigating scientific claims. Music written by Mozart at the age of six—he was then called "Theophilus"—is to be found in the "Philosophical Transactions." In the nineteenth century the number of scientific societies grew rapidly. Our own National Academy was formed in 1860. Specialized societies, like the "Physical Society of London" were formed at the end of the century. The American Physical Society was formed in 1899.

The process of forming scientific societies goes on today, in very much the same way, only more rapidly and more often. The author took part in the formation of the Biophysical Society, and the events leading up to it are of some interest. At a meeting of the already old and respectable American Physical Society, a room for an evening discussion was requested and all those who might be interested in biophysics were asked to come if they wished. The action necessary to do this was doubtless taken in one of the hallways at the meeting by a small group. At the evening discussion many voices were heard—urging immediate action, no action, challenges as to the content of the subject, its relation with other sciences, and so on. The one definite action taken was the organization of a small committee to plan some kind of scientific meeting. This committee met in another such evening discussion at a large convention of biologists, and there made definite plans to set up a National Biophysics Meeting, no society to be mentioned, just a gathering of those who wanted to give papers, and some invited talks to give broader interest. Several hundred attended the meeting. A "business" session was scheduled, and to nobody's surprise the group voted to form a society. In ten years the Biophysical Society had more than 1000 members, thus outstripping the Royal Society —but not the American Chemical Society, which has over 100,000 members.

Today scientific societies live a very sheltered and secure existence, with comfortable bank balances, and a rather special function, which is mostly to hold meetings to disseminate new findings, to publish papers, and to enable a certain amount of high level employment exchange activities to take place. This sheltered existence may become more strenuous and subject to discussion and controversy in the near future. Science is today intimately dependent on society in every nation, drawing its financial support from taxes and the national budget. Science has also grown so that research funds are now a visible item in every national budget; except for war emergencies this is the first time in history that such expenditure has taken place. It is to be expected that before long legislatures are going to ask what the scientists want to do with the research funds. At that point we may see scientific societies in a new role. Already our own National Academy has been asked to form committees to guide government expenditure for special kinds of research.

Even with their present limited function, scientific societies are of major importance to today's scientists. Almost every young scientist seeks to belong to at least one.

A Little Recapitulation

All the knowledge associated with science is by no means equally important. One of the essential beauties of science is the existence of a compact and small set of principles from which it is possible to describe and predict large amounts of behavior. It is not our purpose in this book to do much of the "working out," but it *is* our concern to know that there are principles and what most of them are. We can take it on faith that they work.

Now one essence of scientific thought is a certain degree of exactness. It is not nearly as rigorous as many people imagine, but in places it is quite careful. An analogy is driving a car. It is not enough to know which route to take to get to where you want to go: it is also necessary to keep to the right, to proceed on green, to stop at "stop" signs, to pass on the left and only when the road is clear, etc. The principles of physics are really fewer than the rules of the road, and like the rules of the road they must be understood correctly. Driving in the middle of the road is not the same as keeping to the right: acceleration is *not* the same as velocity.

So far we have five principles of importance. There are perhaps ten more total: it is debatable whether there are that many. The first three are all concerned with an absolutely primary idea, which concerns in its turn *all* our description. These are Newton's three Laws of Motion. These Laws

DEFINE A FORCE

SEGREGATE MOTION INTO THREE KINDS: NONE, UNIFORM SPEED, ACCELERATED

MEASURE FORCE IN TERMS OF MOVEMENT AND A KIND OF SIZE

POINT OUT THAT FORCES OCCUR IN PAIRS

Students usually encounter two difficulties in working with these three Laws. The first is the meaning of "acceleration." It is an easy enough concept, really rather common, and is often called colloquially, for cars, bicycles, airplanes, etc., "pickup." It is *not* the very simplest kind of motion, which is speed or velocity, but is one stage more subtle, one stage further in description.

$$\text{Speed or velocity is } \frac{\text{distance changed}}{\text{time}}$$

$$\text{Acceleration is } \frac{\text{speed changed}}{\text{time}}$$

Force is not concerned with velocity, but it *is* concerned with acceleration.

The second difficulty is the meaning of "mass." A bigger, bulkier, denser object needs more force to move it. The property associated with size, bulk, and denseness we call "mass." The "quantity of matter" in an object is a loose way to give an impression of its mass. Unfortunately, an object which is big and dense also weighs more: it is harder to hold up. Notice the word "up." It is the clue to the meaning of the word "weight," which is related to the earth's gravitational pull and also to the "quantity of matter." When you take your trip to the moon your mass will be unchanged; nothing will leave you or come into you. But the moon will pull you only one-sixth as much as the earth did: your weight will be only one-sixth as much as it was on earth. What is meant by "weight" is really rather difficult and complicated: it depends on several circumstances. What is meant by "mass" is much simpler. In this book we are rarely concerned with weight, but often with mass.

The fourth important principle is the Law of Universal Gravitation:

$$F = \frac{GMm}{R^2}$$

The fifth is Coulomb's Law of Electric Force:

$$F = \frac{q_1 q_2}{R^2}$$

The words "inversely proportional" seem to induce some insecurity in some people. "Inversely proportional" means that one thing gets bigger as another thing gets less, and less as the other gets bigger. As the time before the dentist starts drilling decreases, so does our anxiety increase. Instead of the ratio remaining the same, the *product* remains the same.

With these few remarks, we are in a position to move on to still more discovery and also to introduce one of the basic concepts of physics: the idea of a field. This will occupy the next chapter.

Suggestions for Further Thought

1. Compare and contrast Newton's Law of Universal Gravitation and Coulomb's Law.
2. Refer to the data given in Table 5.1. Plot a graph of angle of twist against $1/R^2$. Interpret your graph. Does your interpretation agree with Coulomb's Law?
3. The hydrogen atom consists of an electron (mass $= 9.1 \times 10^{-28}$ gm. and $q = -4.8 \times 10^{-10}$ e.s.u.) and a proton (mass $= 1.7 \times 10^{-24}$ gm. and $q = 4.8 \times 10^{-10}$ e.s.u.). The separation between the electron and proton is 5.3×10^{-9} cm. Calculate the ratio of electrostatic to gravitational force between the two particles.
4. A scrap of paper with mass 0.001 gm. carries a negative charge e. A glass rod carrying an equal amount of positive charge is placed 1 cm. away and the scrap of paper is observed to be balanced between the gravitational force and the electrostatic force. If each unit of charge has a value of 4.8×10^{-10} e.s.u., calculate the number of charges on the scrap of paper.

References

Guy C. Omer, Jr., H. L. Knowles, B. W. Mundy, and W. H. Yoho, *Physical Science: Men and Concepts* (Boston: D. C. Heath, 1962).

E. C. Stoner, *Magnetism and Atomic Structure* (New York: E. P. Dutton, 1926).

The Kite Experiment

PETER COLLINSON, ESQ; F. R. S. LONDON.

Oct. 19, 1752.

Sir:

As frequent mention is made in public papers from Europe of the success of the Philadelphia experiment for drawing the electric fire from clouds by means of pointed rods of iron erected on high buildings, etc., it may be agreeable to the curious to be informed that the same experiment has succeeded in Philadelphia, though made in a different and more easy manner, which is as follows:

Make a small cross of two light strips of cedar, the arms so long as to reach the four corners of a large thin silk handkerchief when extended; tie the corners of the handkerchief to the extremities of the cross, so you have the body of a kite; which being properly accommodated with a tail, loop, and string, will rise in the air, like those made of paper; but this being of silk is fitter to bear the wet and wind of a thunder gust without tearing. To the top of the upright stick of the cross is to be fixed a very sharp pointed wire, rising a foot or more above the wood. To the end of the twine, next the hand, is to be tied a silk ribbon, and where the silk and twine join, a key may be fastened. This kite is to be raised when a thunder-gust appears to be coming on, and the person who holds the string must stand within a door or window, or under some cover, so that the silk ribbon may not be wet; and care must be taken that the twine does not touch the frame of the door or window. As soon as any of the thunder clouds come over the kite, the pointed wire will draw the electric fire from them, and the kite, with all the twine, will be electrified, and the loose filaments of the twine will stand out every way, and be attracted by an approaching finger. And when the rain has wet the kite and twine, so that it can conduct the electric fire freely, you will find it stream out plentifully from the key on the approach of your knuckle. At this key the phial may be charged; and from electric fire thus obtained, spirits may be kindled, and all the other electric experiments be performed, which are usually done by the help of a rubbed glass globe or tube, and thereby the sameness of the electric matter with that of lightning completely demonstrated.

B. FRANKLIN

Recollections of an Indicator Man

Last night I had dinner with Captain W. L. Pryor, once of the U.S.S. *Semmes*. Talking with him brought back some vivid memories concerning the first navigational radar ever installed on a ship in the United States, and they are worth putting down because there really never has been a good record of any part of the operation of the Radiation Laboratory at M.I.T., which was one of the larger civilian scientific units mobilized during World War II.

Actually how scientists got into the Radiation Lab is of some interest. In my case, it was at the request of Ernest Lawrence, in November of 1940. At that time I was a member of the physics department at Yale. Lawrence explained that it probably would not be long before we were involved in the war then raging between England and Germany, and that it would be worthwhile to spend some time away from nuclear physics and help to get us prepared. The implication was that after a year of this work I could go back to splitting atoms and again be in the forefront of nuclear physics, but that it would be worth taking the year then. So I made the usual arrangements with the chairman of my department, Mr. Watson, left the cyclotron that I had just built, and disappeared into the security of Room 4-133 which then housed the Radiation Laboratory at M.I.T.

I was assigned to the indicator group, then run by an M.I.T. engineer named Bill Hall. All the preparation I had ever had for radar work consisted of teaching sophomore physicists at Yale, having gone through the Cavendish Laboratory as a nuclear physicist, and having generally worked in the nuclear physics of that age, including building a cyclotron. To say that I knew nothing about radar felt like a great understatement. The most frustrating thing of all was that nobody would tell me either. The reason they wouldn't tell me was very simple: they just had no time. What I would do was to get a sort of garbled account of the state of affairs, and go away and begin working. The garbled account was distributed by one or two of the "old-timers"—men who had been in the operation perhaps six weeks. They informed me that we were working on microwave radar, that it was intended to help the British in the night Battle of Britain, that we had the objective of putting together some parts that had already been ordered, and that these were to be an operational system observing ground echoes by February 1. We were to see echoes from an airplane by March 1, and to have a set installed in a bomber and working by April 1. Beyond that we weren't thinking. My job was fairly vital because I was assigned to the part which showed what the radar detects, and makes it of some use.

I arrived in the indicator group in a very befuddled, but nevertheless dedicated condition on January 2, 1941, and promptly began working. At first, working consisted of discussing all possible ways of indicating. We also looked at the indicator that had been ordered from RCA according to some specifications laid down by, I believe, an influential Welshman named Bowen, and presumably copied from the miracle workers of the British laboratories, who had already installed radar in their planes. This indicator consisted of a vast cornucopia with one end closed off and with a screen of some kind on it on which faint spots appeared which could be moved back and forth and which hopefully was to take the signal from the radar set. It was almost as big as an airplane and really about as hopeless a thing as could be imagined. I was rather pleased later when I did actually fly a radar set to find that at least we had obtained priority to put one of these on an airplane. It was put facing a curious direction with no room for anybody to sit by it, and in broad daylight, where it could never have been seen anyway. The reader can very easily detect the solid hatred I conceived for this monstrosity the moment I saw it. Yet we used to go and fondle it and think about it because after all it was real, and in principle it could, and perhaps one day might, have signals on it.

After what must have been a very short time but seemed to include a great many developments we in the indicator group began to take shipment of a few indicator tubes. These tubes were the forerunners of modern TV tubes, they operated on a different principle from what we already had and really showed promise of being used to display the position of one or more aircraft ahead of another aircraft. There was at least hope for it. At about this time we put together the first crude model of an indicator which could go in an airplane and be put where somebody would look at it. I more or less elected myself to the job of getting this on an aircraft because I did feel that although everything else about the radar—the pulser, the transmitter, and the receiver—was operating, what the heck was the good of a radar that hadn't any way to show where an airplane was?

On the way to being put on board the plane I encountered one of the experts at the hanger, who has since done great things. He saw me arrive and observed, rather pityingly it seemed to me—he certainly looked quite supercilious—that it was highly hand-made to say the least of it, and he promptly began to drop it. I don't remember correctly, but I think I caught it before it hit. He then explained to me that anything that went on an airplane had to be able to take shock, et cetera, and he therefore would begin by testing it right then. The traumatic effect of this experience is still with me, and I think it is now apparent to this particular expert just what he did, not in terms of a potentially wounded indicator, but in the effect on the sensitive soul of an indicator man who for the first time thought he might see signals in an airplane. Anyway, when he sees me now he wonders rather plaintively whether I'll ever forget the incident.

The trip that was taken with this B-18 * proved to be historic in two respects. The first was that the indicator did work, in a very feeble and inadequate way. During the flight a ship was observed on the water. Instructions were given by Mr. Bowen to the pilot to fly a wiggly course (which still appears in my notebook) as a course to follow to see whether the radar did actually see the echo of the ship. The idea was to have it swing from side to side to be sure that we had actually seen the ship and that it wasn't just some rock or object, or merely what today in biology we call an artefact of the viewer. So this peculiar bank and turn course was flown, with me observing the indicator, and we did indeed see this object, the first ship echo ever seen by a microwave set from an airplane. At least so I think, although I have no doubt the British will dispute this. However, this is my account and not theirs.

At the moment I didn't realize what had been done to me physically by this operation; I was too much interested in the whole process, this being the very first time I'd been up in an airplane anyway. However, on the way down the second important event occurred—as we landed I became violently sick. This sickness was sufficiently vigorous to convince the other members on board that airborne radar was not for me. The two conclusions—that we had seen so clearly a ship with the set and that I seemingly had no aptitude for flying—resulted in my being assigned to putting an indicator on the *Semmes*. This was the first shipboard navigational radar ever built in the United States.

Being an indicator man, it fell to me to prepare a plan-position indicator, better known as PPI, and the usual weighty laboratory technical decision was taken as to how to do this. The indicator group, which by then had become full of competent and, to my thinking, starry-eyed talent, contained a number of electronic experts who were hot and heavy on putting together a brand new indicator. The technical problem of such an indicator is really very simple. You have at the center of the indicator you yourself—namely, the ship or airplane— you then send the sweep, which is a moving bright spot, out radially, which means straight out, and you want it to go straight out in the direction in which the radar set is pointing. As you do not want the radar set to point in one direction all the time—it obviously needs to look all around—it turns, so you want this spot to go out from the

---

* The B-18 was a slow old crate. Not many were made because they were obviously death traps. They were never used as bombers in World War II, but they existed in 1940, and one of them came our way for laboratory use.

center and show the direction in which the radar is pointing. Then, when the echo comes back from the illuminated object, it comes back with the velocity of light, and this you can show as a little extra-bright spot which shows the correct range and, of course, the correct bearing. The only problem was how to do this. Two ways were suggested. The major problem is that of making the spot go out from the center in the direction of the antenna. To do this, the indicator group proposed to use a wholly electronic method. The British had already done it by a mechanical method. Since I was recognized as the eager beaver who wanted to see results, and since unquestionably it would be nice to have one working right away, I was elected to be part of the group that actually put this indicator, on the British plan, on board the *Semmes.*

To achieve this purpose I was transferred, by some machination or other, to the "roof" group—about a dozen reputedly wild men who actually had one or more operating radars on the roof of Building 6 of M.I.T. and were doing weird and wonderful things behind a very interesting guard who looked with great disfavor on anyone who came up there.

Already in those days, even though we were not recognized by any army or navy outfit, we had our own curious security ideas, and the completed radar was somehow special. Those who worked downstairs in indicators or receivers had a feeling that they were not encouraged to go up and look at it. Nobody really produced this policy at all. It was just a sort of impression we had. (Maybe I had it more than others because I have always thought I had a conscience, though on occasion I have been able to hold it in abeyance.) When I penetrated up into their weird group, I got quite a different impression. The roof was a small, hurriedly constructed, later feverishly-added-to place. There undeniably was a peculiar object which rotated around and around but mostly stayed on one place, with a high-pitched whining sound that kept going all the time, and which after a while you forgot, except when it stopped and you became acutely conscious of it. A group of people milled around it with great vigor.

There was a very fine quotation which somebody cut out of one of the front pages of a newspaper and put on the bulletin board. "What we know here is very little; but what we are ignorant of is immense." Everybody liked that, and it certainly fitted our mood.

Into this milling throng I was plunked, and told that I had to put an indicator on board the *Semmes* where there already were people installing the remainder of the set. I found, as is very often the case, that the bootleg scientific operation such as has been immortalized in the movie, *The Man in the White Suit,* had already been going, and there was this peculiar bootleg operation in which a PPI had already been begun. I don't really know who began this PPI. I have a feeling it was Zacharias, but I'm not sure. Anyway, I inherited what I really consider to be the most grisly mess that any person ever had. The thing that seemed to be available was a sort of a copper can which some out-fit in town had made a dozen or so of, and which would take these new indicator tubes. So here was this can and here was the tube. Undeniably we had a tube. Somebody had cut holes in the narrow end of the can and installed a little yoke which had windings on it and these windings had to rotate, so there were some slip rings and there were contacts which consisted of little feeble pin-like objects and small springs to hold them in place. I was overjoyed by this because it looked as if a great deal had already been done. I promptly put it to one side and forgot it and began work on the circuit which was to produce the sweeps and everything else. Being at that time enamored of vacuum tubes and cir-cuits, I punched holes and drilled and soldered and assembled trans-formers and all kinds of things. In probably not more than three weeks I had something more or less ready to try to drive the indicator.

I have not said anything about Larry Marshall, and this does little justice to the individual or to the group. Larry Marshall, who is still active, and probably will read this, was then the head of the Roof group. He is a very charming and wholly deceptive individual. One never knew whether he knew what was going on or not, but he had a handsome appearance and a charming manner and that kind of air of conviction which somehow got you doing things. It was known that Larry Marshall spoke to the group of individuals who ran the lab. Who they were nobody knew, but somehow one had the feeling that the lab did have direction, not that it mattered much but it did have it, and Larry Marshall would disappear down the stairs for various intervals and after one of these he came back and approached me and said it was time to put the indicator on board the *Semmes*. I explained that the indicator was not working yet and that the circuit was no good and that I had not even had time to try the actual rotating mechanism or even see whether there were any signals. Larry conceded that this was something that ought to be worried about, and suggested that I actually delay the operation slightly and go down tomorrow morning instead of today. That would give me time to do everything else. So I gulped and proceeded to assemble and put all the parts of this indi-cator together for the first time. I was told where it would have to go, that a space had been allocated for me, and that there would be no problem there, and I did indeed succeed in at least getting the end of the tube to light up. I had never seen whether a signal would hit it. This was some remote goal probably never to be achieved by me, but certainly so far away that I did not have to think about it. All I had to worry about was whether the circuit of the diagram was finished, whether it would fit into where it had to go. The rest was off in the wild blue yonder. So the next day or approximately the next day, I picked up with this immense copper can and a tube and the god-awful slip rings and the chassis, and went to New London. We arrived at Fort Trumbull and the first problem began.

The navy, though not yet at war—this was April or May of 1941— had a curious coyness about what its ships did. One just never did know officially where the *Semmes* was going to be. There was a sort of a bootleg way of finding out. This consisted of going to Fort Trumbull and asking. No one would answer until that really human look of distress came over our faces. It is interesting that security is fundamentally limited by human behavior; when you produce a look of distress somebody will break down and tell you what you need to know. At Fort Trumbull we were finally told: "Well, look, they go out every day, and they're back as a rule by five. I saw 'em go out this morning, and if you just sit here and wait, you'll probably find the *Semmes* come in."

This, it proved, was all right, so all we had to do was wait for about five hours on the dock at Fort Trumbull. By the time we had secured hotel accommodations and gone into New London and come back, all the time guarding our precious and highly secret equipment, the time did pass. Later I was to learn that a wait for a mere five hours was essentially the passage of a short instant of time, but at that time I didn't know this, and I remember building up considerable frustration about it. However, at five o'clock or so the *Semmes* did wander in and tied up, and then we had to talk our way on board. This proved to be not as hard as we had thought, because without realizing it, we were exactly the kind of people that the *Semmes* was used to. The *Semmes* was kept for various kinds of experimental work and was an old World War I "tin can" with four stacks and all the trimmings, one of the destroyers involved in the "lend-lease" deal between Roosevelt and Churchill. Before long we were hailed by somebody we knew. I think it was Sam Seely who was on board at the time and who had been installing the modulator and the "spinner" which was a Sperry gyroscope antenna, a flimsy construction intended for aircraft operation which was stuck up fairly high on the front mast on a platform which had already been put there. I privately thanked God that I wouldn't have a great deal to do up in that region because I don't like heights, at least wobbly heights, but as it turned out I got quite used to it, indeed, I got to like the place up there.

We climbed on board and began assembling the indicator into place.

Here we discovered one of the delightful features of collaboration with the navy, and, in fact, the armed services in general. I found this to hold true all the way through the war: the only time you can collaborate with the armed services is when they are not working, because when they are working they have a set routine of tolerably useless operation, which they nevertheless go through grimly and formidably, and you play no part in that; but when they are not working, they will go completely away and leave you alone. If you can learn to operate with nobody around to tell you anything or to discuss anything with you at all, you can do great things. At first this seemed an injustice, and for some time we did burn and curse and try to find the underbodies who were left on board the ship to tell you where the power was and so forth. Gradually we discovered that really there was nothing on board this ship that was for us, that the only purpose was to have a floating platform to get out to sea with one day, and that we had to put everything on board. Fortunately, M.I.T. had a telephone, and by getting back to the hotel and by using guarded language, we could call our friends back there and hash over what had occurred. And this was Larry Marshall's strong point, one which gives me considerable affection for him. If you could get him on the other end of the phone, he would listen and ask questions and take the casual way of his. But in a remarkably short time three people would arrive, always with the wrong things that didn't fit, but carrying with them that air of bouyancy and enthusiasm, and above all, they were three other people to think of methods to improvise, and you would have that sense of belonging and contact which was totally lacking at Fort Trumbull, on the *Semmes,* or anywhere.

As a result of doing this, the indicator got put in. The selsyns, of which we had about the only two in the United States that were not allocated to something, were connected up. The spinner was made to rotate. The peculiar object in the copper can that I have described did for the first time consent to rotate, and we had actually a plan position indicator for the first time on board a ship.

The second phase of an operation such as this is that each member of an engineering team is responsible for one part. You will notice that I have concentrated on the indicator. Well, at the same time somebody was concentrating on the transmitter, and somebody else on the receiver. The likely thing would be that the guy on the transmitter had been out for two days before and it had started working but had just now failed, so he was rushing back to M.I.T. to pick up a new one and talk his way into getting one that might be reliable. The receiver man would be busily wiring up something to make a connection between one plug of one kind which he had been given at the lab and a plug of another kind which he had found down at New London. I myself was in the same stage of a similar kind of operation. Getting the whole thing to work together was essentially an impossibility because each man was busy on his own job. However, curiosity did get the better of us, and after something like three weeks of this kind of operation, going back and forth to M.I.T. and fitting in with the curious routine of the ship, we did succeed in getting the whole outfit together and operating and seeing echoes which did actually begin to appear on this PPI of mine.

I can still remember them. The tube was a purely theoretical concept, again of the British, in which the front surface was a pale, greasy looking yellow-green object, very sickly, and the back surface was a blue screen which was supposed to be excited by the electrons and give out blue light. The blue light was supposed to excite the sickly-looking yellow surface and cause it to fluoresce, and the two together were supposed to give you (a) sensitivity and (b) persistence. I didn't know it, but at the time I was longing for just an ordinary straightforward T.V. screen which later I discovered did exist and which would have been most beautiful to have had. The yellow surface had come away in places and the blue had also come away in places, and so as the spot went around it either flashed up blue or yellow and had a peculiar, sickly appearance. The word, "sickly" comes into my mind for reasons which will be obvious to anyone who has been on a World War I destroyer, and it is not at all without psychological connection that it keeps weaving in as a thread.

Well, the line of varicolored light did leave the center, and as I wound around the control, which was a small knob, and which ultimately had control of the antenna, the line of light would move around, supposedly going to the edge of the tube. This would have been a lovely, attractive, nice-looking sweep which would have been the dearest and most beautiful sight that my eyes could have conceived. However, to do this would have taken something like a thousand volts, and all I had available was about 108. The result was that about one or two inches of the center of the tube had a rather short sweep on it, and within this tiny radius all the operation was confined. I regretted this, but it was the best indicator I had. I remember it very well now, I can almost see it. On this the echoes appeared—the bridge at New London was a nice one, and the various rocks and objects out in the harbor were quite good too. As I would turn this thing around, peculiar objects varying in size from a good-sized pea to sometimes as big as a dime would appear. These were echoes, and since I, at the time, had not learned how to keep focus on the tube, the bigger the echo, the more the tube defocussed, the bigger the blob got, the less beautiful it appeared, so that one had a horrible conflict between a beautiful echo that the receiver and transmitter men were delirious about, and a big boomed-up dime-like object which depressed me intensely, so that here a little scientific dichotomy occurred which isolated me.

This whole thing began to work slightly better, but at this stage the accursed slip rings began to give out. I can think of no language strong enough to describe these slip rings. They wore down. They failed to make contact, which would leave the central spot either brightly on or totally missing, or if they suddenly made contact there would be a beautiful and glorious flash on the screen to be followed by total darkness as they failed to make contact, and this again induced a very bad state of mind.

However, we did ultimately one Thursday take off and go on a trip with the *Semmes*. I didn't realize it at the time, but I was about to have my day. The *Semmes* was associated with submarines, and it would go out somewhere about thirty or forty miles into the near Atlantic and there it would undergo "exercises" with submarines. As far as we could ever tell, the exercises consisted of somebody pinging sounds on the sonar and somebody else shaking their head. I have reason to believe that the sonar equipment did occasionally detect submarines and that there was some value to the exercises, but to my untutored eyes they were entirely futile. They were, nevertheless, of great importance. It was quite clear, or so it seemed to us, that Captain Pryor regarded all our radar operations as effervescent nothingnesses of a group of unfortunate individuals that he had to tolerate because he was told to do so, while the real business was to ping away and shake one's head.

On the trip the radar actually worked. We began picking up objects. We discovered to our surprise and delight that we could actually see buoys, and we tracked these along. We saw other ships and so forth, all at very small distances, and then on a Friday I had my day. I must have been pretty thoroughly sick most of this time because I have no real recollection of what went on. I do remember putting my head into the hood with which one watched the horrible spot going around and standing it as long as I could before disappearing to the side to gain that moment of release and then going back and doing this all over again. It was really quite a devotion to the cause, and I know that many radar operators who may read this one day will have a feeling of kinship with me as I describe it. But on Friday, just as it would have been nice to get into harbor for the weekend, one of the fogs they have around there descended. I discovered quite vividly that fog does stop operations on the water. The scheduled thing to do when fog occurs is to stop, anchor, and wait until the fog lifts. When the *Semmes*, which was quite a thin vessel, stopped even in a relatively calm sea, it began to roll from side to side, a motion I found very hard to get accustomed to. So I had a very strong and compelling reason to get back into harbor, and so did everybody else on the boat, though for quite different reasons from mine. Mine were immediate.

So we kept the radar fired up, and I found to my great joy that I actually could see approximately half a mile ahead and that I could detect an object which I was convinced was a buoy. Now all one had to do was to find the next buoy, because there are enough of them out there so that if you find one and can go to the next, the expert navigators can do the job, and you can get into harbor. I was convinced that this was a buoy. I succeeded in persuading Captain Pryor—though I found since that he was only too anxious to do it anyway and it was simply his manner that made me think he needed persuading—to move the *Semmes* over in the direction of this small blue pea-like object on my screen which I thought was a buoy. It wasn't where he thought it would be, but he did go over, and after a while I could see that the object was essentially right straight in the center and was coming closer. I went out and began looking where I thought it was. This is one of my moments of triumph, because of course I am not an expert at looking through the fog, and there were approximately 65 people scanning through the fog in order to find the buoy. If we could get one buoy, there was hope of getting in. I was, bless my soul, the first person to see it with my eye, and I was able to give the excited yell, not too excited because of the physical discomforts I was experiencing inside, and point accurately to where the buoy was.

Not only was I able to do this once, but a fair number of times at shorter and shorter intervals, until finally we were in close enough, where the fog wasn't too bad, and we were able to make our mooring more or less on time. This got us in for the weekend, which I still feel, even now, to be the important achievement. Captain Pryor, I discovered, proceeded to get on the telephone to the right people in Washington and explain that not only was navigational radar an actuality but it had even been of some use, and that there should be no fooling around with it. Last night I was told that not only did we bring in the *Semmes*, but that three submarines had also followed us in, which I had not known before. So a reasonably good weekend was provided for probably something like four hundred people as a result of the operations of this PPI.

The rest of the story is to me of not such great interest. The operation of building the "SG," as it got to be called, was given to two very competent engineers, Bill Hall and Bill Tuller, who had been transferred to the Raytheon Company, and they did a fine job. As a result, in very short time, the navy did have navigational radar which they made excellent use of.

As for my own further adventures, there were some on the *Semmes*.

I think of it only with affection. It is very hard to describe that curious position the civilian scientist has on board a navy vessel. There is a mood of what might be called friendly hostility. It is not exactly sympathy, nor is it understanding. There is a kind of tolerance, which is really a very fine thing. Probably it is too much to expect sympathy in human beings on any broad, large-scale operation, and certainly one cannot expect understanding, but tolerance may really be the formula around which the world can operate, and this is what one had on board the *Semmes*.

At odd intervals we would discover that we were not alone on board. There were of course the sonar people, and then later a peculiar group of very high-powered people came from the Naval Research Lab who knew all the ropes and who put up a mattress antenna for a long-wave radar. I am convinced it never worked, but it probably did. They were of course in full command of the situation. They knew how to address officers and so forth, and they were not always endeavoring to convert the crew into the proper designation of places on the ship. I remember the trouble we had with upstairs and downstairs and front and back, and it took quite a while before we got the people in the wardroom to recognize these words. One memory I have is of Dr. Mouzon. I found him one day downstairs, a long way downstairs, working on an immense cable. This cable had what looked to me like a thousand ends to it, and he was patiently connecting them, just one wrong from the way the telephone company said to do it. He was doing this under what I considered not ideal conditions, with patience and determination. I've always had a considerable respect for him. Not that his job was any worse than mine, looking into the PPI, but I have a feeling that I got my moment of triumph and maybe he never did, and yet of course we both did what we had to do and I had the luck.

It is really a very fine story in many respects. Perhaps not enough people know the way in which a scientific operation like this is put through. The account I have given has in it the elements of any operation, even those going on today.

ERNEST C. POLLARD, 1958

omit ch. 6
Except. 123 ff.

6

Faraday, Henry, and Electromagnetism: The Idea of a Field

The method of discovery used in physical science has changed in recent times, and now a dual approach, characterized by the words "experimentalist" and "theorist," has emerged as a rather set pattern. As short a time as a century ago, the great men of science were mostly both theorists and experimentalists—that is to say, they framed hypotheses in quite mathematical terms, worked them out as mathematical exercises in many cases, and also designed experiments in the laboratory to test their hypotheses. While this type of man has not by any means wholly disappeared—as witness remarkable men like Enrico Fermi, one of the inventors of the nuclear reactor—there is no doubt that the experimentalist, the expert in the laboratory, generally has well-defined characteristics, notably a skill in designing instruments, in making them, and in making them work, as well as a certain sharp ability to criticize the experiments of others. The theorist is different: he is usually well-versed in mathematical technique, a vigorous arguer, prone to an interest in curious puzzles, and very often a good amateur musician. One of the first superb experimentalists was Michael Faraday (1791-1867), and it is of interest to consider him as a person as well as to see what it was that he discovered in the areas which are of importance to us.

Faraday was the son of a blacksmith, a trade in which skill is not trivial. At the age of thirteen he started to work in a bookstore, and at fourteen to learn the trade of bookbinding, also a skilled trade. By the time he was twenty-one he had read as much as he could find about science, performed what experiments he could afford, and attended a few "popular lectures" at the Royal Institution in London, where the same series of popular lectures is still going on today. Some of these lectures were given by Sir Humphry Davy, one of the great and influential men in English science just after the beginning of the nineteenth

115

century. Davy invented the first practical miner's safety lamp for use with open flames, the only means of lighting at the time, and he had, for those days, quite an elaborate laboratory. After one of the lectures Faraday applied to Davy for a position as laboratory assistant, and got the job.

This letter, by Davy about Faraday, was read at the meeting of the managers of the Royal Institution on March 18, 1813.

Sir Humphry Davy has the honor to inform the managers that he has found a person who is desirous to occupy the situation in the Institution lately filled by William Payne. His name is Michael Faraday. He is a youth of twenty-two years of age. As far as Sir H. Davy has been able to observe or ascertain, he appears well fitted for the situation. His habits seem good; his disposition active and cheerful, and his manner intelligent. He is willing to engage himself on the same terms as given to Mr. Payne at the time of quitting the Institution.

On hearing this, the managers made this resolution:

Resolved—That Michael Faraday be engaged to fill the situation lately occupied by Mr. Payne, on the same terms.

Faraday worked at the Royal Institution for the rest of his life. He is interesting because he is an early example of a scientist making his own way; he did not, like Cavendish, for example, have an independent income. In this respect he is to be compared to Mozart, an early musician-composer who attempted to make a living of it and not depend on the good graces of some Duke. The earning power of science is apparently better than that of music: Mozart had a hard life and died relatively young, while Faraday grew to hold a position of great respect, though not of wealth.

Faraday was described vividly and with deep emotion by his successor, Tyndall, in a series of discourses on Faraday's work. The great experimentalist appears as an imaginative, careful individual, modest about status, forceful about scientific fact, capable of hard work and single-minded steady purpose, and having an innate kindliness toward others. He was happily married and it meant much to him. He lived on an adequate income and rejected ways to add considerably to his means. He was orderly and methodical: he numbered his paragraphs of description consecutively—from 1 to 16041! Tyndall said of him: "not half his greatness was incorporate in his science, for science could not reveal the bravery and delicacy of his heart."

We are concerned with two phenomenon discovered by Faraday, one completely his own, and another which was independently discovered 3,000 miles away by Henry, in Albany, New York, at about the same time. The first was that a magnetic field exerts a force on a current of electricity, a phenomenon now used to a large extent in electric motors;

the second was that a changing magnetic field produces an electric current, which is the discovery in which Henry should also have a claim. Both are concerned with an *idea,* one which we have been busily using in the last sentence: the idea of a *field.*

Fields

AN ELECTRIC CURRENT IS CAUSED TO MOVE WHEN NEAR A MAGNET

If, as Oersted found, a magnetic needle moves when it is near a current, then Newton's Third Law, the law of action and reaction, requires that the electric current experience a force due to the presence of the magnet. That this is so was shown most convincingly by Faraday, though both Ampère and Arago certainly knew of it also. Faraday's experiment, done on Christmas day, 1821, can be understood by looking at Figure 6.1. (This is not Faraday's experiment, but it is much easier to see what takes place in terms of this later experiment.) If a magnet is made in the form of a "horseshoe" (a word we put in quotes because

Fig. 6.1. An Illustration of Faraday's discovery of motion of a current near a magnet. This must happen because the law of action and reaction requires that if a current exert a force on a magnet a magnet must exert a force on a current.

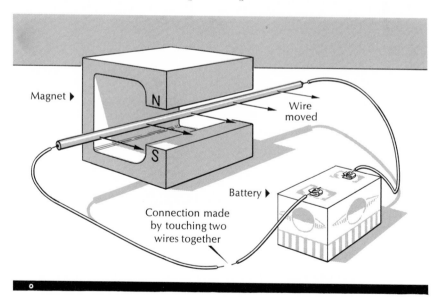

the poles actually face each other and this would be a shade uncomfortable for a horse), a strong magnetic effect can be created in the
space between the two poles. If a wire is introduced between the poles
and arranged to be free to move—for example, if one person holds it
there while someone else completes the experiment—then a connection
to a battery can be made. When this is done, the wire moves in the
rather odd way shown. The force on the wire is neither in the direction
of the current, nor toward either of the two poles of the magnet, but in
the third direction, which is perpendicular to both the others. This
odd behavior, which an old teacher used to describe as knocking a man
down by hitting him on the chin and then seeing him fall sideways,
is one of the unexpected things about electric and magnetic effects,
and it shows that there is something not quite simple in the relationship of the forces we have been describing. This lack of simplicity we
will later trace to a cause: the magnetic force we have just described
is due to electricity *in motion:* the force discussed in Coulomb's Law
is due to electricity *at rest.* The two have different characteristics, as
we have just seen. We will discuss this later on.

It would be a shame to leave out Faraday's actual experiment, because
it is so very elegant. His apparatus is shown in Figure 6.2. Faraday
wanted to see the wire with the current flowing in it rotate continuously, because this was, in itself, an achievement, and it also made a
strong demonstration. He had the idea of immersing one end of the
wire in mercury—which is a metal, and hence a conductor, and also
liquid, so the wire is free to move—and then pushing one pole of a
magnet in the shape of a rod through the mercury and near the hanging
wire. The wire was of platinum, which is not magnetic, and it hung
down touching the top of the magnet until the current was created
by connecting the hook at the top and the pool of mercury at the
bottom to the battery. Faraday's experiment showed that when this
happened the wire was urged to one side, left the magnet, and constantly rotated in the manner shown. Increasing the current made
the wire rotate faster.

A CHANGING MAGNETIC ACTION PRODUCES AN ELECTRIC CURRENT

Faraday's second discovery was that there can be a production of
electrical effects by magnetism. This is the discovery which was made
separately by Henry, and we shall describe both methods of showing
what happens. Faraday spent many years looking for the production
of electricity by magnetism. For him, it was not sufficient to see that
the force produced by a current on a magnet was equivalently matched
by a force produced by a magnet on a current. He doggedly followed

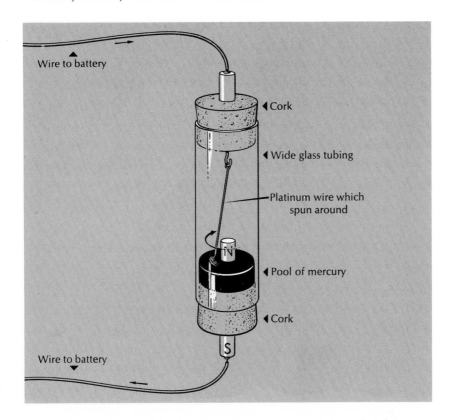

Wire to battery

◀ Cork

◀ Wide glass tubing

Platinum wire which spun around

◀ Pool of mercury

◀ Cork

Wire to battery

Fig. 6.2. Faraday's apparatus showing that a wire carrying an electric current moves when near a magnet. The moving wire was of platinum and was connected between a loop and a pool of mercury, which allowed the wire to move while still making connection. A magnet was fastened in the lower cork and projected above the mercury. When the wires were connected to the battery the wire spun rapidly. This was the first electric motor.

the idea that a current could be produced magnetically, and he kept putting more and more sensitive devices for the measurement of current near magnets. They obstinately refused to budge. Stationary magnets did *not* produce electric currents. His experiments took a different form in 1831, when he began to realize that the momentary, fleeting effect he observed when the magnetic action was changing was real. To show the effect he did many experiments; we choose one of the simplest to describe. It can be understood a little more easily by consulting Figure 6.3.

One of the major elements in the discovery was his use of a sensitive

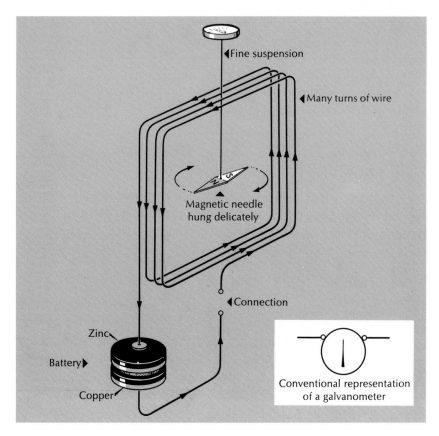

Fig. 6.3. Representation of the modification of Oersted's experiment to create a current measuring device, the *galvanometer*. All turns of the wire urge the needle the same way. With a good magnet, many turns, and a fine suspension, a very small current can be measured.

means of detecting a current, called in those days (and still so called by some of us old-timers) a *galvanometer*. A galvanometer is a refinement of Oersted's device, in which many turns of wire are coiled up and a magnetic needle is set at the center of the coil. The effect of a current is magnified many times by the many turns, and by suspending the needle very delicately so it is restrained as little as possible, the motion of the needle can be made to show very tiny currents. An explanatory figure for a galvanometer is shown in Figure 6.4. Faraday had one of these instruments, which he had designed and made, and he used it in a "circuit" as shown. He devised a coil of many turns of wire, simply wound by hand. The two ends of the coil were connected to the galvanometer, which we have represented by the needle and two places to hook on the wire, or "terminals." Near the coil of wire Faraday held a magnet. What he observed was that as the magnet was pushed into the turns of wire of the coil, the needle of the galvanometer moved over and back, indicating that a momentary current flowed. As the magnet was withdrawn, the needle went the other way, again only momentarily. He tried it many times and he found that the key to the production of an electric current by magnetism was that the magnetic element had to be changing.

Another of Faraday's experiments was almost the same in principle, the only difference being that instead of using a magnet to produce the magnetic action in the coil of wire, he used a second coil, which we already know produces magnetic effects. Only when the current in the second coil was altering did Faraday see any effect in the galvanometer. This experiment is the one which was done independently and perhaps better by Henry, at almost exactly the same time. We will describe this experiment in a little detail, as it is important to see what took place at this very exciting time in the emergence of knowledge about electricity.

It is possible to make quite powerful magnets. Usually these are of the "horseshoe" type—the magnet is bent so that the north and south poles are near each other. This discovery was made fairly early, and the corresponding discovery, after Oersted's finding that an electric current caused a magnetic needle to move, was that if soft iron was wound with many turns of wire and a current sent through the wire a strong magnet

Fig. 6.4. A moving magnet produces an electrical effect. One of Faraday's great experiments which showed that electricity could be *generated* from magnetism.

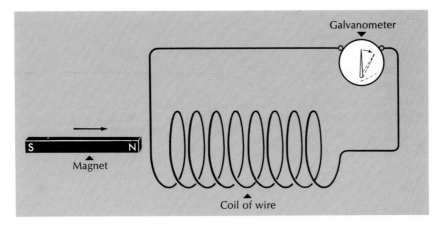

was also made. It is rather interesting to notice how this development actually came about. Almost as soon as Oersted's experiment was known, Arago, in France, and Davy, in England, found that steel needles could be made magnetic by winding a wire around them and connecting the ends to a battery. The actual electromagnet, the horseshoe-shaped piece of soft iron with a current sent through the wire, was not made until five years later, by Sturgeon, in England. Sturgeon used bare wire and only a few turns. Henry produced powerful magnets: he made one for Princeton University which could lift 750 lbs. and another made for Yale which could lift 2,086 lbs. Henry had much interest in this question of ability to lift weights, and in a way he was interested in an irrelevancy, because this quite interesting and obvious property of electromagnets is still one which is concerned with many details, like how many turns of wire and how much iron, rather than being one which leads to further discovery.

Henry used one of his electromagnets in the experiment illustrated in Figure 6.5. He placed a piece of iron across the poles of the magnet, wound wire around this iron, and connected the ends of this wire to his version of a galvanometer. In order to start and stop the current in the electromagnet he simply pulled the plates of different metals out of the acid bath which formed the battery. Pushing the plates in caused the chemical action to start, and the electric current to flow in the coils of the electromagnet; while this happened, and *only* while it was happening, the needle of the galvanometer swung. When he removed the plates the needle swung in the opposite direction and came to rest.

This experiment done by Henry, without knowledge of Faraday's work, is much more dramatic than Faraday's. The battery and iron ring produce a powerful magnet, so powerful that the lower iron plate across the poles of the horseshoe cannot be pulled away at all by hand, so there is no question of what we have just called a "magnetic effect." The galvanometer need not be very sensitive at all, the pointer moves firmly and positively, and just as firmly and positively comes back to rest, even while the battery and coil are connected and the magnet is fully "on." When the battery plates are removed, the process repeats, but in reverse: again, this happens only while the current is being taken away. No electric current is generated in the second winding unless the magnetic effects are *changing*.

Thus Faraday and Henry found that:

A CHANGING MAGNETIC ACTION PRODUCES AN ELECTRIC CURRENT

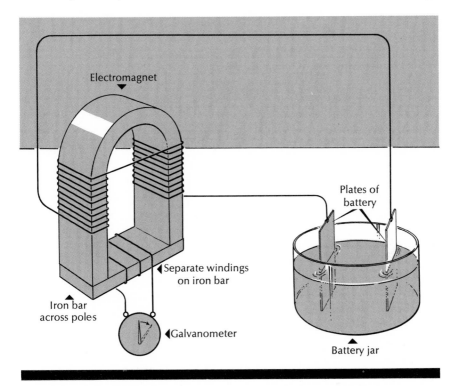

Fig. 6.5. Joseph Henry's experiment, which showed that when the current in the electromagnet was changed by lifting the plates out of the battery a current flowed in a separate winding. Thus a *changing magnetic effect* produces an electric effect.

WHAT IS A FIELD?

The reader may have noticed that in the last few paragraphs we have been doing a little evasion. We have continually spoken about rather vague notions such as "magnetic action" or "near a magnet." We had to do this because there is an essential idea, suggested by Faraday, which we really need in order to describe what is happening in the experiments. This is the idea of a *field*. This idea is dominant in all physics, and, indeed, very few theoretical physicists could get on for a minute without it. It is not at all easy to say what is meant by a field. Faraday himself thought that each electric charge radiated a set of whiskers which he called "lines of force." The strength of the effect of the electric charge depended on how many whiskers could be found in any area and naturally grew less the further away one went. This is not a bad description, but it leaves a lot to be desired.

Our experience is that it is not easy to convey the idea of a field in a few words. It is hard to define. Thus we have to discuss it and to give examples of fields until gradually the idea becomes settled. Such "acquired" ideas, like "acquired" tastes, very often get a stronger hold on us than any other kind.

In its essentials, a field is a region in which one body is influenced by another. It is necessary that the effect be spread out, and usually that it vary in a more or less uniform way. If we consider young men as the bodies influenced, then a good-looking girl can be said to have a field of influence around her. If one had a way of measuring the amount of influence, it probably would be found to become less as the distance increases. In this case there is no great problem about understanding the nature of the field, although the psychology experts make a fuss over it. The fields of electric charge and gravitation, and, to a great extent, magnetic fields are more prosaic, and, incidentally, also more predictable. Because we want to give some expression to the idea of a field, and because the fields of electricity and gravitation are the simplest of all, we intend to consider them first and then introduce the notion of a magnetic field.

If a model of a field is useful, and we have to admit, reluctantly, that it probably is not, then the idea of two balloons in a soft jelly might help. If one balloon is blown up hard, it compresses the jelly all around it, and this makes a difference to the other balloon, which will squeeze smaller. The first balloon produces an effect around it, in the jelly in this case, and the jelly then transmits the effect to the second balloon. This field of influence will not be simple, and we should not push it too far.

The same idea is to be found in the transmission of sound. Sound goes through *matter*—solid, liquid, or gas. If we put an alarm clock in a vacuum chamber, set it ringing, and pump out the air in the chamber, we find that as the air is removed from around the bell the sound dies out. The air is acting like the jelly mentioned above.

THE ETHER

The jelly idea appealed to the first proponents of fields. They suggested that there exists an all-pervading, invisible, intangible "luminiferous ether," which bears the stress imposed on it by electric charges and transmits them to other charges. The ether was thought of as being like a jelly—in better terms, an "elastic solid"—and an electric charge was thought of as producing a strong distortion in the elastic solid, which then spread its effect all around, being only observed when another electric charge was somewhere near it. Quite elaborate theories were worked out, using this idea of an ether. It was given specific properties; in particular, it was thought to be the means by which light was propagated. Nowadays the idea of an ether has quietly faded away. It has faded largely because no properties were found to belong to the ether except those needed to describe fields. "Why not describe the fields directly?" is the question asked, and the answer is, "why not?" So we speak of the ether no longer.

LINES OF FORCE

Faraday conceived one of the most useful ideas for describing a field, and we have already touched on it. He thought of each electric charge as having associated with it a certain number of lines of force, directed outward in a uniform way. In the units of electric charge used by Faraday, called the electrostatic system, a single electric charge had 4π whiskers, or lines of force, sticking out from it. It may seem odd to have a number which is not a whole number, but really this is not important, because one can easily have fractions of charges in Faraday's system of measuring charge. The appearance of an electric charge is then as shown in Figure 6.6.

Now Faraday went one stage further; he suggested that if you draw a unit area (one square centimeter in his units) perpendicular to the lines of force, and then count the number of lines which stab through that unit area, the number of lines acts as a measure of the strength of the field. This quantitative measure is very useful and we will adopt it for the moment, but before we do so, we need a preliminary idea or two.

If we return to the influence field exerted by the good-looking girl, we soon find that the effect we measure depends on whose eyes are being tested. An equally good-looking girl will not waste any time on her, while the same would not be true of a man aged 23. A pair of field glasses lying on the table will not turn spontaneously. They will be unaffected. In the same way, an electric field exerts its influence only on other electric charges. Upon them a force develops, to repel or attract. To complete Faraday's idea of measuring a field we therefore have to say that we can measure a field strength as he suggested, by the number of lines of force threading a unit area, where we desire to measure the field. This idea is expressed in Figure 6.7. The unit area has been drawn at three locations, and it can be seen that the number of lines passing through it is markedly different depending on the distance. In fact, we do not have to stretch our imagination at all to see

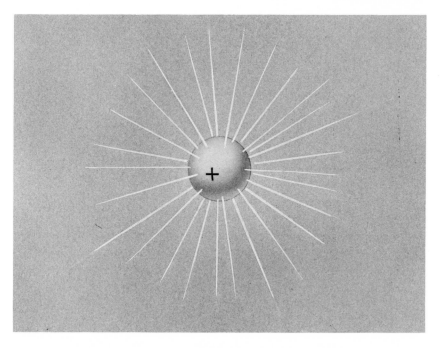

Fig. 6.6. Faraday's concept of the lines of force emerging from an electric charge. The lines go straight out as far as we can think. The more the charge the more the lines.

that the field strength goes down about as the square of the distance—as we, of course, expect.

Now we say that if we put q_2 units of charge at the place where we measure the field, the force they experience is q_2 times the field strength.

In this chapter the reader has been unnaturally free from reading any mathematics. Partly this is because of the influence of Faraday, who used very little mathematics himself, though he thought accurately and clearly. In any event, we now need to alter the situation and use some mathematics. Suppose we call the electric field strength at some place E. This means that there are E units of such field. Then, as an equation, if we call the force which is experienced by our q_2 units of charge F, we find that

$$F = q_2 E.$$

Let us see if this conveys any idea of how Coulomb's Law works. If we have not one unit charge, but q_1 of them, then there are $4\pi q_1$ lines sticking out from it. Suppose we measure the field strength at a distance

R units away. The lines of force all go through a sphere whose area is $4\pi R^2$. So the number per unit area is

$$\frac{4\pi q_1}{4\pi R^2} \text{ or } \frac{q_1}{R^2}$$

Thus we see that

$$E = \frac{q_1}{R^2}$$

Then the force

$$F = \frac{q_1}{R^2} \text{ times } q_2 = \frac{q_1 q_2}{R^2}$$

This, you will notice, is Coulomb's Law.

Fig. 6.7. The use of lines of force to express the size of an electric field. The more lines going through the unit area the greater the field strength.

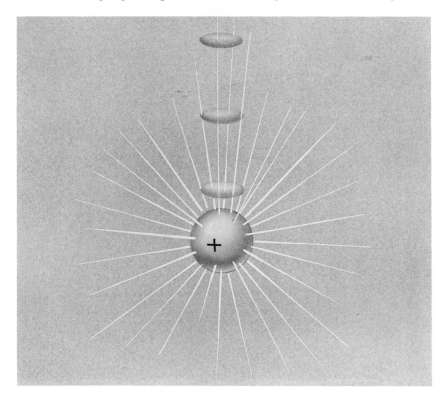

GRAVITATIONAL FIELDS

Almost the same statements can be made about gravity as about electricity. A massive body has around it an influence which results in the attraction of another massive body placed near it. If we denote the gravitational field of one massive body by the symbol X, and a mass of size m_2 is placed on the field, then a force develops of size F such that

$$F = Xm_2.$$

Notice how nearly this is the same as the equations we wrote about the force for electrical effects. The only really big difference lies in the fact that gravity, as we have so far observed, is only attractive. No known repulsions occur.

The reader will note that we say "no *known* repulsions occur"—a weaseling word, *known*. The reason for this is rather interesting. One of the discoveries of modern physics has been the existence of a series of "anti" particles, which have opposite charge, and other opposite properties, to the normal particles. The positron, for example, is the antiparticle to the electron. It is speculated that "antimatter" is repelled by regular matter, thus providing the repulsive kind of gravitational effect which we do not ordinarily observe. Such "antimatter" has been produced in the laboratory, but in small amounts and with some difficulties, and so far no experiments to see what happens to it in a gravitational field have been possible. One of the favorite concepts of science fiction writers is the "antimatter" universe, where antimatter is commonplace and regular matter rare, because the various consequences thereof are helpful in moving the plot forward. Up to the present, all we can say is that gravity, to our knowledge, is monotonously attractive.

MAGNETIC FIELDS

A magnetic "pole" (which we shall see later on is really a fiction) can be said to exert a magnetic field which influences another magnetic pole. Magnetism is really rather different, because as we have stressed, poles always occur in pairs, a north pole and a south pole, which are rather close to each other. It is still possible to retain the idea of a field, although we must realize that a magnetic field has rather different characteristics from an electric field.

Change and How To Describe It

While we have just discussed the idea of a field, we have not really made a description of Faraday's law relating the production of an electric current to the change of a magnetic "effect," a word we can now decently replace by magnetic field. To do this we have to spend a little time on the question of how to describe any change, not only a change in a magnetic field.

In physical science we are continually dealing with changing things. Think of the examples so far:

Speed is $\dfrac{\text{change of distance}}{\text{time of change}}$.

Acceleration is $\dfrac{\text{change of speed}}{\text{time of change}}$.

A changing magnetic field produces an electric current.

It is necessary for us to find a way to describe change in a useful manner.

Let us take refuge in the favorite device of the physicist—a graph. Suppose we draw the speed of a football player, (naturally we are writing this in the fall term) as he streaks for a touchdown. He starts as fast as he can after he gets the ball, slows to avoid running into the blockers and then gets up speed and keeps it up until he is over the line, where-upon he slows down. The graph of speed versus *time* is shown in Figure 6.8. Speed versus *distance* is also shown. The two are similar, but not the same. Slowing down and starting up take time, but don't use up distance. Think of the speed-versus-time graph. If we want to describe the change of speed versus time we first divide the graph into small intervals of time, shown by the vertical lines in the Figure, where we have given an enlarged version of the beginning part of the graph. Then in any small interval of time we can find the change in speed. The change in speed divided by the small interval of time in which it took place is the rate of change of speed with time. It is also common usage to call this division the ratio of the change in speed to the time taken for the change. The two mean the same thing. Now this division, or ratio, is rather clumsy to write in algebra. For instance, if we number the little intervals of time as:

$$0, t_1, t_2, t_3, t_4, t_5, t_6, t_7, \text{etc.,}$$

and the little sections of speed as:

$$0, s_1, s_2, s_3, s_4, s_5, \text{etc.,}$$

then any one of the division processes, or ratios, might be, for example, $\dfrac{s_4 - s_3}{t_4 - t_3}$. A shorthand for this clumsy notation has been devised, but before we introduce it we must ask ourselves whether this method of subdividing the time, and so the speed, is what we need to understand the process of change. One thing seems to be clear. If we make the

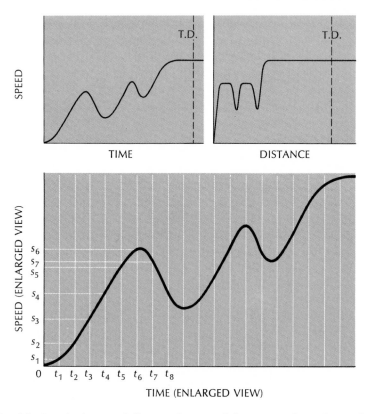

Fig. 6.8. Speed, time, and distance in a touchdown run. In order to describe the *changing* speed, the first part of the run is shown magnified and divided into many little segments. The interval of speed divided by the interval of time measures the change of speed.

subdivisions numerous and therefore the scale large, we are certainly deriving a tremendous lot of detail about the way the runner progresses to a touchdown. Suppose we say that if the subdivisions are as numerous as we can ever want, and the scale as large as we can ever want, then the algebra will indeed be very messy, while our konwledge will be very detailed. So under those conditions, we agree to use the shorthand. Newton used the most compact notation, which is $\dot{s}$ (note the small dot over the symbol), and he called the ratio a *fluxion*. Another notation is $f'(s)$. The notation now used almost universally by physicists is $\frac{ds}{dt}$. This was introduced by Leibnitz. The letter "*d*" is used as a prefix to mean "a tiny increment of"—in this case, "a tiny increment of *s*" and "a tiny increment of time." More elaborately, ds and dt are called "differentials," and the ratio the "derivative." To be mathematically exact we must also specify that the number of slices be enormous, so that ds and dt are both very nearly zero in each case. This exacting requirement is not so important in physics.

We shall, to a small extent, use this notation, though we do not expect to work a problem with it.

Some examples:

$$\text{Velocity, or Speed, } v = \frac{ds}{dt} *$$

$$\text{Acceleration, } a \quad = \frac{dv}{dt}$$

We are now in a position to look at Faraday's experiment with the moving magnet and the moving wire. While the magnet moved, the galvanometer deflected. To make clear what is happening, we repeat the diagram for Faraday's experiment a little differently in Figure 6.9. Emanating from the approaching magnet are a few of Faraday's "lines of force," or of the magnetic field, as we now say. Inside the wire we see the electric field, shown as many arrows urging the current through the galvanometer. The field in the wire is caused by the moving magnet, and now we should attempt to give a quantitative relationship between the moving, or rather, the *changing* magnetic field, and the electric field. But before we can do this we must answer a very penetrating question. Is the electric field which makes the current flow *only* in the wire? Or is the wire just a place where electricity can flow, and so reveal the presence of a current? In the former case, we have to fix our thoughts on the wire alone; in the latter, we must consider that there is an electric field everywhere near a changing magnetic field.

The latter of these two is the true situation, and the clear statement of this was first made by Maxwell, of whom more later. Because this is so we must analyze Faraday's experiment somewhat further. We propose to do this by forcing our minds to think of a very simple and special case of Faraday's experiment, designing this case so that we can elaborate it. In the left-hand insert at the bottom of Figure 6.9 is a very small rectangular loop of wire, and exactly perpendicular to it we have imagined a magnetic field to be present and changing, so that in the little loop the electric field must be created. What is the form of that electric field? From Faraday's experiment it must be as drawn, so arranged as to go around the loop. The field at the bottom is opposite to that at the top,

---

* It cannot hurt to state clearly that ds and dt are each *one number*, not a product of d and s, or d and t.

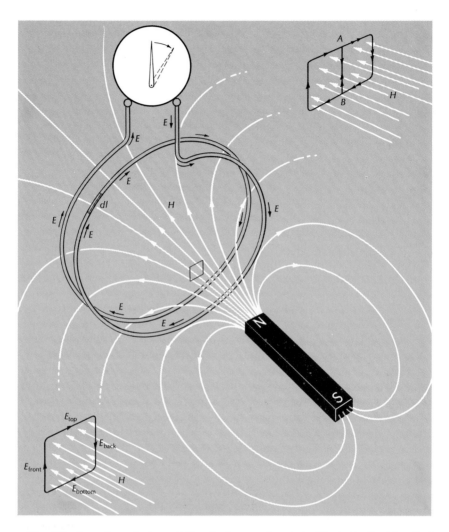

Fig. 6.9. An enlarged view of Faraday's experiment to illustrate the idea that the electric field produced by the changing magnetic field is *everywhere*, not just in the wire. The lower insert shows a very small loop, which can be thought of as somewhere in the space in the middle of the coil. The electric fields in the loop are examined. The upper insert shows two adjacent loops and it can be seen that the common wire has equal and opposite fields in it. So only the wire at the edge actually shows an electric field.

and the field in front is opposite to that in the back. Now we are in a position to give the quantitative relationship, which we propose to do in a mixture of words and equation, and we shall, for the present, write as laboratory experimenters and not as mathematicians. E stands for the electric field. What is found, as stated by Maxwell, based on Faraday's work, is that $\dfrac{E_{\text{bottom}} + E_{\text{top}}}{\text{height}} + \dfrac{E_{\text{front}} + E_{\text{back}}}{\text{width}} = -(\text{constant}) \dfrac{dH}{dt}$. The subscripts should not bother the reader. We ask, for now, that the constant be thought of as being introduced by how we measure. What we want to concentrate attention upon are two features which stress *change*.

The first is not too hard to see, it is the $\dfrac{dH}{dt}$ which is the rate of change of the magnetic field. Since we have steadily insisted that only while the field is changing is there any effect, the reader should not mind this part of our expression. Now if we look at the left-hand side we see that the electric field generated depends on the *size* of the little loop. If the height is twice as big, our formula says that the two fields at the top and bottom will also be twice as big, and the same is true for the width. What we have to say about the meaning of Faraday's experiment in words is, therefore,

THE FASTER THE CHANGE OF THE MAGNETIC FIELD (IN TERMS OF TIME), THE GREATER THE CHANGE OF ELECTRIC FIELD (IN TERMS OF DISTANCE).*

Notice that the relation is between change and change, only the change is change with time in one case and with distance in the other.

This relationship, while startling and significant in one respect, is very clumsy when we return to Faraday's experiment; an elegant device introduced by Stokes enables us to see it very much more simply. In the second insert in Figure 6.9, two loops adjoining each other are shown. It can be seen that where the two loops join, the electric fields, represented in one case by single arrows and in the other by double, are opposite and *cancel*. Thus if we were to add up a whole lot of loops, we feel safe in saying that only the outside of the many loops would have any net electric

---

* The correct mathematical way of writing this expression is to consider E in terms of one direction, and let the opposite character of the fields on each side of the loop appear automatically. When this is done, with the three directions as given in the sketch, the correct statement of one component of Maxwell's second equation is

$$\frac{dE_z}{dy} - \frac{dE_y}{dz} = \frac{1}{c}\frac{dH}{dt}$$

The strange three-dimensional intertwining of the relationships is referred to as a "curl."

field in them. So if some way can be devised to add up the effect of many loops—and these loops need only exist in our imagination—we expect to find the *boundary* alone important; in Faraday's experiment we will make that boundary the wire. Stokes noticed the very simple piece of mathematics we repeat below. If, for each loop, we multiply both sides of our equation by the area, which is the width times the height, we get a new equation:

$$(E_{\text{bottom}}+E_{\text{top}})(\text{width}) + (E_{\text{front}}+E_{\text{back}})(\text{height}) = -(\text{constant})\frac{dH}{dt}(\text{area})$$

or $\qquad\qquad E \times \text{length of loop} = -(\text{constant})\frac{dH}{dt}(\text{area}).$

A glance at this will show that the left-hand side is the electric field times the appropriate length of the wire in which that field is found. On the right-hand side is the area times the rate of change of the magnetic field. Bearing in mind the fact that the loops add up, Stokes said that if we take the product of the electric field in the boundary (the wire) and the length, this will be equal to the whole area times the appropriate change in magnetic field per second. The product of the electric field and the length, added up for the whole circuit, is called (traditionally but rather unfortunately), the *electromotive force,* and the product of the magnetic field and the area is called the *flux.* So we have a famous relation, much used by physicists and engineers, and by Faraday:

THE TIME RATE OF CHANGE OF THE FLUX IS PROPORTIONAL TO THE NEGATIVE OF THE ELECTROMOTIVE FORCE.

Now for that "negative." In one sense it is not significant, for there must clearly be a direction to all the above and we use sign to represent direction, and negative is quite legal as a direction. In another sense it is very significant, for it can be shown, by combining this experiment with Oersted's, that the way the current is created, with the negative sign, is such as to resist the approach of the magnet, an opposition first pointed out by Lenz. This tendency to create a change to resist, in part, another change, is often observed.

This chapter, as the reader will have noticed, has begun to show a different character from the chapter describing Galileo and Newton. In the first place the subjects discussed are all unfamiliar unless one is a man of science. They involve rather complicated combinations of specialized things: magnets and wires with batteries; galvanometers and electromagnets; and so on. And the ideas which result from these studies are a little more abstract even than the ideas of force and acceleration. What is reallly more strange than these experiments and the ideas is the realization that such experiments concern things which are at the very basis of the way in which we must explain Nature. In fact, even more of the same is going to have to be described before we can make an attempt to put it together. As we have said before, this is one of the reasons why it is hard to "put science across." To do so we have to ask that nearly all the obvious things and the common sense impressions that we have must be considered as really secondary, and the findings from odd experiments with electricity and with coils of wire must be considered primary. Lest the reader start to develop a faint heart, we wish to say that, in terms of the ideas on which we must build, we are about half way. So we aren't doing too badly.

Suggestions for Further Thought

1. Write an essay on electricity and magnetism, including an account of the individuals involved and the experiments they did.
2. Discuss and illustrate the concept of field.
3. Look up the outline of the personal history of Faraday and Henry. Henry proved influential in the organization of American Science. Faraday did little in the same way for English Science. Comment on the possible reasons why this was so.
4. Electricity was first studied as a rare phenomenon; it has developed, in our thinking, into one of the basic elements of physics. Compare this with the discovery of penicillin and the growth and use of antibiotics, or the discovery of genetics by Mendel and the modern idea of heredity.

References

William F. Magie, *A Source Book in Physics,* 8th printing (Cambridge, Mass.: Harvard University Press, 1963).

John Tyndall, *Faraday as a Discoverer* (New York: Thomas Y. Crowell, Apollo Edition, 1961).

Faraday as a Discoverer

SUMMARY

When from an Alpine height the eye of the climber ranges over the mountains, he finds that for the most part they resolve themselves into distinct groups, each consisting of a dominant mass surrounded by peaks of lesser elevation. The power which lifted the mightier eminences in nearly all cases lifted others to an almost equal height. And so it is with the discoveries of Faraday. As a general rule, the dominant result does not stand alone, but forms the culminating point of a vast and varied mass of inquiry. In this way, round about his great discovery of magnetoelectric induction, other weighty labors group themselves. His investigations on the extra current, on the polar and other condition of diamagnetic bodies, on lines of magnetic force, their definite character and distribution, on the employment of the induced magnetoelectric current as a measure and test of magnetic action, on the revulsive phenomena of the magnetic field, are all, notwithstanding the diversity of title, researches in the domain of magnetoelectric induction.

Faraday's second group of researches and discoveries embrace the chemical phenomena of the current. The dominant result here is the great law of definite electrochemical decomposition, around which are massed various researches on electrochemical conduction and on electrolysis both with the machine and with the pile. To this group also belongs his analysis of the contact theory, his inquiries as to the source of voltaic electricity, and his final development of the chemical theory of the pile.

His third great discovery is the magnetization of light, which I should liken to the Weisshorn among mountains—high, beautiful, and alone.

The dominant result of his fourth group of researches is the discovery of diamagnetism, announced in his memoir as the magnetic condition of all matter, round which are grouped his inquiries on the magnetism of flame and gases; on magnecrystallic action, and on atmospheric magnetism, and its relations to the annual and diurnal variation of the needle, the full significance of which is still to be shown.

These are Faraday's most massive discoveries, and upon them his fame must mainly rest. But even without them, sufficient would remain to secure for him a high and lasting scientific reputation. We should still have his researches on the liquefaction of gases; on frictional electricity; on the electricity of the gymnotus; on the source of power in the hydroelectric machine, the last two investigations being untouched in the foregoing memoir; on electromagnetic rotations; on regelation; all his more purely chemical researches, including his discovery of benzol. Besides these he published a multitude of minor papers, most of which, in some way or other, illustrate his genius. I have made no allusion to his power and sweetness as a lecturer. Taking him for all in all, I think it will be conceded that Michael Faraday was the greatest experimental philosopher the world has ever seen; and I will add the opinion that the progress of future research will tend not to dim or to diminish, but to enhance and glorify the labors of this mighty investigator.

John Tyndall

7
Other Ways To Think About Motion:
Energy and Momentum

Having ventured into the world of electricity and magnetism, we are now going to go back a little and examine the character of motion in a rather different way. We do this because we have come to realize that the first way in which we perceive the truth may not be the most convenient way to develop the power which our perception of truth has given us. Putting it a little differently, our minds are very much human, and they work according to human fashion. At the moment we cannot analyze and explain the human fashion, but we, quite surely, have had to learn to live with it and use it. So it would not be surprising if we were to find that there are several ways to look at motion, all truthful, and that some of these ways are better suited to us than others for some purposes. So we are going to examine this possibility, which has proved to be a sensible thing to do and has given us two new concepts, those of *energy* and *momentum*.

Of these two the concept of energy has come to have great influence. It has proved to be a way to unify thinking about many areas of science, even those as far removed as astronomy and biology. It would be almost unthinkable to "go back" on the Principle of Conservation of Energy, and most scientists would not listen for a moment if such a suggestion were made. While this is true, it is also true that the Principle itself had to become convincing to science. Two such Principles have become established in a relatively gradual and cumulative kind of way, as opposed to the demonstration-and-discovery kind of way. Both are concerned with the idea of energy, and the first of them is our concern here. The second is more subtle, concerns the way in which energy transfer can take place, and is not in place in this book. Our problem is therefore to discuss the way in which the Principle of Conservation of Energy became a strong doctrine and to do so quite honestly. This proves to be a little difficult,

137

but because it illustrates so very well the manner in which a general
Principle *emerges,* it is worth effort. We ask the reader to have two
concerns as we go ahead with the development. The first and perhaps
most important is to see the *process* of development, how relatively simple
and almost trivial thoughts lead to general ideas, and the second to
acquire a sharp idea of *what energy is.*

When the development has reached its first phase, which is toward the
end of this chapter, we shall have reached the idea that bodies can move
in such a way that two properties, *Potential Energy* and *Kinetic Energy,*
exchange between each other. The sum of the two remains the same.
This illustrates the Principle of Conservation of Energy. We can now
show how this idea originated.

Newton's laws form the starting point for all our thinking about motion. Granted that this is true, it doesn't mean that we are prohibited
from looking carefullly at these laws to see if there are other ways of
expressing them which are just as true, but which appeal to us more and
perhaps enable us to understand some things more simply than we can
by just using Newton's laws in their original form. There is a very simple
way to put them into different terms, and when this is done we have two
"principles," both of which are very useful. These are the *Principle of
Conservation of Energy* and the *Principle of Conservation of Momentum.*

Both principles are deduced by two mathematical devices, the same
in each case. A short word will explain the devices, which are quite easy.

The first and most important mathematical device is called *integration.*
It amounts to a sustained addition. The second device concerns what is
added. Let us look at the way they work. We take the second, simpler
idea, first.

Newton's Second Law, for a single force F and single mass m, in the
symbols which should be getting a bit familiar, is

$$\text{Force} = \text{mass} \times \text{acceleration} = \text{mass} \times \left(\frac{\text{change in speed}}{\text{change in time}} \right)$$

or

$$F = m \frac{dv}{dt}.$$

Now, when we use our second device, we think ahead that we want
to add something and we use a little skill in designing what we add,
always keeping our equations correct, which means that we always say
essentially the same thing, making only the appearance different. In
their heart of hearts, many physicists think that this restatement is all
the content to be found in mathematics. They usually do not say so
because they have a strong desire to keep on good terms with mathematicians. The reader will wonder what we mean by the words "think

ahead that we want to add something and use skill in designing what we add." If he is alert, and maybe a trifle irritated by the attitude of the scientist, he will denounce us for hypocrisy, something he would like to do anyway, only we seem to have a kind of impregnable (and annoying) virtue. In this case he would be quite right. What is going on is a human process: we try new things at random, and if one works, or, in the psychologist's not too wonderful expression, "gives us reinforcement," we do the now no longer new thing once more. If it keeps on working, we go at it some more. Then after a time we begin to invent fables about what we did; one of them is that we planned it from the start. The reader can be sure that the original notion of what we are about to do was strictly trial. That it worked is something else.

We consider the very simplest conceivable example of force and motion, a single massive body of mass m at rest acted on by a force F. We watch the resulting motion as it starts and moves until it has gone a distance S_m and attained a speed v_m (See Figure 7.1). What we now do is multiply both sides by a small change in distance. We can do this because an equation which says two things are equal still says they are equal if we multiply both of them by the same thing.

$$\text{The equation now reads:} \quad F\,ds = \frac{m\,dv}{dt}\,ds$$

and we remind the reader of our notation of "ds" to mean a "small change in distance."

Now the right-hand side can be rearranged to look differently in a way which is rather interesting. Instead of writing

$$m\,\frac{dv}{dt} \times ds$$

Fig. 7.1. A representation of a time-lapse photograph of a mass m acted on by a single net force F. The mass speeds up, with an acceleration a, and goes from position 0 to distance S while starting with zero speed and attaining a speed v_m. We consider this, the simplest motion involving a force, in such a way as to lead us to the concept of energy.

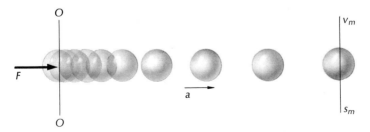

write:

$$m \times dv \times \frac{ds}{dt}.$$

Looking at $\frac{ds}{dt}$ we can see that it is a change in distance divided by a change in time, *which is speed,* for which we have the symbol v. So the right-hand side is:

$$m \times dv \times v$$

and our modified equation, which is derived from Newton's Second Law, and so is just as true as Newton's Second Law, is

$$Fds = mvdv$$

In mathematical terms, we have found it possible to change the variable on the right.

Now that we have the equation in this form, we can employ our other device, the process of repeated addition which we have called integration.

To do this, it is helpful to resort to one of our favorite methods—representation of things by lines on a graph. It will be necessary to look at two graphs: the one of force versus distance, of F versus s; and the other of "mv" versus speed or v. The reader may again wonder what superior wisdom suggests that we pick these. There is a simple reason this time. We want to look at a picture which tells us at a glance what is meant by Fds. These symbols mean that a small change in distance occurs while a force acts. The product of the force by a small distance is what we want to look at. Now if we represent F by a vertical line of the proper size and ds by a little piece of horizontal line, the product of the two is the area of a rectangle. This area is something we can see and so can hope to understand. So in Figure 7.2 we draw on the left a line showing how big the force is. If we want to look at the area corresponding to one increment ds, the area we look at is like the one shaded. It is really very easy to see how to add up all the rectangles for Fds: the reader can see, at a glance, that it is just the same as the area below the thick line which represents the steady value of the force, all the way from the axis to the dotted line, which corresponds to the place where we suppose our study of this motion to end. So in this rather easy case, the area we are interested in is just a big rectangle; it does not introduce any surprises.

The right-hand side of the equation, for which we have the corresponding graph on the right-hand side of Figure 7.2 is not quite so simple, though it is only one step harder. The difference lies in the effect of the force on the speed. Because the force makes the body speed up, the

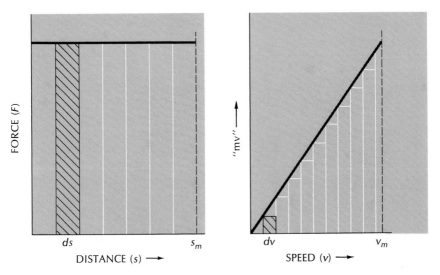

Fig. 7.2. Ways of adding up products Fds and $(mv)dv$. This kind of graph shows these products as areas. By making the size of dv small and having many segments, the addition is seen to be the area of the triangle.

speed is not a fixed value, but starts out from zero at the beginning and steadily increases. So we have a real problem with the little rectangles which are going to tell us what to think about the size of $mvdv$. What we do is to show courage and go ahead. Clearly, at the start there is no rectangle. But as soon as we look at the second small section of speed, we realize that the force has had an effect, so we multiply the little element of speed by the value of mv, and we produce a small rectangle, which is the one shaded. The next tiny interval is even more apparent and we derive another rectangle, a little bit taller, and so we construct a sort of staircase of rectangles which go all the way out to the dotted extreme, which we designated in advance.

The reader will argue that this is rather an odd figure, because he knows that the speed increases steadily, and yet we have a "staircase," which would seem to say that the speed went in steps or jumps. But he won't argue with the statement that if the number of steps is made to be very great, with only a tiny piece for each step, then the graph would appear to show the speed going up steadily along a line. It is this development of a good approximation to the steady case which is the trick we have called integration. We want to talk about the addition of all the little rectangles, and we want this addition to bear some relation to the smooth motion of the object which is being made to go faster. So we say we will add up rectangles, and we will make the rectangles vast in

number and minute in individual size, so that adding up the rectangles
will be the same as going carefully along the actual line of the motion of
the body. In doing this we have once more used the basic idea of the
calculus, the idea of a limit. In this case, the limit is of a sum, or total,
and not of a ratio, or proportion. In this case it is the *integral* calculus
we use. It is not really a hard idea. Interestingly, the limit idea is usually
easier to grasp for adding than for dividing. We say, in this case of the
calculus, that the difference between the tiny staircase and the line can
be made as small as we wish by making the steps many and small, so that
the *limit* of the staircase is the area. Once again, the result is rather easy.
Adding up all the small rectangles will be the same as finding the area of
the triangle, which appears to connect the top of the steps in the right-
hand figure of Figure 7.2. This area is easy: it is half the product of
the base times the height, which is one-half the fastest speed, which we
will call v_m, where the subscript m stands for "maximum," times the
biggest of "mv," which is mv_m. This is $\frac{1}{2} mv_m^2$. This term has a name:
it is *kinetic energy*. It is our first development of the ideas involved with
energy.

Now let us go back to our equation which described Newton's Second
Law as it applies to motion when a force acts. We have said that the
equation permits us to write $Fds = mvdv$. New we are going to assert
that if we make a great addition sum of both sides, as below:

$$Fds_1 = mv_1dv_1$$

$$Fds_2 = mv_2dv_2$$

$$Fds_3 = mv_3dv_3$$

$$Fds_4 = mv_4dv_4$$

$$Fds_1 + Fds_2 + Fds_3 + Fds_4 \ldots = mv_1dv_1 + mv_2dv_2 + mv_3dv_3 + mv_4dv_4 \ldots$$

then adding up both of these whole sets of equals will give a totality
which is also an equality. We have already said that writing this in this
way is very clumsy, so we look for a more elegant way to say it. In
mathematics we use the symbol $\int$, called an integral sign, which is derived
from an elongated "s" for "sum:" At the bottom of this sign we put the
starting point, while at the top we put the finishing point. The result is
a very impressive equation.

$$\int_0^{s_m} Fds = \int_0^{v_m} mvdv$$

One reads this equation in English as: "The integral of *Fds* from 0 to
s_m equals the integral of *mvdv* from zero to v_m."

Very often, but not always, it is possible to see that the integral has a certain form. Thus in this case, the left-hand side is the rectangle, Fs, and the right-hand side is $\frac{1}{2} mv^2$. When this is true, the limits of the integral tell us to subtract the value of the term of the lower limit from that at the upper limit. Thus in the case above, which is a special case where the force is fixed, we have

$$\int_0^{s_m} Fds = Fs_m - 0 \text{ and } \int_0^{v_m} mvdv = \frac{1}{2} mv_m^2 - 0.$$

So we get the relation

$$Fs_m - 0 = \frac{1}{2} mv_m^2 - 0.$$

We will not use this relation in this form but will modify it as described below.

Now if we return to the impressive-looking equation between integrals, we find that we never did anything which required that the force be fixed in value. So we suddenly realize that for *any* kind of force acting on a body this strange relation is true.

The relation is

$$\int_0^{s_m} Fds = \frac{1}{2} mv_m^2 - 0.$$

The force can be like gravity, quite steady, or it can be like the resistance of water or air, getting much greater as the speed goes up, or it can be like the force between electric charges, depending on how far they are apart. This tempts us to do a bit more with it and see if it has any payoff. The early workers in the science of mechanics knew what we are about to say, but they were quite unimpressed; nevertheless, events have shown that this type of trickery does lead to a result of great value. What has evolved, after quite a lot of discussion, is the use of this equation to describe the behavior of two kinds of energy. The right-hand side we have already designated as "kinetic energy." The left-hand side is by no means so simple, and in fact is really more elaborate and has quite strong restrictions.

Tradition says that we define a quantity, which, for the moment we leave without a name, as $- \int Fds$. The negative sign is sensible, as we shall see, but the rest of the matter is not so straightforward. Let us agree about the negative sign first, and then introduce the philosophical difficulties. The negative sign is an artifice to enable us to say that two kinds of energy add up to one value, but that the two kinds can change amount, always maintaining the total. Let us put it in very simple terms. Suppose you have $100 in the bank. The accountant at the bank keeps this fact in a record. Now you draw out $20. He correctly records this fact by saying that the money you have is − $20, as far as your account is concerned. But if you want to find out how much you have all together, you want to add your money in your pocket to his reckoning, and we all know it will total $100. But to do that you must reverse the sign he has put on your money and call it + money. The same is true in our equation. The statement of the equation of motion, or of Newton's Second Law, is made from only one point of view, and it won't let us add up a whole sum of something we are going to call energy. So we change the sign of one side, and that has always been the left-hand side. Now we come to the trouble. If we look at the strange symbol

$$-\int_{0}^{s_m} F ds$$

and do the necessary mathematics on it for the case where the force is gravitational, or electrical (not magnetic) we find a pretty result. The value of the integral depends only on the two ends, and never on how the two ends were reached. For example, if a book has to be taken from the bottom of a building to the top, it will not matter if it is taken upstairs, hauled out of a window half way up and then pulled up the stair well, or picked up by a helicopter, taken out of town several miles, and returned to the top of the building. The value of the integral is always the same. On the other hand, an even simpler case that of familiar friction gives an integral which is anything *but* the same if the process takes place differently. If I try to move a book on a rough table from one place to another, it will matter a good deal whether I take the shortest way, or whether I slide the book all over the table before I bring it to the right place. The same would be true of motion in a tank of water, or at high speed in air. It is because of this obvious difficulty that the early workers in mechanics did not worry too much about "energy." For the case where the integral does *not* depend on how the transit between two points is made, the force is called *conservative*.

Let us have a little faith, however. Suppose we say that we do not understand all about Nature anyway, but where she is simple we want to study her carefully. So we will agree to consider *only* conservative forces and we go ahead and say that the value of this integral, with the negative sign, is equal to the difference between the two values of something we call *potential energy*, which we designate as V. Then we get

$$V_m - V_0 = -\int_{0}^{s_m} F ds$$

Suppose we introduce the symbol T for kinetic energy, and then we have

$$T_m - T_0 = \tfrac{1}{2} m v_m^2 - 0$$

for our rather special case, using T_m for the kinetic energy at the end and T_0 for that at the start.

If we try out the equation above, which says

$$\int_0^{s_m} F ds = \frac{1}{2} m v_m^2 - 0,$$

we will see that

$$-(V_m - V_0) = T_m - T_0 \quad \text{or} \quad -V_m + V_0 = T_m - T_0$$

and some simple rearranging gives

$$V_0 + T_0 = V_m + T_m$$

and now we say that *the sum of potential and kinetic energy is conserved.* This is the first phase of the discovery of the *Principle of Conservation of Energy.* Thus, if we want a definition of *potential energy,* we must first establish that the force or forces concerned are conservative. When this is done we can say that the potential energy measured from a definite point we call zero is $-\int_0^{s_m} F ds$: s_m is the point at which we desire to know the value of the potential energy. It is not a clear, satisfying, and simple statement. Rather it is special and intellectually confined. We shall later see that it is capable of development to an extent not apparent from the above and, in its way, forming a surprising turn in science.

All the above is a reasonably thick patch of mathematical trickery. We hope that the reader will go over it several times. We did not like writing it, because we never like to write about manipulation of symbols, but we did not think we could give the reader an honest idea of the subject without it. It is included, not because it is a tremendous logical fact, but because it shows the very humble origin of the idea of energy, one which, in a more developed form, gives comfort and cheer to vast numbers of scientists. We suggest that the following can be distilled out of this analysis:

1. It starts with Newton's Second Law.
2. It uses a summation over distance.
3. Only in certain cases does a potential energy exist.

Quite a lot of problems became easy if, instead of thinking in terms of Newton's Second Law, we start with the Principle of Conservation of Energy, which we have derived from that law. The problem of a roller coaster is a good example. In Figure 7.3 we show a representation of one. Suppose we are asked to find how fast the car is going at three places, A, B, and C. To do this using Newton's Second Law directly we would have to discover how the rails act on the car all the way down, and see how this compounds with the effect of gravity. We would also have to keep in mind the fact that the effects change all the time. None of this process is appealing, though it can certainly be done. On the other hand, if we say that the car has a certain potential energy at the start, and that the meaning of the word "start" is "when the car has zero velocity," then the initial kinetic energy is automatically zero. So the original potential energy must be changed into less potential energy and correspondingly more kinetic energy. If the car goes back up the hill, as at B, potential energy is restored and kinetic energy depleted. The reader probably wants us to do this problem for the roller coaster, as we have drawn it, is a bit intriguing. The potential energy must be measured from somewhere. Let us choose the bottom. Then the start is at a height h, and other places are h_A, h_B, etc. The potential energy is

$$-\int_0^h F ds$$

where we put h as the highest point, which is supposed to be the start. Now the value of F on a car of mass m is familiar to us; we have discussed it before. If M is the mass of the earth, and R the radius of the earth, then

$$F = G\frac{M \times m}{R^2} = \left(\frac{GM}{R^2}\right)m.$$

Since G, M, and R, are fixed we propose to lump them together and call all the symbols in the bracket g. Then $F = mg$. However, we measure h *upward*, while we know that gravity acts downward. So if we are going to do as we have indicated in Figure 7.3, we must admit that the force is opposite to the way we measure, and so $F = -mg$.

Fig. 7.3. Representation of a roller coaster for the purpose of applying the Principle of Conservation of Energy.

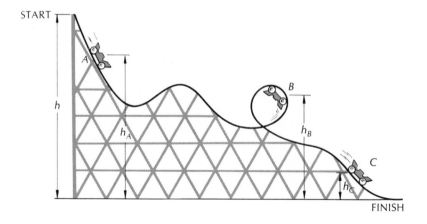

Now we shall find, if we look back at the left-hand side of Figure 7.2, that for this simple case, where F is fixed, the value of the integral is the same as the area of the whole rectangle. In this case, it will be Fh, or $-mgh$, and the value of *minus* this integral is $+mgh$, or simply, mgh.

By the same token, the value of the potential energy at the place A is mgh_A. Now if we say that the speed at A is v_A, the kinetic energy at A is $\frac{1}{2}mv_A{}^2$. So now we use our conservation principle, remembering kinetic energy is zero at the start, and we write

$$mgh + 0 = mgh_A + \tfrac{1}{2}mv_A{}^2$$

which can be rearranged to produce

$$v_A{}^2 = 2g\,(h - h_A)$$

The reader can amuse himself by putting in numbers if he likes. If the heights are measured in feet, then g is 32 feet per second per second.

Solving the problem for the places B and C only involves changing the subscripts appropriate to the height. In other words, the speed of the roller coaster only depends on the height from which it started and its height where you want to know the speed, and not on whether the riders are standing on their heads, as in the case of B.

While in problems like the one we have just discussed the use of the Principle of Conservation of Energy is very powerful, it becomes awkward in many others. For example, any situation involving friction to any degree is *not* one to which one can apply this method. One might think that because of this apparent need to select problems the concept of energy would not be very useful. This was the view taken by the early workers in mechanics. By rather an odd turn, the exact reverse has proved to be true. This calls for a little philosophical thought.

If we speculate on the form we choose for all the things we need to express or describe, we usually see that there are many choices open, but that one seems to have the most appeal. Sometimes different choices are taken—as, for example, one drives on the left in Japan and England and on the right almost everywhere else. Choosing energy as a means of describing many properties of Nature was really not dictated by necessity. However, the idea of a conservation principle in which a certain total amount of energy existed to be shuttled between various forms had a very great appeal. This idea, that there is a certain amount of money in the bank and it can be spent in various ways, is one which seemed to be a solid way to think and did not have too many subtleties in it. So we have learned that by applying quite considerable mental skill to the idea of energy we have been able to develop this idea of conservation. In consequence the idea of energy has persisted and has now reached a dominant position in physical thinking.

Momentum

If the reader is shrewd he will have noticed something surprising about our discussion in the last few pages. We have made no mention of the Third Law of Motion. Nowhere did we say anything about the fact that there is a reaction to every action. This lack of a full analysis is another of the reasons why it might seem odd that the conservation of energy should prove to be an important general principle. A treatment similar to our discussion can be applied to a problem which also involves Newton's laws, only this time all three of them. Suppose we consider a very simple process in which an explosion causes two objects to separate and fly apart from each other. Suppose we designate the masses of the two objects as M and m. Now the act of explosion probably produces quite a complicated set of forces—or better, two forces which change rapidly and perhaps even unpredictably. Regardless of this unpleasant uncertainty in the nature of the forces, there is one absolutely certain feature that they must have. *At any time whatsoever,* the force exerted by the first mass on the second must be exactly equal and opposite to that exerted by he second on the first. This is required by the Third Law of Motion. (See Figure 7.4.)

Then we can suppose that at any particular instant the force is F acting on m and therefore $-F$ acting on M. Now if we write down the requirement of the Second Law of Motion, it is that the force must equal the mass times the rate of change of velocity. In symbols this is

$$F = m\frac{dv}{dt} \text{ on the first body}$$

$$-F = M\frac{dU}{dt} \text{ on the second body}$$

The reader will note that we have used the symbol v for the speed of

Fig. 7.4. An explosion creating two masses M and m out of one piece. The force F is equal and opposite on each piece all the time, by Newton's Third Law. This leads to the *conservation of momentum.*

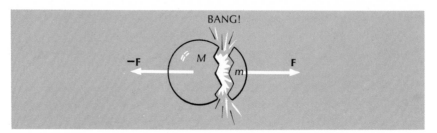

the first mass and U for the speed of the second. The two derivatives we have written are already familiar to him.

Now the two equations above only describe the situation at one instant. But *at all instants* the force on one mass is equal and opposite to the force on the other. Let us therefore perform the same mathematical manipulations that we went through to see the origin of the Principle of Conservation of Energy. There is one difference this time, instead of multiplying both sides by the little element of distance, let us multiply both sides by the little element of *time*. When we do this the equations become

$$Fdt = m\frac{dv}{dt}dt$$

$$-Fdt = \frac{MdU}{dt}dt$$

and we can simplify these by canceling the dt on the right, so the equations will read

$$Fdt = mdv$$

$$-Fdt = MdU$$

The reader will remember that the other mathematical process we used was the process of integration, or multiple addition. If we now do the same, we find that the equations look very impressive:

$$\int_0^{t_m} Fdt = \int_0^{v_f} mdv$$

$$\int_0^{t_m} -Fdt = \int_0^{U_f} MdU$$

Now in this case the right-hand side is the simplest yet. Neither of the masses, m or M, changes at all. So all we have to do is to add up the elements dv and dU and they each give v_f and U_f. Thus we can write

$$\int_0^{t_m} Fdt = mv_f - 0$$

$$\int_0^{t_m} -Fdt = MU_f - 0$$

We have supposed the explosion to start at time 0 and speed 0; we end our consideration of the events at time t_m and velocities v_f and U_f for the small and large masses, respectively. The left-hand side is not easy, because we have already said that the force is changing, and not too predictably. But we have also kept saying that at each instant the forces are equal and opposite. So all the way through the adding process we are adding, step by step, the same thing, only reversed in sign, in each equation. This being the case, we are justified in writing the conclusion that

$$\int_0^{t_m} Fdt = -\int_0^{t_m} -Fdt$$

and from this it also follows that

$$mv_f = -MV_f \quad \text{or} \quad mv_f + MU_f = 0.$$

This result may not impress the reader, but a few words will make it look more interesting. The product of mass and speed is what we call *momentum*. In our treatment, the sum of the momentum at the end proved to be zero. Yet both masses were moving, perhaps with the speed of bullets. They *must* move so that the momentum of one is exactly equal and opposite to the momentum of the other. Had we been willing to include the initial speed of the body before the explosion, we should have found that the momentum before the explosion had to be equal to the momentum after, a result which is in agreement with a very important general principle called the Principle of Conservation of Momentum. This principle has no odd cases and exceptions: it works. It is not so useful for much of our thinking, because it retains something which we could just as well do without some of the time—the need to consider the direction in which things are happening. All the same, it is very useful, and plays a great part in any kind of collision or explosion problem.

Angular Motion

The laws of motion, together with the integral calculus, can be used to consider motion around, as well as in a straight line. When this is done, it is found that there is a third principle—the Principle of Conservation of *Angular* Momentum. Speaking rather roughly, angular momentum is the same as linear momentum only multiplied by the distance to the axis about which the turning is taking place. It is this principle which underlies the law of planetary motion discovered by Kepler, that the planets sweep out equal areas in equal times. This means that something like *mv* times the radius has to be fixed if the Principle of Conservation of Angular Momentum is valid. This principle, seemingly of special use only, proves to be very important in the physics of atoms. One would expect as much, for an atom must almost certainly contain small particles rotating about each other somewhat like a miniature solar system and it does.

Suggestions for Further Thought

1. Discuss the origin of the Principle of Conservation of Energy.
2. Discuss perpetual motion machines in relation to the Principle of Conservation of Energy.
3. A car doing 66 m.p.h. (100 ft./sec.) stops in one case in a distance of 1 ft. and in another case a distance of 100 ft. The head of a passenger has an average mass of 10 lbs. Calculate (a) the change in kinetic energy, (b) the change in momentum. Estimate (a) the average speed while stopping, (b) the acceleration while stopping, and (c) the force applied to the passenger's head in each case. Comment on the possibilities of survival. (32 lb. ft./sec.^{2} = 1 lb. weight).

Reference

Gerald J. Holton, *Introduction to Concepts and Theories in Physical Science* (Reading, Mass.: Addison-Wesley, 1958.)

Recollections of the Cavendish Laboratory

The Cavendish Laboratory at Cambridge University is one of a very small number of places where the teaching of physical science and achievements in research have taken place long enough to have a real history. The teaching of science in anything like an organized way is scarcely a hundred years old. That there should be such teaching at Cambridge was decided in 1851, and by 1871 plans had moved far enough to appoint Clerk Maxwell as the Cavendish Professor of Physics. That title and the name of the laboratory do honor to Henry Cavendish, a great physicist who made the first good measurement of the constant of gravitation and conducted deep researches into the nature of electricity, extending and confirming the work of Coulomb. The laboratory was not built until sixty years after his death, but the funds for the building and the original equipment were provided by the Duke of Devonshire, who was of the family of Cavendish and then the Chancellor of Cambridge University. One of Maxwell's great occupations as the Cavendish Professor was editing Cavendish's scientific papers, including repeating some of his experiments. Maxwell did not live long to occupy this position; he died in 1879. The next occupant was Lord Rayleigh, who besides being a great scientist, had the interesting and surprising attribute of being a successful dairy farmer. He held the professorship for five years before going to the Royal Institution in London. The next appointment proved to be one of the most brillant ever made, one which must have made many a dean and provost think wistfully. Instead of appointing some very able senior man, among the many who were, so to speak, on the premises, the University chose a theorist, a man only twenty-eight years of age. He was J. J. Thomson, almost universally known as "J. J." It seems strange to think of him as a young "firebrand," for the author recalls knowing him in the time after his retirement; yet this active, penetrating mind produced a steady stream of superb work over a quarter of a century and attracted to the laboratory some of the most capable men in the world. Under Thomson the promise of a laboratory, started by Maxwell and Rayleigh, became a sriking reality. One has only to look at a list of those working in the laboratory to see the names of the great performers in physical science from all over the world. This era continued until just after World War I.

In 1919, Thomson, while not exactly retiring, made a place for a new Cavendish Professor, Ernest Rutherford. Unlike Thomson, Rutherford was already widely renowned, already a Nobel Laureate. Perhaps the really surprising thing about Rutherford's term as Cavendish Professor was his ability to move toward even greater levels of achievement at once. Within a year of his appointment he had proved that nuclear reactions were possible and predicted the discovery of the neutron. These discoveries were the forerunners of the atomic energy of today. In very little time an amazing group of men were gathered at the laboratory: Fowler, Chadwick, Kapitza, Ellis, Cockcroft, Walton, Dee, Ratcliff, Oliphant, Blackett, with Thomson and Aston as continuations. At this time, in the area of nuclear physics, the laboratory was unassailable, and in several other areas was more than competent. At the Observatory, C. T. R. Wilson, one of the great men of Thomson's time, was working, and associated with that operation were men like Eddington.

Rutherford died in 1937. His successor was W. L. Bragg, whose field is that of structural analysis by X-rays. The laboratory began to look different. New experiments began, and a new wing was added. The real difference of note, however, was the spread of scientific activity throughout England, and the threat of World War II. Thus Chadwick, Dee, Blackett, and Walton took Professorships at outside universities and started their own schools of physics. At nearly the same time English scientists began to disappear into strange organizations working on such things as radar for warning against air raids. With the outbreak of war almost all Allied science began to be channeled into inventive effort for the military. (I have described three of these in other essays in this book.) The Cavendish Laboratory was emptied of its key personnel and went into a kind of twilight existence, remaining open but clearly with a low key performance. This was engendered by the need for instruction even in a time of emergency.

At the conclusion of World War II a group interested in the problems of biology, using the thoughts and techniques of physicists, assembled, and this completely new aspect of the laboratory produced evidence for the structure of protein and nucleic acids, and a steady stream of Nobel Laureates which is still going on. For over eighty years the laboratory has been a place of sharp intellectual stimulus. It is quite a record!

Since I began my career in science the character of the Cavendish Laboratory has changed considerably. I realize today that my sharp memories of some very great men may be more worth recording now than at the time I knew those men, when I was a young graduate student. Accordingly I have set down a few personal recollections, choosing those which can give an idea of what the place was like, a little after the start of Rutherford's era, a whole span from 1926-35.

In July of 1928 I showed up at the Cavendish Laboratory and underwent a small transition time in between being an undergraduate and being a graduate student. The summer life in Cambridge is really quite idyllic. Only genuine scholars are there because there are no formal courses other than laboratory courses, and so the Colleges are full and the lodging houses not so full. I was able to use my old room in Caius College and operate out of there. Since I had one of the more desirable rooms on the corner, it was really quite pleasant. The fortunes of my assignment to begin work brought me into contact with Jack Constable. We were shepherded into the "nursery," which is a small attic room in the Cavendish Laboratory, in which incoming graduate students were given "busy work" until one or other of the faculty members were ready to take them on as students. There was equipment for vacuum purposes, which I remember that P. B. Moon used, and Constable and I were set to counting scintillations. At that time the best method of detecting single particles was still the observation of scintillations, and graduate students were put to counting these things to see if they were unduly sharp of eye. If they were, they were set to a problem involving this method of counting. Since sitting in the dark with eyes glued to a microscope for a fairly large fraction of each day is somewhat hard on the eyes, there were, in 1928, an unusually large selection of people with poor vision in the Cavendish Laboratory. Constable and I were not quite that shrewd, and we were acceptable to work on this project for a little while. Into the midst of this group of raw, somewhat scared, very talented individuals Dr. Chadwick would come about twice a day. He would stomp up the stairs at the end with his quick step, his glasses covering the glint in his eye, take in at a glance what was happening in the room, and start talking to whomever he thought would be interesting. He would spend time with those who seemed to be close to the competence necessary to

get them out working with one of the faculty members all the while
carefully considering the best way to use the abilities of those students
who had been taken on in the laboratory. He was not friendly in the
sense of being *gemütlich* or having any comradely character; he was
factual, very busy, and obviously had a sharp mind fully at work. He
taught more by letting you see what you should do than by instruction.
It is a very powerful method with good students who are dedicated and
sure of themselves; it is not always good with those who want instruction to get started. I found him very interesting, rather frightening, and
in the mood I was in, searching for my own identity, I felt he was
neither good nor bad. He had a good deal of personal character: there
were many stories about him. In fact he ran the laboratory with complete understanding of what went on, tight control, very hard work,
and an extremely shrewd, accurate mind. I do not believe there could
be a more devastating critic of a piece of experimental work than Dr.
Chadwick. We would read some German article and present it to
him with enthusiasm as showing our competence in the literature; with
a few well-chosen words he would puncture the balloon, and we would
realize that there were many critical things which had not been considered.

   At the end of a rather longer than normal incubation period in the
nursery, Constable and I were put together and set to work personally
with him. It was great good fortune for me and I have always been
most grateful for it. I didn't think so at the time, but now I realize that
it was formative and constructive and, in a certain sense, my salvation.
We were asked to develop a proportional counter, or, as it was then
called, a Geiger-Klemperer counter; Constable and I tried to do this
with very inadequate equipment, including an old-fashioned electrom-
eter, and nothing really suitable for the purpose. It can be done, and
done well, with excellent electronics, but it was hopeless with the equipment we had. We spent about five or six months in acute frustration,
long after every one else had left the "nursery." Altogether this period
wasn't the very best period. I do remember one occasion when we were
putting the high voltage on a piece of equipment, and a bee lighted on
it just as Chadwick came in. With that rather strange fixed look that
he had and a deadpan expression he turned to me and said, "Put some
volts on him, will you?" I did, and of course the bee was quite unper-
turbed. He was somewhat surprised, however, when he flew off, because
there was some change then; but it didn't seem to do more than give
him a slight traumatic moment. Chadwick produced one of his rare
smiles then.

   Meanwhile, two very talented electronics students, Wynn-Williams
and Ward, had been developing a wholly new method of counting particles and had used this to make an accurate count of one radioactive

measurement. Since the equipment seemed to have worked, we were put to constructing one nearly like it, with one or two modifications, and Constable and I entered the world of vacuum tubes, electronic amplifiers, and so on. This occupied us for the next nine months. During this time we worked in Chadwick's own laboratory and were next to Lord Rutherford's lab. Wynn-Williams and Ward were his students. I soon began to have quite a feeling for the sort of individual Lord Rutherford was. He was a big, bluff, healthy, outgoing person, quite conscious of his power as a scientist, quite conscious of the position an individual such as he should occupy in the scientific society. At that time he was president of the Royal Society and we watched while he gathered together the equipment for his Royal Institution Lectures. He used to come in, often with his hat still on, just a little after nine o'clock in the morning, chatting with people as he came in, but mostly getting right into his laboratory. He had many things to do in his office, but the laboratory was where he generally came first; and I'm sure he did this out of choice. Woe betide his students if they were not there. Even if he knew they were in the midst of a construction job and were to be found in the shop, still he wanted them on hand for him to brief and talk to the first thing in the morning. As he came by our laboratory, he would generally make a comment or two of varied nature, sometimes kindly sarcasm, about the equipment, especially if it had an unusually haywire look about it, or if he thought there was some manifest absurdity there. With our valiant attempts to conquer some of the problems, there *were* some manifest absurdities. Constable believed everything he read, up to a point, and at one stage he had a miraculous series of suspensions to get rid of all vibration in the equipment. I was always skeptical that they would do any good, but went along and for a while we had quite a construction. It took about five minutes of undoing things to turn on the amplifier and five minutes of putting them back to see what happened, but we were trying our best and Constable was happy. Rutherford didn't let this go by without some comment. However, his comments on it, while sharp and sometimes a little cutting, never had the effect of stopping us from trying. At no time did we ever feel that Rutherford had a contempt for our work, although he might be amused. We might feel that he had watched this sort of thing before and that this was a stage we had to go through, but we always had the feeling that he did care, that he knew we were trying the best we could, and that he was not going to stop us. We also felt that he had considerable faith in our ability. He did this, not in a way in which he *said* he had faith, but in a *real* way. His great skill in criticism of students included his ability to make it apparent to you that if you stuck with it and kept going you would almost certainly make out.

Rutherford had some little idiosyncrasies. He smoked a pipe, liked
to talk, and wasn't always conscious of what he was up to when he
was in the laboratory. At one stage the detection of particles involved
recording in the dark and, since his entire laboratory was adapted to
being darkened, the idea was to keep the place dark. When Rutherford
would come in, there would be a traumatic moment as the door opened
and all efforts were bent on keeping him from turning on the light.
Then he would want to smoke his pipe and talk about what was going
on. He would be fully aware of the fact that the room was dark and
the experiment was going on and he would be most interested, but the
inevitable stage would come when the well-packed pipe, which was
associated with getting out of the office and into the lab, needed to
be lit. Depending upon his degree of absorption in what was going
on the match might or might not be struck. The great trick on the part
of the graduate students was to watch this and to keep at least one
good thick back between him and the apparatus when the match lit.
When he was really interested he would some times light matches so
often that one could tell where he had been standing in the lab just
by looking at the floor.

At one stage we put in a little dark room to keep our equipment
dark without keeping the whole room dark. The door on this room
wasn't readily closed, since it had been built rather quickly. Rutherford noticed this difficulty of closing one day and promptly suggested
that we put on (in his words) one of those little catches one sees on
"country doors." This was a piece of wood with a screw through it
that one turned, and it certainly was highly successful at keeping the
door closed. The only difficulty was that anybody inside was promptly
trapped and would have to wait in the dark room until someone let
him out. What happened was the characteristic thing that happens
with very great men. The catch was, indeed, put on the door, but it was
so fixed that it would not quite turn and latch the door. Otherwise
considerable danger could result, particularly with an individual like
Constable, who was quite capable of closing the door and going off to
lunch knowing that someone was inside. If that someone happened to
be Pollard, it was quite all right, but if it had happened by any chance
to be the lab assistant or Chadwick, it would have been an error.

This stage in nuclear physics was one which was really very exciting
and very interesting personally in the Cavendish lab. The nucleus is
a realm in which the most sophisticated and modern physical theory
will be needed, and even today one can hardly say that it has been
conquered in terms of understanding. At the same time the nucleus

had been "created," in a certain sense, by Rutherford, who had dis-covered that it existed and who had shown how to change nuclei from one kind to another; he was undoubtedly the top man in the world on experimentation with nuclei. On the other hand, Rutherford was a very factual thinker, one who had a sharp picture in his mind of what it was he was thinking about, and not one to accept, without a rebellion, the dicta of quantum mechanics, at that time called wave mechanics, which suggested that all one could ever calculate was a probability. As a result, the laboratory was a certain sense torn in two. We had co-existing, on the one hand, the first-rate mind of a tre-mendous experimenter, and, on the other hand, perhaps the most revo-lutionary concepts that have ever hit physical science. It was a difficult time, and the Cavendish lab underwent a certain degree of confusion in direction.

I remember the debates and discussions that were held on the subject of wave mechanics; I remember that it did seem to be more difficult than perhaps it needed to be at the time. We were not a laboratory that was used to working in spectroscopy. Such laboratories were more commonly found in the United States. In fact, I believe it is true that there was not a single spectroscope in the Cavendish lab at that time; and so the experimental evidence that might have made us happy with the new theory wasn't there. Instead the experimental difficulties were very strongly present. In the midst of this Rutherford and Chadwick and their group of very talented students and junior faculty endeavored to function. They were fully aware of the need for new experimental approaches, and had two most interesting individuals, Cockcroft and Walton, working on a method of accelerating particles which would then be capable of making changes in nuclei just as Rutherford had done with the alpha particle. The experiments were proving to be harder then they thought, and the apparatus was growing larger and larger and seeming to take more and more time to become effective. Calculations on the equivalent energy necessary to produce effects had been made crudely, but carefully, and these indicated that quite con-siderable energy would be necessary. All this time suggestions were coming from the theoretical group, among the most notable of whom was Fowler, Rutherford's son-in-law, that one might see things com-pletely differently if the new wave mechanics were right. I remember Chadwick designed a most difficult experiment with great labor and care to test one of the crucial points of the new theory. I think of all Chadwick's many fine experiments this is the hardest, and in one respect, for the laboratory in which he worked, the most incisive. He studied a very symmetrical collision between identical particles and, according to the new theory, he should have discovered, where all angles are the same, a number twice what would be expected based on the old theory. He found it! Thus, in the laboratory, one of those who might be called the "old guard," those who had their training with Rutherford at Manchester, became convinced that there was something to the new theory, and one could see the laboratory beginning to slide in the direction of thinking in terms of these new ideas.

At about this time we had a visit from Gamow. He was a Russian, with a high-pitched voice and somewhat enthusiastic manner. He listened to all the experimental information, and came out with a suggestion for the way in which Rutherford's own personal particle, the alpha particle, was emitted from nuclei. This is the theory of alpha radioactivity now agreed on today. The theory was a strange one to scientists then, in that it required the traversal of a barrier without going over the top of it. It was very unpalatable to Rutherford, and he grumbled away at it, but nevertheless it seemed to work. Cockcroft and Walton began to realize that they could do their experiments without pushing their apparatus to the extent they had thought necessary and this was done. All the excitement following their famous work was after I had left the laboratory.

The Cavendish laboratory had some rules and customs. One rule was that it was open from nine to six every weekday and from nine to one on Saturday. This was unswervingly held to, sometimes under quite difficult circumstances. The general strike of 1926 occurred when I was an undergraduate. Nearly the whole of Cambridge University was very tense about it; this strike was regarded as a very close thing to a labor revolution. Many of us, including myself, went off to London to act as special police. Rutherford took no part in this action and kept the Cavendish laboratory open, continuing to hold classes, as I remember, for the whole of the ten-day period. It was really a very courageous thing for him to do, and, in my opinion, rather than giving Rutherford the stamp of being a conservative in the sense that has sometimes been suggested, it shows that he was a liberal with a rather confident idea of the freedom of action of people.

The customs of the Cavendish Laboratory were almost as strongly followed as the rules were. One of these customs was tea at 4:30 every day. This was a strange phenomenon, and one which served a very useful purpose. A fairly small room next to the library was set aside essentially just as a tea room and was hardly ever occupied at any other time. At almost exactly 4:25, the female attendant in the laboratory, who had a job of continually sweeping and generally looking after the corridors and classrooms, appeared with three huge teapots, which were placed on the table with the suitable number of cups already there. The person who was the secretary of the "tea club" (I was the victim for one very sad year) then produced something to eat. This consisted of a variety of what the English used to call very tersely "deadlys," which we call french pastries, and assorted very sticky things known as "Chelsea buns." In those days a large supply of these could be had for very little money. At 4:29 and 30 seconds the first person would arrive for tea, and at 4:32 the room would be absolutely jammed full, with the contents of the teapots badly depleted and the Chelsea buns and deadlys in a definite state of wreckage. By 4:42 the room was beginning to empty and at 4:45 the only people left were two or three intent individuals who had discovered some mutual scientific point they had to settle. Nothing was left in the teapots but leaves, and definitely nothing was left on any plate that had contained solid food. This tea ceremony served a very useful function. It was an excellent method of communication of all sorts of things from gossip to scientific knowledge, and it had the effect of bringing the whole group together and making them feel like a unit. There actually is a good deal of difference between the eminent men and the students in an English university. This is not distance which is desired by anybody, but it forms part of the English pattern. The use of tea as a mitigating influence on this age-old traditional pattern of superior-inferior relationship was very good, and I look back on it almost wholly with pleasure. I do not look back with pleasure on the problem I had of collecting funds for the tea; and I am very grateful indeed to Sir J. J. Thomson who at a later date left money to provide for the tea fund in perpetuity. This means that one graduate student per year is (a) saved considerable embarrassment and (b) wealthier by something on the order of $50, not a trivial sum in the life of a graduate student.

About once a year we would find ourselves invited to Lord Rutherford's house for a Sunday tea. This was a rotational affair and about ten of us would appear. We were really very stupid about this whole business and I look back on it with a strong sense of shame. Lord and Lady Rutherford were very human people. We were caught in this strange feeling that because somebody lives in a house on Queens' Road and has a garden and is a professor and a great man, he is necessarily a formidable person to be afraid of and, particularly, a person to be silent with. Rutherford was none of these things. He truly loved his position and his students and he really did wish, not as a formality but as a reality, that he could know them personally. We would show up in our best clothes, arriving sheepishly in twos and ones, get introduced, sit around the fireplace and take tea, wondering about whether we were doing it right, while Rutherford would try to keep us talking. Constable was not too bad at this; however, in some ways he was a little unfortunate, because he seemed to be one of those people who are quite willing to say the first thing that comes into their heads. It was quite a while before I realized that he actually did exert *some* censorship. He and I got along fairly well and, on the whole, I think our session with Rutherford was not too bad. I do remember for a minute or two Rutherford expressed some pleasure at the fact that we had not been silent and inveighed against the tongue-tied character of graduate students, wondering why it was they had no lives they were apparently willing to discuss and no interests seemingly outside of the next screw they would have to put into their apparatus.

Part of the trouble I think was that Lady Rutherford appeared to us to be formidable. We had only experienced Rutherford as a scientific man in the laboratory and the classroom and, suddenly, we discovered that he had all the appurtenances of a home. We somehow knew that Lady Rutherford would have nothing to do with any discussions of nuclear reactions or vacuum systems or anything like that; and then we suddenly also realized that there were a huge number of unknown areas of interest which contained subjects so far from the interests of the ordinary graduate student that it would be almost impossible to imagine anyone discussing them. So we tended to be a little quieter than we needed to be and, while I know she acted graciously in a very friendly way, it was on the whole the ordeal of the year to go to the professor's home.

There are two more things I would like to record about Rutherford, both in my opinion, very favorable to him as a man and human being. Almost the very first thing I encountered at the Cavendish Lab was a conference on nuclear physics which involved a great many international experts. Most of the greats in nuclear physics from Europe were invited. Naturally, so were the graduate students. At least we were able to sit in the back row at the sessions and watch what went on. I noticed that when Rutherford was presiding he made little or no distinction between men of very great reputation and his own students. At one stage a point was up for discussion and L. H. Gray, who was a year or two ahead of me, and certainly, at that time, no international "great," wanted to say something. Others at the meeting seemed to feel that perhaps he had no status, but Rutherford just said "Come on, speak up, what's on your mind?" or words to that effect, and Gray had his turn in court. This made a great impression on me. It is very easy for a great man to move among his peers without regard for the future great men. Rutherford had nothing of that in his character. The other thing that I noticed about Rutherford was the stage at which people left the laboratory. Rutherford took most seriously the problem of placing his students where they would be most effective, have the greatest influence, and receive the highest salary. He took this as a very serious task, and even with students who had hardly been near him, but, nevertheless, were members of his laboratory, was unremitting in his attempts to place them, coming back time after time to the problem if the student failed in an interview or somehow didn't seem to fit into the position. He did not have to do this, because we were already benefited so much by having been in his laboratory that our chances for a position were very good; yet this was not the attitude that Rutherford took. He seemed to feel he had a responsibility to the students who worked in his laboratory. He accepted this when he admitted them and went through with it quite resolutely. I know in one or two cases he did so with great pains and some difficulties. I have always respected him since I knew this last side of him. The odds and ends of the world have given me a chance to see a large number of great scientists; not all of them are in the same class with Rutherford.

The great men of the Cavendish Laboratory, like Rutherford, Thomson, Chadwick, and Fowler, could hardly be said to be great lecturers. This was not because they did not, all of them, on occasion, give excellent lectures, but because their own philosophy was essentially to show the student what was to be acquired, and to assume that the student would then go ahead and acquire it—the difference between actively teaching and suggesting what to learn. The whole spirit of the place was that you were there because you wanted to learn; the function of the professor was to show you what to do and then leave you to do it. I do remember one or two scattered incidents about the courses. For instance, I remember that Rutherford's lectures were, to my mind, not very deep, but always inspiring in the sense that once or twice in each classroom session one would suddenly see with profound insight into a branch of the subject which just wasn't in any book anywhere. I also remember the occasion when he started to repeat his previous lecture; he grew a little uncomfortable as he watched the class. On finding his mistake, he asked Hayles to go and get his notes; we all waited in silence while the three minutes necessary for this took place. Then, with notes, Rutherford went on with a lecture which was quite good. The more professional teachers like Alec Wood, Ellis, and Ratcliff were excellent. I particularly remember what a first-class job Blackett did, and how he opened my eyes to the kinetic theory of gases, which is really not ordinarily very inspiring.

The mood of the place was a mixture of competition and unity. Everyone among the students felt that he had to prove himself; that he had to do a job that would require his intellect and his skill; that it would be difficult; and that he had to do it. At the same time the students fully realized that they were among selected individuals, individuals whose friendship would be worth a great deal to them all their lives. These friendships began in odd and strange ways, but they were real friendships, and I have retained a good many of them in spite of a change of nation and a change of subject over all these years. My partner, Constable,* was a man of many enthusiasms, and among the things that he worked up was a scheme of a short walk before breakfast, sometimes followed by having breakfast together, sometimes by just dispersing. These morning walks were quite strange things. They would slowly accumulate people who tramped about the odd quarters of Cambridge with stomachs rumbling away, and then dispersed to each other's rooms in groups of four or five to have breakfast together. It wasn't at all a bad way to get to know one another and this sort of thing was going on quite a bit. I remember that Walton induced me to run in the slow pack of the "hare and hounds." I had never done any running in my life and I have always been last whenever I ran, but I discovered that jogging along about as slowly as you can jog through the fields on an autumn afternoon in company with others might be strenuous but also very pleasant. I have always felt kindly toward Walton ever since that time because I think it did me some good.

These are the sorts of human factors that entered into the unity part, and competition, the other part of the mixture, isn't bad if you are competing in such a way that your success will bring you real pride. If you compete and feel that when it is over somebody else who has not done so well will get more credit, then you don't feel very successful. We never felt that way in Cavendish Lab. We felt that our associates really could judge our success or failure accurately and that it was safe to leave the judgment of our ability in their hands. It was strenuous, and at some times strenuous almost to the point of extreme stress on the nerves and mind, but nevertheless it was exhilarating and worthwhile. It was certainly an experience we could never forget.

---

* Lest I seem to be flippant about Jack Constable, let me set it straight. He was my close friend and I owe him a debt I can never repay. His early death, solely due to our lag in biological skill, has been a permanent sadness in my life.

ERNEST C. POLLARD, 1963

8

Spread of the Idea of the Conservation of Energy

In Chapter 7 we described the way in which the equations of motion can be recast in such a way as to suggest two "principles"—the Principle of Conservation of Energy and the Principle of Conservation of Momentum. The former of these is interesting because it actually does not involve all the laws of motion, and it also does not involve direction. The derivation we presented formed the first phase in the emergence of a new concept of "energy" as a firm and useful idea. In this chapter we want to show how that idea became established and what position it now occupies in physical science.

Let us first look at a simple example of what can be called the restricted idea of the conservation of energy. A pendulum will serve as an example: for us a pendulum is a heavy weight suspended by a wire or string, as shown in Figure 8.1. Before we begin to think about energy at all we can consider the motion we are all so used to. We know that if the bob of the pendulum is pulled to one side and then released it goes back and forth. A really long pendulum, as the one that can be seen in the Smithsonian Institution, is truly fascinating to watch, especially as such a heavy slow motion can easily be maintained all day, and then the earth rotates underneath it so that the pendulum seems to have changed its direction.

Now one feature is very easy to demonstrate. The pendulum never goes *past* its point of release. A favorite lecture demonstration is to stand with one's nose at the release point and to let the heavy weight come right back without flinching. Its safe, so long as the lecturer knows how to stand still. The other feature is that the weight steadily gains speed on the way down, until it is going very fast at the bottom of the swing, and then loses it on the way up. It is very hard to look at this kind of motion without wanting to say that it is characterized by the

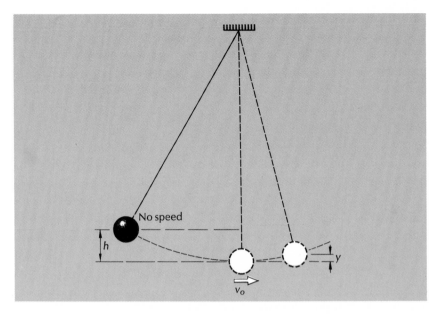

Fig. 8.1. The motion of a pendulum illustrates the conservation of energy. The interchange between height and speed can be figured.

possession of some property which changes form from speed to position, back and forth.

If we now go over the same discussion we used for the roller coaster, find that the force of the earth's attraction on the bob, of mass m, is mg, and to find the potential energy at any place we must designate a starting point and then find the value of

$$-\int_0^{s_m} F\,ds$$

Exactly as for the roller coaster, we find that this integral tells us that the potential energy, V, is

$$V = -\int_0^h F\,ds = -(-mg)h = mgh$$

If the bob is not at the maximum height, but at some intermediate lesser height y, the potential energy is mgy, because everything is just the same, only y replaces h because y is the height which has been attained against the force of the earth's attraction.

Now when we let the bob go it will swing to the bottom where the excess height is zero. So the potential energy at the bottom is zero. But, on the other hand, the speed will definitely not be zero there, but will be quite high, say v_0, and so the kinetic energy is $\frac{1}{2} mv_0{}^2$. At the same intermediate place, where we said that the height was y, we can say that the speed is v. The kinetic energy at the top is zero, for the bob is not moving at that point.

The Principle of Conservation of Energy then states that

$$mgh + 0 = mgy + \frac{1}{2} mv^2 = 0 + \frac{1}{2} mv_0{}^2.$$

Looking at this we see that the sum of potential energy and kinetic energy at the top, where it is all potential, is equal to the sum of the two part way down, where it is partly potential and partly kinetic, and to the sum at the bottom, where it is all kinetic. With these equations, and the knowledge of the particular value of the height h, we can calculate the speed of the bob at any height on the way down, and of course, at the bottom. What we notice is that we do have the balance sheet kind of description. There *is* some property which changes form from being associated with speed to being associated with position: that property is energy.

The authors want to give a word of caution here. They would like to give it with considerable emphasis, for experience has led them to find their readers have a desire to look at this process superficially. Many readers will approach these two chapters with some concept of energy. It is our contention that man *developed* the concept and was not born with it. Thus, to say that "potential energy is energy of position," which is a familiar statement, is meaningless until we say *what energy is*. We must realize that potential energy, at any event, is not a simple concept; it is definable only in a limited way.

ASIDE ON SYMBOLS

In physical science we try to use symbols which remind us of what they represent: h for height, and so on. When we do this we soon run out of letters, and so the device of using subscripts has come in. Thus we spoke of v_0, to represent the velocity at the bottom. It looks formidable, and is a great headache to typists and typographers, but for the rest of us it is rather convenient.

THE GROWTH OF ELABORATION

Before we embark on a further study of the various kinds of energy, it is worth while to think about how things become elaborate. We touched on this before when we discussed the number system.

Almost everyone is struck by the elaborate nature of even simple music.

Learning to play music on any kind of instrument is hard, harder than learning a language. Yet a great deal of music is based on a very simple structure. If we look at the three chords drawn, usually denoted by the numbers 1, 4, 5, they represent very simple sounds indeed. Over the

years, the human ear has developed a liking for these, particularly in a progression 1, 4, 5, 1. One might think that music based only on such a progression would be very tedious and boring (and incidentally, it can be); nevertheless, quite a lot of music which we hear around us all the time is to a large extent founded on these three chords. Obviously more chords can be added. If we add three more, the 2 and 6 chords and a seventh on the 5, making only six chords in all, then we really do have the basis for a large part of ordinary music. Even the truly great composers, Mozart and Beethoven among them, did not use much more than double this number. Their music is intricate and subtle and bears listening to hundreds of times without becoming cloying.

The point of this digression into the structure of music is to show how complexity can develop out of relative simplicity. Language is another illustration. The Chinese never constructed an alphabet; they use a separate character for each word; yet with only 26 letters in our alphabet we can write all the words the Chinese ever write, and possibly many more.

In the same way, in physical science, there are relatively few basic laws —not a dozen in number—perhaps fewer than used in music and certainly fewer than used in language. At the same time we see from the analogies of music and language that a great amount of elaboration can develop. The interesting thing is that the elaboration we develop fits the facts of Nature. In fact, so confident has the physical scientist become that the failure to fit even once would distress him acutely. He would spend years trying to dissect the situation where the failure occurred; usually he would discover that the failure lay in the description being faulty and not in the elaboration of his beloved principles. Once in a long while this is not true, and then there is an upheaval and new principles emerge.

Simple ideas like potential and kinetic energy can be used in a development, just as in music one can develop more and more progressions of chords.

Heat as a Form of Energy

We have stressed the "humble" origin of the idea of energy. When it was first advanced, it was limited to systems like pendulums, falling bodies, watch springs, and so on. Anything involving friction, or tubulence, or human muscular action was excepted. Chemistry was not even considered to be related to energy in any way.

In 1842, Mayer, a German physician, became convinced that the idea of mechanical energy could be extended to heat, electricity, chemistry, and sound. He showed that existing heat measurements on gases fitted very well with the idea of a definite relation between mechanical energy and heat and he calculated the exact relationship correctly. He ran into much scientific hostility, partly because he propounded too broad an idea, and partly because he himself did not do experiments. Also, we must add, partly because there is such a thing as prejudice among scientists. Two years later, Joule, a wealthy English brewer who had a private laboratory in Manchester, performed the direct experiment of causing a change in potential energy, due to the falling of two weights, to churn up water in a heat insulated container. The frictional churning of the water causes the falling of the weights to take place very slowly and thus there is no appreciable kinetic energy developed as they fall. This is the familiar action of a dissipative force, in this case inside the container. The apparatus is shown in Figure 8.2.

What Joule sought was a relation between the change in potential energy due to the slow lowering of the weights and the amount of heat developed in the water. To measure heat in the simplest way we measure both the mass of water heated and the rise in temperature of the water. So Joule watched the thermometer shown in the figure, and as the weights slowly sank and as the water was churned up by the paddlewheels, the thermometer did rise. He carefully measured the rise and weighed the water, so measuring the amount of heat. Was it related to the amount of potential energy change? It was. The more potential energy used up, the more heat generated. Thus he observed, in this system, a transfer of one form of mechanical energy, potential energy, into heat.

This is the most celebrated of Joule's experiments, but by no means the whole of his work. He set out to prove by experiment that whenever a process takes place in which mechanical energy is lost by friction or turbulence or some similar dissipative process, an equivalent amount of heat is generated. One of his lesser-known experiments is interesting because it shows that the loss of kinetic energy by a system can result in the development of an equivalent amount of heat. The apparatus is shown in Figure 8.3. He suspended two blocks of lead from the roof beams, and in the larger of the two be placed a thermometer, dipping it

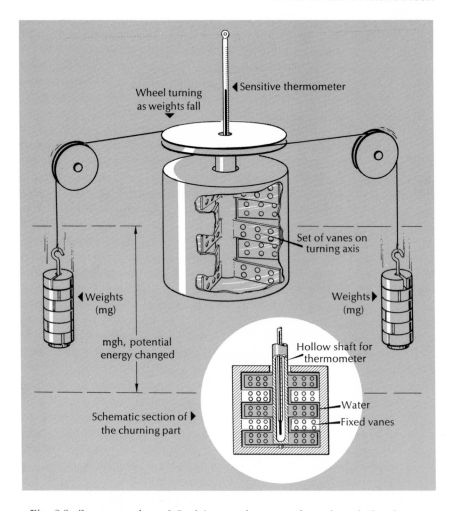

Fig. 8.2. Representation of Joule's experiment to show the relation between potential energy and heat. The development of heat by friction is measured by causing water to be churned up and so heated. The loss of potential energy as the weights fall has an exactly equivalent gain in heat.

into a small pool of mercury so that it made contact with the lead. Then he pulled back the smaller block, let it go, and allowed it to collide with the large block. The lead was so soft that the two blocks stuck together. When this happens it is not hard to show that some kinetic energy is lost. Joule observed that each time the collision was made to occur the thermometer rose. He watched it carefully and made the necessary calculations in terms of the mass of the lead and its heat capacity, and found

Fig. 8.3. Joule's proof of the relation between kinetic energy and heat. The lead blocks were allowed to collide in a known way. At each collision a measurable amount of kinetic energy is lost. There is a corresponding rise in temperature.

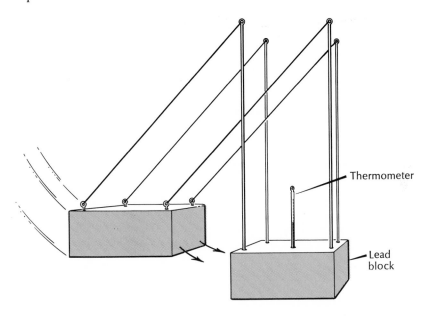

that the relationship he had found with the rotating paddle wheel and the falling weights (in which potential energy is used up) also held for the case where kinetic energy is used up. An equivalent amount of heat was produced. Joule performed many such experiments, including electrical measurements. After his work was completed no one could doubt the reality of the equivalence between heat and energy.

Others, notably Rowland in the United States and Hirn in England, repeated Joule's work, not so much to test the truth of the relationship as to measure its quantitative value. The conclusion reached was that *heat is a form of energy;* and as a result, the idea that a fixed amount of energy could be distributed into various forms—kinetic and potential energy, now included *thermal energy.* Thus, the idea of energy became elaborated. Soon after this, electrical, chemical, and acoustical energy were also added. Today we can include *nuclear* energy.

We now can set a chart, as shown, to represent the behavior of energy, and we must complete the chart with many criss-cross lines. Note again how simple is the basic idea, and how elaborate the development.

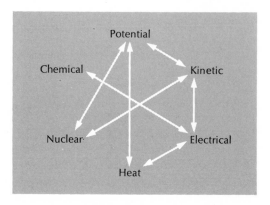

Chart 8.1. The interrelationships of energy.

The Molecular Hypothesis

This last idea of the interconvertibility or exchangeability of energy leads us to try to simplify it. The simplification is based on the hypothesis that all we are really ever concerned with is the exchange between kinetic and potential energy, but that we have sometimes to admit that a part of the process is taking place on a very small scale, so small that it carries us beyond our powers of visualization and we have to use our imagination. In physical science, when we use our imagination, we call it "framing a hypothesis."

Let us take one of the simplest ways in which mechanical energy (for example, the energy due to muscular force pushing a book across a table) is converted into heat by friction. The mechanical energy appears as a force times a distance and nothing ever seems to want to return it to us once we become involved with friction. We keep exerting a force to move the book, and each time we change direction *we* must use the force: the back never presses of itself. On the other hand, we find that, as the mechanical energy disappears, heat comes to take its place. Let us start by considering the bottom surface of the book and the top surface of the table as the one is pushed over the other. At the first glance, they look as in (a) in the Figure 8.4. In (b) we have enlarged the part between the two lines and we see that there is quite a lot of roughness; only a few places actually touch each other. One such place is *yy*. In (c) we have enormously enlarged a part of *yy* and *used our imagination*. We have enlarged it to the point where we can see molecules. We represent the molecules of the book by circles and those of the table by squares. They are actually somewhat different things, so it is fair enough to have them look different. The arrow indicates that the book is moving.

One thing this picture tells us at once is that our hypothesis is barren without any further ideas. One idea we obviously need. We have no right to draw such a regular arrangement unless there is a reason for it. There is. Forces are present which attract molecules one to another. Because of these forces, the molecules are almost touching one another. (For the moment we will leave that "almost" unexplained, through it is important.) We need still another idea. We must imagine that molecules need not be still: they can jiggle or vibrate back and forth, and so long as they are not too vigorous in their jiggling, no harm is done. Now we are ready to use the hypothesis. The molecules of the book which are right next to the table are attracted by them. So as one book molecule moves by a table molecule, it pulls it and actually moves it out of position. The book molecule doesn't pull hard enough to tear the table molecule completely away. As it gets rather far out of position, the other table molecules, which are also pulling on it, win the tug of war, and the table molecule snaps back to its normal place. The book molecule also snaps back, because it has been pulled back by the other book molecules; both molecules follow the law of action and reaction. After this event is over, both molecules jiggle or vibrate extra hard.

Fig. 8.4. Various scale views of the contact of a book and a table. At one of the points of contact, y, the scale is greatly enlarged so that the molecules can be seen. They are in different, but regular, arrays, held in place by electrical forces between the molecules.

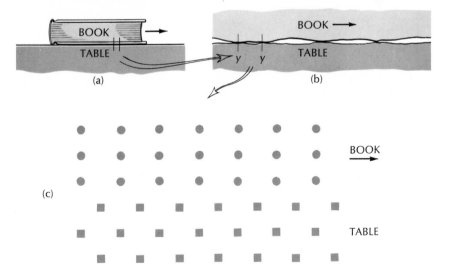

We thus see the primary event of friction. The apparently steady motion of the book produces the local disturbance of the molecules at the surface, and while the book moves, the molecular attractions will continue in this pulled-and-released way. There is a secondary effect which also happens; the forces between the molecules are now acting between the vibrating molecules and those in layers farther from the surface. The motion of a surface molecule pulls and pushes at its neighbors and they also begin to vibrate, so that the vibration is not part of the surface alone. This influence, which conveys the jiggling into layers below the surface layer, is the molecular explanation for the conduction of heat. (See Figure 8.5.) When everything is over we have a spread of extra vibration in all the molecules of the book and the table. To make a consistent description we need to add an extra hypothesis: the word "heat" refers in some way to the motion of the molecules in their vibrations. We can now say that because the vibrations are faster and more extensive and they are spread out into the book and table, there is more heat, and so energy has gone into heat. We return to the topic of the nature of heat and temperature later on. While we are on this subject we can see one very interesting consequence of this way of looking at the process of moving the book across the table with friction. We notice that if we wanted to get mechanical energy *back*, that is to say, have the vibrating molecules all go still, and have the book propelled across the table, then we have to find some way of getting all the separate molecules to cease their motion, and to conspire to have only molecules at the surface move, and all move in the same direction and so push the book. It sounds improbable, and it is. While mechanical energy can readily, by friction, go into heat, it is not so easy (though to an extent possible) to persuade heat to go into mechanical energy.

Fig. 8.5. The result of holding and snapping free. The molecules vibrate most rapidly at the surface and this vibration goes from layer to layer, forming *heat conduction.*

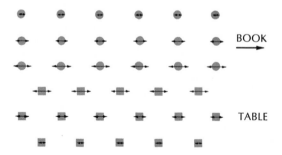

We can ask why the two surfaces don't bind together—often all the attraction of the molecules should work as much between wood and book as between wood and wood and book and book. The answer lies in the roughness of two surfaces. They only touch really closely at a very few places. The person pushing the book actually tears these places apart. Very carefully flattened surfaces *do* stick together and will not come apart.

ELECTRIC CURRENTS

Now that we have described the process of friction and its relation to heat, we may as well get some dividends from the molecular hypothesis. One very nice one is in the description of an electric current.

It is quite hard to find things in which electric currents flow. They do not flow in wood or glass or air or in many ordinary things. They *do* flow in metals, especially metals like copper and silver, which we refer to as conductors. So, we first have to ask why electric currents only flow in conductors and not in *everything*.

We can suggest that it is because the molecules which make up matter are themselves compounded of electrical parts. These parts must be equal plus and minus, or we would know it by the charge they would show. Suppose that a conductor is a regular array of atoms (or molecules; at the moment it doesn't matter to us) and that some of the atoms have released part of their structure to roam freely throughout the substance. Today we know that this is what happens, and that the freely roaming "parts" are electrons—negative particles. Let us now consider what happens to a conductor when an electric field is applied to it. The conductor is shown in the Figure 8.6a. The dots are positive nuclei of atoms, the large circles are electrons attached to atoms, and the three little shaded circles are free electrons. As drawn, there is no electric field applied. Now suppose a positively charged plate is put on the left and a negative one on the right. Now an electric field, urging the negative electrons to the left is present. Things will happen. They would be very simple if all the atoms and electrons were still. But they are not. Especially the electrons. Because the conductor is at ordinary temperature, and not extremely cold, the electrons (and the atoms) have energy. The electrons, particularly, are going fast but aimlessly all over the place. Now when the field appears, the electrons feel a force urging them toward the positive plate. They start to go toward it, but as they do they encounter atoms and get deflected one way or another. Between encounters with atoms, they make some headway, and as a result, they show a tendency to *drift* toward the positive. This drift of the electrons is the electric current. Seen pictorially, it is as in Figure 8.6b.

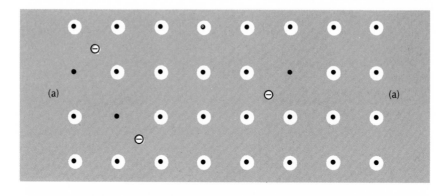

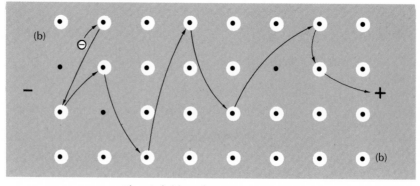

Electric field on electron ————▶

Fig. 8.6. A conductor with free electrons (a) and a suggestion for the motion of
one of them when an electric field is applied (b).

A little boy in a football crowd hears his mother calling him. He is
buffeted by people's legs, but he gets there.

RELATION BETWEEN CURRENT AND FIELD: OHM'S LAW

It is reasonable to suppose that a big field causes a bigger speed of drift
and so more current. This means that we can say that current is proportional to field. If E is the electric field and i the current, then we
recall that a proportionality is an equality with a constant in it, so

$$i = (\text{Constant})\, E$$

This is *Ohm's Law*.

We usually find that one of the small points of sophistication about our readers is that they may have heard about "Ohm's Law," and also that it did not seem to be just as we have stated it. The trouble lies in an unwillingness of the practicing electrician to use the idea of an electric field: he prefers to use something else, which is *related* to the electric field. This is "potential difference," generally shortened to "voltage." In a simple case, this "voltage," divided by the length of the wire across which it is to be found, is a measure of the electric field. So, if we substitute the symbols V for potential difference, and l for the length of the wire, then we get:

$$i = (\text{Constant}) \times \frac{V}{l}$$

and we can see that current is proportional to voltage, which has a familiar ring to it. If we aggregate the length and the "Constant" into a lovely, rather vague, though very comforting word—"Resistance"—we can put:

$$\text{Current} = \frac{\text{Voltage}}{\text{Resistance}}$$

This will certainly bring back fond memories. Theoretical physicists use the law in the form we have given earlier.

Solids, Liquids, and Gases: The Three States of Matter.

In inquiring into the nature of friction and of an electric current, we have essentially said what we consider the structure of solids to be, on the molecular scale. The molecules are in a regular array, generally so regular that the outline of regularity extends all the way to the visible boundary of the solid and confers a regular shape on it, which we call a crystal. Thus sodium chloride—salt—has its atoms in a cubical array, with sodium and chlorine atoms exactly alternating. This means that salt occurs as crystals,—not cubes, as a rule, for in that case all the sides of the cube would have grown exactly equally as the crystal formed, which would be surprising. However, the edges of salt crystals have the right angle of a cube. Not all solids are crystals, and not all solids have perfect molecular arrays, particularly if the solid is made of a mixture of substances, as wood is, for an example. Even so, the molecules are close together, and do have an arrangement; and there are relatively few places where a molecule could be which do not have a molecule in them.

A liquid is very nearly the same thing, with a small difference which produces a surprisingly large effect. In a liquid, the molecules are close together, just about as close as they are in a solid, but there are a small number of vacant places that are not filled by molecules. This has the effect of making it possible for molecules to slide one over the other, moving so as to push a whole line to fill a vacant place, and then leaving a vacancy behind, which can be filled by another slide. The liquid thus has only one big requirement: the molecules must stay very close to each other, so that they keep the general pattern of arrangement. But there are a very large number of ways of keeping this arrangement, and for this reason a liquid can adapt itself to the effect of gravity on it in a container, and will seek to sink down as far as it can; thus it is able to take the shape of the container, which is the property we associate most with liquids. In Figure 8.7 we show the transition from a solid to a liquid. On the left the molecules of the solid are shown as almost still. Once in a while we have indicated an unusually active molecule by an increase in the little "fuzziness' which is shown for each one. On the right we have shown the same solid which has been heated to a higher temperature, and there the fuzziness is much more marked. We have also tried to indicate that the molecules are a little farther apart, though this is a little difficult. Neither of these actually determine whether the substance is a solid or a liquid; it is the *vacancies,* outlined by the dotted lines, that actually make the difference.

Using this figure, we can easily work out the "form" of a gas using the molecular hypothesis. Just as the vibrations of the solid cause an enlargement and the possibility of vacancies, thus producing a liquid, so it is possible for the vibrations to increase still more and permit a few molecules to escape entirely from the more dense form of matter. What happens to these? If the space above the solid or liquid is a vacuum, the molecule which is liberated from the surface has no neighbor and nothing to attract (or be attracted to) at all. It just goes, and it continues going

Fig. 8.7. Molecular array of a solid and a liquid, the latter with vacancies in the array, shown by dotted circles.

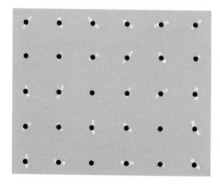
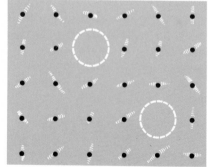

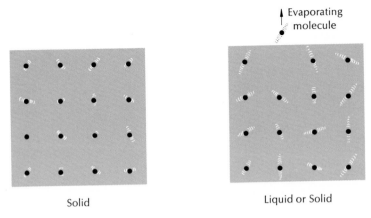

Fig. 8.8. Increased molecular vibration can cause a molecule to break free: the process of evaporation.

until it encounters something. If such a gas molecule were released in the space between the planets, where there is almost a perfect vacuum, the distance traveled by this molecule before it hit anything might be many thousands of miles. In our ordinary experience, the molecule will find itself in some kind of confined space and will hit the walls of this space. When it does so, it bounces off, and in the act of bouncing it causes the wall to experience a force. The force, when produced by very many such molecules, we call a pressure. More correctly, the force divided by the area of the wall on which it acts is called the pressure. In Figure 8.8 we show the sort of process which results in the departure of a molecule from the surface of a solid or a liquid—the process of evaporation.

The essential character of a gas is to be found in the great separation between the molecules; they are so far apart that they hardly attract each other, but remain as separate entities all the while. It is interesting that so long as the molecules do not attract each other, they are, effectively, a gas. Thus the molecules of something, for example, sugar, dissolved in a liquid are far apart from each other and they do not attract each other very much. They actually behave in many ways as a gas. This simplicity has proved of great value in physical chemistry, and it has been considerably exploited.

MORE DETAILED CONSIDERATIONS OF GASES

We have just seen that a very good description of a gas is obtained by supposing that it consists of untrammeled molecules, free from each other's attraction. We can state that the pressure exerted by a gas obeys the relation

$$P = \frac{1}{3} mnv^2$$

where P is the symbol for pressure, m the mass of one molecule, n the number of molecules in a unit volume, and v^2 the square of their speed.

We cannot, in this book, easily prove this formula, not so much because it is difficult, but because it takes rather a lot of mathematics. We can show something about it which makes it more easy to believe. In doing so we actually follow the example of Joule, who used the trick we are about to employ to get some idea of how fast the molecules are actually traveling. We think about a cubical box, whose side is of length l, and which is filled with a gas. Now we imagine that the molecules are going back and forth in three streams aimed exactly perpendicular to the inside walls of the cube. They all have the same speed v. Think about one of the streams—for example, the one which goes from left to right. One molecule in the stream is going to hit the wall and bounce back off it. As it goes toward the wall it has a momentum mv, and when it bounces off it has a momentum $-mv$; the change at each bounce is $mv - (-mv)$, or $2mv$. This momentum is really the "motion" of Newton's Second Law, and if we could find out how much of this change of momentum took place per second, we could find the force on the wall that is being hit. To do this we suppose that there are n molecules per unit volume, making nl^3 altogether, for the volume of the cube of side l is l^3. Only one-third of these are going back and forth in our chosen direction, so we have to deal with $nl^3/3$ for our purposes. Now in one second each molecule goes a distance v, but it has to do this by making many trips back and forth. Each trip back and forth occupies a distance $2l$, and in one second the whole distance gone is v, so the number of trips in one second is $v/2l$. This is the number of times it will hit our particular wall. We must remember that in order to get back in the direction which will cause it to hit our wall, it has to hit the opposite one. This will be important in a moment. Now the amount of momentum change (in one second), which is the force, is therefore the number of molecules, times the number of hits per second, times the momentum at each hit. This is

$$\frac{nl^3}{3} \times \frac{v}{2l} \times 2\,mv$$

and this is the same as

$$nmv^2l^2/3.$$

Now what we mean by pressure is the force on an area divided by the area, and the area of the side of a cube is l^2, so when we divide by l^2, we get the formula we have been talking about:

$$P = \frac{1}{3} nmv^2.$$

The fact that the other wall was struck while the molecule was on the way back and forth is quite pleasant, for there will be a force on *that* wall and it also has an area of l^2, so that the pressure on that wall is the same as the one we chose to think about, in fact, the pressure is the same on all the walls. Figure 8.9 is useful if a picture of the process helps.

This very crude and approximate way to think about a gas leaves much to be desired, but it does make us think about the very essential features of what is happening: the way in which each molecule, as it bombards the wall, transfers momentum to it, and so makes a force come into being, and the number of molecules which can do it, and the impacts per second, which is also a factor. When the mathematics is done carefully, it turns out that Joule's "heroic" simplification of the motion into three streams is not right, but that something quite equivalent *is* right, and that is the fact that the only part of the motion of a molecule which matters is the part which is aimed at the wall: the part which is *along* the wall does not matter. Then what proves to be true is that we must average the force over all possible squares of speeds. The reader can sense that we are becoming technical. We do not intend to do so. The formula we

Fig. 8.9. Joule's way of looking at the molecular reason for the pressure of a gas. One molecule going back and forth is being considered. Very many are needed to develop the pressure.

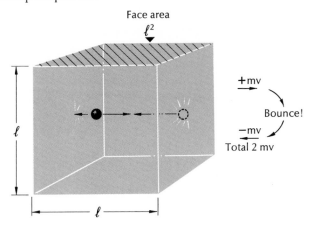

have proposed, and in a manner justified, is very useful to us; it will help us to develop a concept which we are anxious to discuss.

At this stage we have to give way to an aside. When we were students one of the maddening things about our professor of physics (and there was a set of such maddening things) was his seemingly casual mixture of very exact and obviously inadequate thinking. He seemed to be able to choose when he would require the most precise logic and deep mathematics, and when he could throw all such rigor away and indulge in what seemed like wild fancy. If we did the same the result was always catastrophe. And here we have just perpetrated the same thing on our students: we have produced absurdly inadequate "proof" of a formula, and are apparently cheerful about it. The reason for the seeming inconsistency is to be found in the mixture of experiment and theory which is the basis of science. The formula above suggests that there should be a certain average speed for the molecules of a gas. The method used in finding the formula also suggests that there are some better ways of doing the mathematics. So two means of gaining confidence exist: we can see what meaning we extract from the simple theory, and we can go ahead and design a better theory. Both these have been done and the formula stands up. Now we have the problem of telling the student about this. The professor often discusses the history of ideas a little, and if the historic procedure included some rather vigorous approximations he is liable to think that the student should not object too much to getting the first ideas in the way they came originally, and too often he forgets to point out the stronger evidence which is just beyond the level of the teaching he has to employ. So that is partly why we use this very crude and approximate way to look at a gas: Joule did it a hundred years ago and it made some tentative sense to him. Not long after, Maxwell and Boltzmann worked out the theory much better, and fifty years later Stern measured the speed of the molecules directly.

Incidentally, we can actually use the formula to find the speed of the molecules in a gas, which this is really why Joule went through the approximation in the first place. The pressure of air at sea level, "one atmosphere," is 1,000,000 dynes per square centimeter. The symbol m stands for the mass of one molecule and the symbol n for the number of molecules there are per unit volume, which in this case is 1 cubic centimeter. The total mass of all the molecules in one cubic centimeter is $m \times n$; this is also the "density," which is 0.00118 grams/cc. The formula then says that

$$1,000,000 = \frac{1}{3} \times 0.00118 \times v^2$$

and this can be solved to tell us the value of v. It turns out to be about 50,000 centimeters per second, or 500 meters per second, one third of a mile per second, or 1,200 miles per hour, as fast as a jet and twice the speed associated with sound. Molecules are in very rapid motion and this explains why the chemistry lab smells all over so very well.

So far we have made no mention at all of any *experiments* on gases. This is not doing justice to some very famous men: Boyle, Charles, Gay Lussac, and Avogadro. Avogadro made the good and correct suggestion that equal volumes of gases, under the same conditions, should have the same number of molecules in them, regardless of whether they are molecules of hydrogen, air, carbon dioxide, helium, or even alcohol. This last might be a bit of a stretch, but it would be right if the temperature were quite high, well above boiling point. Boyle, Charles, and Gay Lussac showed that there is a relation between pressure, volume, and temperature, and this relation, if combined with Avogadro's hypothesis, is so simple that it is very appealing. The relation is

$$\text{pressure} \times \text{volume} = B$$

and the value of B is very interesting.

If we plot a graph of the value of pressure times volume against the temperature, we find the relationship shown in Figure 8.10. The product goes marching accurately up as the temperature goes higher, and if we

Fig. 8.10. Graph of pressure $\times$ volume versus temperature. It is a straight line and the pressure would be zero at $-273°C$. This is absolute zero, or 0 degrees Kelvin.

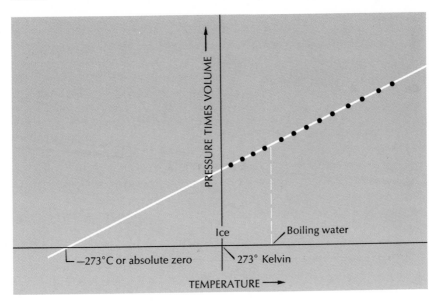

draw the nice straight line back until it corresponds to a point where there is no pressure, we find a temperature of $-273°$ C. "C." here stands for Centigrade, which are the kind of degrees used in Europe and almost everywhere else (except in England, where they are weakening, and the United States, where the people are still a bit old fashioned). There are 100 centigrade degrees between the freezing point and the boiling point of water at sea level. These degrees are used universally in science. If we go the Europeans one better and not only use the Centigrade temperature scale, but *start* from $-273°$ C., we find that the relationships found by Boyle, Charles, and Gay Lussac become very simple. If we call temperature measured in that way, usually designated as "absolute" or "Kelvin" temperature, T, then we find

$$pV = kN_1 T$$

where N_1 is the number of actual molecules in the volume V, and k is a constant of a universal importance which is called "Boltzmann's constant."

Now this experimentally established formula and the theoretical formula are remarkably nearly the same thing. At a first glance, they seem somewhat different, for the experimental formula includes the volume V and the theoretical formula,

$$P = \frac{1}{3} nmv^2,$$

does not. But it soon appears that we can fix this up. In the theoretical formula n is the number of molecules in a unit volume. But so is N_1/V. So we can divide both sides of the experimental formula by V and we get

$$P = \frac{N_1}{V} kT$$

which is the same as

$$P = nkT.*$$

Now suppose we ask ourselves what it would take to make the two formulas agree exactly. It is important to ask this, for one of the purposes of theory is to try to make experimental results have meaning. So if we can get the formulas to agree, we should find something which will make our understanding deeper.

If we make the two formulas agree exactly, then we must have

$$\frac{1}{2} mv^2 = \frac{3}{2} (kT).$$

---

* n is the number of molecules *per unit volume*, which is the total molecules divided by the total volume.

Now the left-hand side is the kinetic energy of a molecule. The right-hand side is a constant times the temperature. This is a very exciting result; it tells us that we can now clearly understand what is meant by temperature. It is a measure of the kinetic energy of the molecules: strictly, of the average kinetic energy of the molecules. When we feel the water is cold, it is because the average energy of the water molecules in the lake is less than ours, and the difference is something we have developed nervous responses to, and so can react to.

Notice that in order to measure temperature in this way we must measure it from absolute zero. No one should be surprised at this; there is hardly anything so very basic about the temperature at which water freezes, which is the mistaken "zero" the Europeans picked. The Kelvin scale, which measures from the true basis for temperature measurement, is really much simpler. Most physical scientists have no difficulty in translating their thoughts from "Centigrade" to Kelvin. They get used to "room temperature" being $300°K$.

There is one last thing to say about this way to interpret temperature. One might argue that we have looked at gases rather carefully, but that if we had some way to look at solids equally carefully we might come to some different conclusion. If this were to happen it would be a disaster. We can say, right away, that no such disaster occurs. All studies of solids show a very consistent description, and exactly the same meaning is found for temperature in all of them. While we are about it, we should note one instance where this relationship proved to be much less easy. If we examine *radiation,* for example, sunlight, we can, quite readily, formulate a description of the relation between the energy in radiation and the temperature. At the turn of the twentieth century, it found that sense could not be made out of the relation between temperature and the transfer of energy from radiation to a solid unless some drastic restrictions were made on the way in which such transfer could be made. These restrictions formed the genesis of the *quantum theory,* and their discovery was, in the first instance, due to Max Planck.

For the present we will leave such difficulties alone and accept the idea that the average energy of the molecules is a measure of the temperature.

Suggestions for Further Thought

1. Discuss Joule's experiment as related to the conservation of energy.
2. Write short essays on (a) evaporation, (b) conduction of heat, and (c) absolute scale of temperature.
3. A man throws ping pong balls of mass 5 gm. at a wall 1 meter square. If he

throws them with a velocity of 5 m./sec., how many must he throw per second in order to exert a pressure of one atmosphere on the wall?

4. Assume a value of 2.4×10^{-23} gm. for the mass of an "air molecule" and 1.4×10^{-16} ergs/$^\circ$K. for the constant k. Calculate (a) the speed of the air molecule at room temperature (27°C.), (b) at the freezing point of water, (0°C.), and (c) on a hot day (37°C.).

References

George Gamow, *Biography of Physics* (New York: Harper & Row, 1964).
John Tyndall, *Heat: A Mode of Motion* (New York: D. Appleton & Co., 1915).

High Power Ground

There needs to be a sequel to the story of the indicator man. The Radiation Laboratory at M.I.T. grew to be one of the largest laboratories in existence; it had a very limited assignment and it comprised some of the finest minds in physics and engineering. The Laboratory was the place of inception of at least one Nobel prize winner's idea, and the scientific material published after the five years of the laboratory's existence formed the "Radiation Laboratory Series"—some twenty-odd volumes. As these took shape, Jim Sheridan, one of the well-loved members of the laboratory, called them the "five-foot book of shelves." Yet the bare technical record, most impressive as it is, does not say anything about the human undercurrents in the laboratory. In a "mission-oriented" laboratory, especially in wartime, these are very strong and they often came to dominate the operations. So it is that the intimate operation of such a great laboratory, of national significance, is a story that needs to be told. It should be told by more than one member. I would like to think that these essays might start the reminiscences of some others. For now I would like to take the opportunity of carrying my recollections a little further and describing some of the events associated with my next assignment, which went by the name of "High Power Ground."

When the testing of the radar on the *Semmes* had come to some kind of conclusion—and I must stress that very many people had a lot to do with this, notably Ray Herb, who was out at sea with the *Semmes* in better times, and who showed that it was far and away the best instrument for navigation available up to that time—I returned to the laboratory and began trying to improve the indicator. This was rather an interesting era; we were not yet involved in the war directly, and though the laboratory was growing very rapidly, the emergency had not reached

its full degree (which came after Pearl Harbor), and the laboratory had
a certain relaxation about it, at least it seemed relaxed in comparison
with the emergency situation later on. It was in this period that the
laboratory even had time to take part in amusements like Art Roberts's
operettas,* which later became famous among physicists. In all this time
the most familiar feature of the laboratory was the arrival of new faces.
One of these was Ralph Meagher, now a Professor at Illinois. He came
in one day and Larry Marshall assigned him to help me with the
indicator.

Many people think that scientific work is impersonal and cold, and
involves merely the knowledge of what is in the handbook and the
application of precise principles to achieve certain results. This is not
true. Consider my psychological condition before and after the arrival
of Ralph Meagher. Before his arrival I was furiously working as hard
as I could, thinking as best I knew how, trying to get the spot on my
indicator to focus better, to get a bigger sweep—and to do all this as
rapidly as I could. I was, without a shadow of doubt, out of my depth.
Ralph had a clear instinct for the whole process of electronics which
I lacked. When he came in, he listened to my troubles and in a matter
of a few days began pointing out some things I already thought of,
but which had much more relevance to the problem than I had believed.
As a result we began the necessary politics to get local industry to make
transformers and basic circuits that would give us what we needed.
The indicator began to work right. This is one of the very few occasions in my time in the laboratory when I actually had a sense of satisfaction and achievement and enjoyed a certain amount of pleasure in
the work. Nearly all the rest of the time the work had to go out before
it was ready, and I felt a mixture of inadequacy and high accomplishment. This is a split condition and does not give rise to a happy mind.

The laboratory still permitted some vacations. I remember that we
were allowed three weeks off and I took my family down to Buzzards
Bay. I had left Yale with many commitments still unfulfilled. One of
these was the writing of a book on nuclear physics. Bill Davidson and I
had a contract for it, and we were valiantly trying to get it done. I
still had two chapters or so to go and at the short spell at Buzzards Bay
I succeeded in writing these two. I remember the driven condition in
which I felt myself. All my interests were now in radar, fighting the
war, and so on, and this book on nuclear physics seemed to be as purely
academic a procedure as one could ever want. The idea that a few
doctors and scientists could want to use radioactive tracers for studying

---

* "Snow for Uncle Joe"—a skit on the problems of procurement with the now famous
"Conant, Compton and Baruch" song.

things, and therefore one should publish a book for them, seemed to be so trivial that it was very hard to get to work on it. However, I had a certain underlying wisdom and I remember driving myself mercilessly to get it done, because I knew in the long run the basic scientific record would be of more importance than just the problems that went on in any laboratory from day to day. It proved to be an interesting book to have written and since it is now out of print I can be forgiven for mentioning it. It appeared in 1942, when there was almost nothing with which to educate the vast number of people who had begun to work on the development of the atom bomb. As a result it had a sale in most unusual places. I would have bet a hundred to one against a book on nuclear physics being sold in Tennessee, and yet the sales rose sharply and significantly in that location. It had the distinction of being translated into Japanese and into Russian and also, I am told, into French. The Japanese edition paid me about $50 for it, the Russians paid me nothing for it, and the French put somebody's else's name on it.

When the vacation ended I found myself back in the laboratory. Ralph Meagher had greatly improved the indicator, and I looked forward to a time of constructive work. This benign condition did not last. One day I was called downstairs by Ken Bainbridge. This interview took place down in the lower regions of the laboratory, in an odd room where Ken had momentary "squatter's rights" on a desk. Bainbridge had made a very rugged and difficult trip over to England to study at first hand what was going on in radar over there. British radars were very different indeed from the sets that we had. They seemed much more conventional, often used much longer wavelengths. The British had greatly stimulated our work by sharing with us their discoveries in microwave transmission; but now it was felt that our skill in microwave radar should be applied to solve some of the traditional problems, and not merely the problem of the detection of aircraft from another aircraft or that of the navigation of ships. So Bainbridge was setting up a new group which was to look into the problems of higher powered radar and the name of the group which was to be formed was to be called "High Power Ground," the title of this reminiscence.

I had the utmost difficulty communicating with Bainbridge. This was for rather a strange reason. He held me in high respect, something I did not know at the time, but which I found out later, and he had almost unbounded confidence in my ability to understand anything no matter how it was said. I was too polite to stop him and say, "Now, Ken, I don't understand one thing you are saying." So we went on in this curious mixture of high excitement and incomprehension on my part for something like an hour, at the end of which I realized that I had been tapped by Ken to be the second member of a new group which he was to head and which was to endeavor to do something about high powered transmission with longer ranges.

To say that it was an immense challenge is total understatement. If I had felt out of my depth on the indicator situation I now felt completely lost. It is a strange thing that a laboratory of size functions to keep an individual going in spite of this feeling. I have stressed before that all of us felt this condition. We felt it in common, and our remedy for it was a mixture of thinking and talking which slowly got us past the stage of a kind of despair and actually started us doing something. I soon found that I need not be quite so worried and lost because Ken Bainbridge had already a sharp and clear comprehension of what it was he was setting up. It was my failure to communicate with him that led to my feeling of uncertainty at first. Gradually I began to realize that he had a clear idea of what he wanted to do. I also began to realize that Bainbridge had a strong affection for the United States Navy. Bainbridge, while calling his group "High Power Ground," returned from a trip to Washington with something else in mind. This proved to be radar for aircraft carriers to help them locate and control aircraft.

I don't want to go into the technicalities, because this is a great waste of time, but I do remember sharply the way this group built up. We were assigned space in the "roof laboratory." This is an incorrect statement, because the space was not there when we were assigned it, and instead the long-suffering M.I.T. carpenters put another roof on top of an already temporary roof and banged and hammered and put up plywood and things far above the sidewalks. Ultimately we had space in which we could function. It was minute in terms of what it did, but it did contain an office, a laboratory, and a place where we could install a radar and where we could begin experimental transmissions. We were to be what was later called a "systems" group: that is to say we had to put it all together and make it go. However, under Ken Bainbridge's rather wide-ranging direction we found ourselves free to do a great deal of development, and indeed, research. He had introduced a whole number of concepts into the design of this radar which were partly derived from his trip to England and partly out of his very competent and fertile mind. As a result we found ourselves needing more and more people, and more and more people began coming up the stairs. I had an office in the corner and I had the first secretary I ever had. She was Genevieve Fundingsland, and of course she was available largely because she was married to somebody who was on the laboratory staff. She was an enormous help. It is a shame that we so rarely give recognition to this kind of most useful and very

positive source of strength, not technical in any way, but which nevertheless makes a laboratory move forward. The Radiation Laboratory
had more than its share of such help.

We began the usual battle of the memoranda which goes on in
such labs as this, and up the stairs came the new people. These people
would first be interviewed by Dr. Wheeler Loomis who was second in
command of the laboratory working out of Dr. Dubridge's office. I
have the normal paranoia still with me about the people that I got,
and I was convinced at the time that Wheeler Loomis looked over all
the people that came in, and if they seemed to be any good he either
gave them to the airborne division or to one of the divisions working
on components and only if they seemed extremely oddball and effectively useless did he send them up to me. I'm quite sure this is a
strong distortion of the truth and I wouldn't write it if I didn't know
that I will be listened to in a kindly and amused way, because in
point of fact what turned out could hardly have been more in the
reverse. I don't remember the order in which these individuals came
in: one that wandered up was Andy Longacre. Andy was a physics
teacher at Phillips Exeter and he had somehow managed a year's leave
of absence and had got Wheeler Loomis to let him into the laboratory.
He is a very striking person with a very strong personality who must
have been by all odds the most magnificent physics teacher anywhere
in the country at the time that he took his leave of absence. He had
that strange mixture of an absolutely genuine humility and tremendous
competence which characterizes so many really great men. It took very
little time indeed for me to convey to Andy Longacre my sense of inadequacy, this was no problem at all, but what interested me was that I
seemed also to be able to convey to Andy Longacre my confidence that
we were going to do it regardless. How I did that I don't know.
Possibly I didn't do it, possibly Ken Bainbridge did it, but in any
event Andy Longacre showed up, resisting almost all the way, and
began working on the hardest part of the job, which was the problem
of the transmission of microwaves at high power.

Another person who worked with us was John McKendry. John
was a very quiet, almost silent individual, with the ability to produce
extremely apt, very funny, very pungent remarks almost under his
breath. I had him working on circuitry. He had about the same degree
of skill as Ralph Meagher, but I think that, unlike Ralph Meagher,
he didn't like circuits. I think Ralph *liked* vacuum tubes, while John
McKendry thought of them as unwilling slaves that he had to beat
all the way to get them to perform. Undoubtedly he did beat them
and undoubtedly they did perform. I will mention a few others: Ed
Schneider came in from the Stevens Institute and also began working

on circuitry, John Hall, an astronomer from Amherst, "Binks" Curtis from Harvard, Robert McConnell, Mike Karelitz and Dave Jacobus. These formed the nucleus of the "High Power Ground" group.

Of course we had our usual battle of conferences, decisions, and struggles with getting equipment but in a very short time, certainly not long into 1942, we had a high powered radar blasting out under all the proper circumstances and detecting aircraft at greater and greater distances from the roof of the M.I.T. laboratory.

At this stage we began to encounter a new phenomenon of science: in World War II there had to be a close collaboration between the scientists and the military. The use for our radar was thought of primarily in terms of what the British found they needed in the Battle of Britain. It was first intended to detect enemy aircraft at close quarters and to guide our own aircraft to intercept them. It proved to be the only thing possible for the navy to use on aircraft carriers for just that purpose. So our work was moved up very high on the laboratory priority list and a group began working under white-hot pressure to put this radar out.

In the process we had to give it some sort of a field trial, and it was decided that a first model at a field station should be put where the navy might be able to take a look at it and learn something from it. We scouted around and found that a place could be had at Jamestown, Rhode Island, and a site was picked there. The question arose as to what to name this field station, and we also ran into the problem that we could not buy new cars very easily during the war. Since we needed a station wagon to get us back and forth we bought a used one. The name had not yet been painted off this wagon and I remember it, it was "Spraycliff." So we decided rather than give the wagon a new name we would save money all around and simply call the new station "Spraycliff" and go ahead. As one would expect, as soon as we made this decision it became necessary from the point of view of security to remove the name from the wagon and that was done. Here we put up the new radar and as the person who was supposedly in charge of the operations, I had to spend a fair amount of time at Jamestown along with other people from the laboratory. I remember with interest one of the things that happened down there. This radar was extremely good at spotting things on the water and a very clear and obvious set of echoes appeared which were precisely one nautical mile apart except for two miles at the end. These were so loud and clear and appeared so often that we demanded an explanation for them and since they were not on any chart, we encountered a strange silence from the Navy in this regard. The local experts tried to persuade us that they were multiple reflections exactly a mile apart and this we wouldn't buy either and so we knew perfectly

well scientifically that there was a line of objects out there south of
Jamestown and yet officially nothing existed. Later we found out that
this was a torpedo range and that these were actually buoys on the water
which were spaced in this way for determination of how far torpedoes
had gone.

We used to be able to pick up and watch aircraft from the Quonset
Naval Airbase and we began the problems of learning how to use the set
for the purpose of interception. I remember some of the excitement we
had in this regard and indeed I think some of the greatest fun I ever
had in my whole life came when we had a two-way radio installed
so that we could tell pilots what to do. The astonishment of the pilot
at the other end when he realized that we were actually able to tell him
the location of his target ship, was often most interesting and the sounds
that came over the radio were genuinely fascinating. The experience was
rewarding and interesting and taught us a lot and in due time we found
ourselves with stations all over the world. I remember putting one in
Panama, one went in England, and I finally wound up in the middle of
the war in England at a station in Dover Castle where one of these was
set up. There we watched, *not* on the radar, eight of the V-1 rockets in
the air at one time flying on their way to London and we were well
aware that this new problem in the war had come our way.

I really don't want to keep on the subject of the radar but I would
like to say something about what happened in terms of personalities and
people. At about the stage when we were ready to put our first radar
on board the U.S.S. *Lexington* (where it performed quite well in actual
combat) I was once again called down to Ken Bainbridge's office and
this was an occasion which I shall certainly never forget. Ken Bainbridge
had been caught in the expanding need for help on the atom bomb.
Those who read the accounts of the Trinity test where the first atom
bomb was exploded at Alamagordo will realize that Bainbridge had the
responsibility for the actual test itself. Prior to this he was my boss. Ken
had just received the word that he had to leave: that he had to go to
this more demanding work. What interested me was the misery of decision which he must have undergone before doing it. Bainbridge had
his heart very much indeed in the war. He had no question whatsoever
of the absolute necessity for victory. No one more firm and more resolute
in the need to destroy the Nazis could have been found anywhere in the
lab. He was also, I feel sure, convinced that we were doing as much as
could be done by any scientific group to win it right where we were. He
had watched his very inventive, very careful, very closely engineered ideas
come to a stage where they were of great use to the navy and he had no
question that more application could be found for radar developments in
other areas that would prosecute the war and win it in other respects. Ob-

viously our efforts in our laboratory plus those of the British were winning the battle of the Atlantic and we were actually at the stage of seeing the numbers of sinkings by submarines per day go down and we knew that this was partly due to our efforts in microwave radar and airplane search. He told me he was leaving. He didn't tell me why or where he was going. It's rather interesting that he never had to. We had a strange knowledge of what went on as regards the atom bomb development and this knowledge had nothing to do with any security leak. All of us nuclear physicists knew perfectly well what had to be going on. We all knew that the separation of uranium 235 could result in something exciting and we sometimes in an idle way discussed what might be its potential. These discussions were very few in number because we were most of the time concerned with radar and the problems of radar in our work. So Ken Bainbridge didn't have to tell me where he was going or what he was going to do: I knew. What was most interesting to me was the clearly tortured state of his mind. He was no longer going to be involved in something which to him was honorable, straightforward, clean and simple. The development of a new and horrible type of weapon was of course of great necessity, but it was perfectly clear to me that he saw right then the moral issues which he would face as having had to take part in it. I remember him saying that there were among the leaders in science some very hard men. He wasn't sure he could go along with them and he did not name any names, at least that I remember. I did know to whom he referred because we scientists have our own ways of estimating our leaders. He finally asked me point blank if I had any reactions to what he ought to do. This was after he told me he was leaving. I remember my simple and very banal speech to the effect that if it would in any way shorten the war or guarantee the saving of lives that it was something that ought to be done and that his decision ought to be made in those terms. In any event he left. I would like to say that the element of scientific leadership is something of much greater importance than most people, including scientists, recognize. The usual statements made with regard to science are that it is something impersonal, it will happen anyway, if it is not discovered in one place it will be discovered in another, and little or no difference is to be found in the long run between whether there is adequate research guidance or not. All of these statements are true in the long run but in an immediate and urgent situation they are anything but true. Where you have a desperate need to develop something, minutes, hours, and days are of genuine importance. I remember at a later stage the problem of the V-1's. These were producing something like 300 severe explosions every 24 hours in London and the method for combating them *did* exist. Had it not existed then a very serious morale disruption would have occurred in London. Seen from our point of view it was possible to make a decision to put radar and fire control on the South coast to shoot these things down as they came in. We were able to convince the command to make the deployment in a matter of days and start shooting down the V-1's. The ability to do this fast unquestionably made a huge difference, and the ability to have the kind of leadership available to force such a decision, and to produce the quick response, unquestionably saved thousands of lives and made it possible to face the task of the defeat of Hitler much more resolutely than could have occurred otherwise. By the same token, if Hitler had started firing over the V-1's six months earlier, events might very well have been closer to a decision in his favor than any of us care to realize. So there is a close matter of timing on discoveries that have to be made to order and for a purpose. Under those circumstances scientific leadership is extremely important if not vital.

The High Power Ground project which Ken Bainbridge was running was not as decisive in the war as the atom bomb or fire control radar: we were just one useful instrument that might make a difference. Nevertheless, we had to regard ourselves as being as important as anyone else and certainly within our group we did so. All I can say is that the removal of Bainbridge from the leadership of our group dealt us a blow from which essentially we never recovered. I found myself having to take over and having to do the job, having to provide that kind of leadership which was his, and which was his by right, because the whole project had essentially been conceived by him. Jealousies, politics, relationships with the army, with the branch of the army that was to become the air force, with the navy, all went worse and went with more friction and with more difficulty and all of the day to day decisions in which we had to speed things up, force them, drive them, went harder and the whole project slipped back. In essence only I as the person who took over can say this. I know that the loss of a scientific leader, while it left a situation that seemed to be under reasonable control, and while the later productivity was not too bad, nevertheless did produce a permanent and irremediable setback to this project.

For this reason I believe that scientific leadership is being very much undervalued today. The persons who are directing some of our important laboratories (and we have many important laboratories today) are absolutely crucial individuals, and their health, their state of mind, and everything about them is of the utmost importance. If we take the director of a large laboratory and put him into some government administrative position, we should realize that we do not do so without definitely altering the character of the output of that laboratory and possibly altering its course and definitely harming it. It is for this reason that the incredibly superb job done by Oppenheimer, which put us in the position of having a new weapon probably six months to a year earlier than we might have had it under any other circumstance, has never been fully recognized. There has been a kind of shrugging of the shoulders. We say that after all Oppenheimer did what he had to do, and he did it well, and aren't we grateful. But we are not grateful enough to think about the whole role of scientific leadership and what is the genuine respect that we should pay such a person when he has achieved that role, and actually given his country that much of himself.

Things were never the same with me after Bainbridge left and this dilution of our laboratory by the loss of men capable of great leadership did come, in my opinion, to start it on a downward path.

I should say something about what it feels like to take over the leadership of a scientific group when there are blue chips on the effort in the laboratory. It is murderously hard. It is hard because there is a squeeze from two directions. On the one side you simply do not know, until you have done the necessary work, what is the scientific potential of the thing you are working on. On paper, had our high powered radar been able to perform all the things that it should have been able to perform and which today it can do, our operation would have been eagerly sought by everyone. In fact we could never come close to that situation no matter how we tried. The power we could put out on the air, the receiver sensitivity that we could use, were not adequate and our performance always fell below that which could have been operationally of service. The navy was glad to take all it could get and there's no question that we served them well. But in regard to the army and the air force it was by no means so easy to convince them that we had a product they could use. This brings me to the other side of the squeeze. In order to be useful to the armed services at that time one had to make contact with them and this was something I found myself having to do in increasing amounts. The Radiation Laboratory operated in a very permissive way, one of the things greatly to the credit of its director, Lee DuBridge. He trusted me, even though he hardly knew me, to make contact with the representatives of the army, discuss things with them, relay the knowledge to him and to keep within the policy of the lab. This went so smoothly that I remember only one occasion when perhaps my discussions may have been a little out of line and that one occasion was quickly, almost instantly, rectified. But in spite of that, there began to be endless trips to queer rooms in the Pentagon where odd people had to be met and where all kinds of prejudices had to be overcome. Some of the places where prejudices ran very high were among our own scientific elite. In a time of emergency one of the things that are spawned by government are studies. These studies are done by the people that do the studying and not necessarily by the people that make the hardware.

These studies, in war time, soon came to have tremendous authority. If one were made so that it didn't agree with something going on in the laboratory then pain and anguish would result. So I spent many patient hours in the Pentagon, in many rooms, trying to explain, trying to discuss, trying to pick up ideas, trying to make suggestions, trying to show the way in which the formulation of policy could also fit in with the work being done in the laboratory. Each of these trips was immensely exhausting. One would go down with one's heart light, and head high, believing that one had a real contribution to make and that this would be picked up eagerly and that support for it would rapidly come. One would encounter a group of three officers, all technically competent, two of whom understood the situation and agreed with you, and the third who was going to fight it all the way for probably quite honest, quite valid reasons but which were nevertheless reasons which were scientifically unsupportable, at least in my terms. Very often the third person can win if he is resolute enough. He can convince the other two and then you leave Washington with no support and the need to go back and see your program changed, and the successes which you think you are winning becoming negated. This aspect of life is terribly hard for a scientist to take. Ordinarily in his own laboratory when he is on his own research project he faces this kind of decision with some equanimity. If today I find that a request for funds from some granting agency is not forthcoming, it doesn't mean the cessation of work in my lab nor does it mean a slap on my wrist. It simply means that I have to go to work to prove the validity of my suggestions and try again. In point of fact it may prove to be a stimulus. But in war time when human lives are at stake, these decisions cannot be handled in a like way and they must be sharply responded to or the laboratory is not fulfilling its function. If one returns from a trip with a decision made against your group, and one realizes it is technically a wrong decision, and that this technical wrongness may be in part due to your inability to explain correctly or to carry a conviction which you should have done, the burden on the spirit is tremendous. It is here that the scientific leader shows his true qualities. What has to be done is to understand sharply and accurately the condition of the affairs in his laboratory as regards performance and as regards promise. He must be capable of projecting with precision where the laboratory will reach in ten days, a hundred days and a year and his projections must be very good indeed. On the other side he also has to be able to take what is being done in his laboratory and state it with conviction and simplicity so that others may understand it. Achieving these two ends is so hard that the number of individuals that can do it is extremely small. Where they have been found, the service that they perform is extremely great.

A very interesting revelation of the place occupied by scientific leadership in our society is seen in the recall of General MacArthur by President Truman and the removal of security clearance from J. Robert Oppenheimer by the Atomic Energy Commission. I do not in any way wish to diminish the luster of General MacArthur. Yet I do wish to point out that Oppenheimer had led an effort which gave us exclusively the greatest weapon ever made, years ahead of anyone. This lead did, in the opinion of many statesmen, decisively influence the affairs of the world in the direction sought by our country. Now when MacArthur was recalled there was an outcry in Congress, hearings were held, and a big national concern developed. Hardly any such events took place for Oppenheimer. Scientists were concerned and there were hearings, but on an altogether different scale. At the time of Oppenheimer's death most Americans did not even know of him or what he had done. This contrast is sharply felt by scientists.

In my own case I found, to my surprise, that I could often convey conviction to the armed services. I could not convey conviction in terms of a prepared position but if I was able to mingle with them for a sufficient length of time to catch the realities of their demands and to return to the laboratory and put together equipment which fitted their needs at least to some extent, then I found that this aspect of working with the armed services became relatively simple and pleasant. As the war moved on to further stages the work we did in what came out of the High Power Ground group bore very little relationship to the work which it began, and a great many of the ideas that Ken Bainbridge started, wound up used only in limited ways. On the other hand the potential and drive of the group which was able to be combined with the needs of the services produced very creditable results in which I have a good deal of pride. I remember that as we got better and better at this, a stage came in which we were actually able to combine our design of a radar with the training and equipping of the officers and men who were to use it and we even finally wound up having them build the set which they were going to use in actual service. Some of the times for radars to go from the design stage to the use stage got to be so short that at times people don't believe me when I tell them. Nevertheless, the story that one writes about this later development of High Power Ground is different. If one takes a simple thing like the indicator, one has a simple function, a great need, an initial performance which is poor but which is very full of promise and one sees that promise develop and one has nothing but a sense of achievement with it. On the other hand in High Power Ground we had a scientific development full of promise but which was questionable in its end use, and which therefore had to find its purpose. This was something which was mixed and in which there was not the simple, clear, easy and rewarding set of conditions which are to be found in the earlier stages. Those people who are watching science to-day should bear this in mind. There will be a complete difference between the kind of mission which actually puts three men on the moon and the kind of mission which then works on the problems which have been decided to be important thereafter. It may very well be that in terms of the whole scientific advance as seen in fifty years' time, the third and fourth missions may be more important than the first. Nevertheless, it will be harder to find scientific leadership for them, it will be harder to find support for them, it will be more tedious to explain what good they are, and it will be much more frustrating for the people working on them. Those who are concerned with the relationship of science to ourselves should bear this in mind and should be watchful for it.

ERNEST C. POLLARD, 1965

9
Electromagnetism: Electrons and the First Splitting of the Atom

Vectors

It may seem strange to introduce a chapter with such an impressive title with "vectors," a very specialized word. The truth is that we have been shirking a responsibility and our delinquency is now beginning to put a restriction on us. We have talked in the past about fields. Now a field, whether it be gravitational, electric or magnetic, has a direction associated with it. This direction is very important and we can not seriously develop any subject in physical science if we don't recognize the property of a direction. A name has been given to all things which must be measured by both size and direction: they are called *vectors*. If you say that you have walked a mile, that is not a vector, but if you say that you have walked a mile toward Philadelphia, then it is a vector. It will be recalled that the lines of force which Faraday drew to represent an electric field were drawn *straight out,* away from the electric charge. So at each place the field is *aimed* and by this we mean it has a direction. Figure 9.1 shows the direction of an electric field at a certain place due to three charges placed near it. Thus, even though the field might be the same size, the direction differs and so the vectors are different.

VECTOR ALGEBRA

If we are going to have to deal with vectors and think about them, and if the ideas of algebra are important to us, then we have to think about the rules of addition, subtraction, and so on, for vectors. Addition and subtraction are easy. Multiplication is hard, and division of vectors by vectors is not used in vector algebra. We are only concerned with addition and subtraction. They are very simple. There is a familiar notation

197

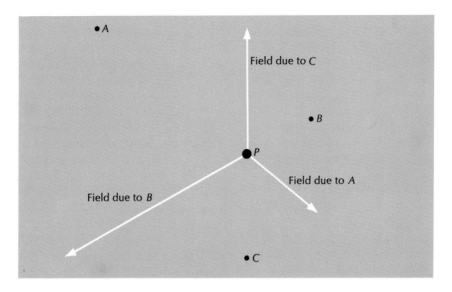

Fig. 9.1. Representation of the fields produced at *P* by three electric charges *A*, *B*, and *C*. All three fields are *directed,* away from each charge. Somehow there is a total effect at *P*. To find it we have to add vectors.

for a vector; we write it in **BOLDFACE**, like **A.** In this way we can always distinguish vectors from ordinary numbers.

ADDITION

Consider a person walking. Let us say he walks one mile east and two miles south. In terms of vectors these would be described as drawn in Figure 9.2. Now it is really very easy to think where he reached; and, in fact, the only question really is: "How simple can you get?"

The only slightly difficult idea comes when we give a name to the airline distances and direction between the start and the finish. We call this the vector sum. Then we would redraw the above in Figure 9.3.

To add vectors, we use the following rule. Make a line in the proper direction with a length equal to the size of the vector in some units you decide on. At the arrowhead of this line draw a second line in the right direction for the second vector and of the proper number of units for the second vector. Draw a line from the tail of the first vector to the arrowhead of the second. This is the vector used to represent the sum of the two vectors.

Two features of vectors need to be described. The first is that only the

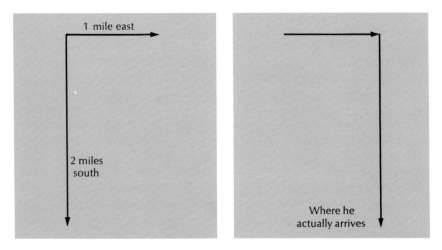

Fig. 9.2. Walking under separate instructions and how to figure where it actually gets one.

magnitude and direction matter, not the starting point: the second is that a vector is never curved: it is always straight.

SUBTRACTION

Subtraction of vectors is easy. You add a reversed vector. A negative vector, like any negative number, is the same as the positive vector only exactly reversed in direction. So $\mathbf{A} - \mathbf{B}$ is the same as $\mathbf{A} + (-\mathbf{B})$ and we

Fig. 9.3. Addition of vectors, using the idea contained in walking under separate instructions.

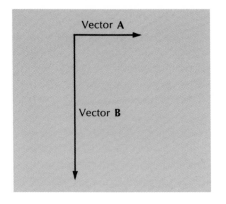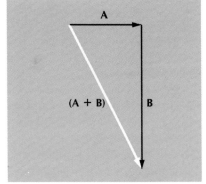

now draw the diagram as in Figure 9.4. Notice that we freely move the vector lines about on the page, but we don't alter the way they point (except for — **B**) and their length.

These two rules, which are a little trouble to learn at first, are nevertheless simple and useful. All we ask is an appreciation of what the rules are. The solution of problems involving them is not going to be an important part of the book.

The Full Relation Between Electric and Magnetic Fields

Having used the reader's fresh enthusiasm at the start of a new chapter to get him to think about a special way of description, we can return to the all-important subject of electricity. So far, we have described Coulomb's Law, electric currents, the magnetic effects they produce, and the discovery, made by Faraday and Henry, that a changing magnetic field produces an electric current. One of the greatest geniuses of electricity was James Clerk Maxwell, a mathematical physicist who assimilated Faraday's ideas and discoveries, including, in particular, his idea of an electric field, and proceeded to express them accurately in mathematical terms. When he did this he was struck by a very important lack in the description which Faraday had given. He became convinced that if it were true that a changing magnetic field produced an electric current then the current must be caused by an electric field so that another way to state Faraday's discovery is to say that a changing magnetic field caused the production of an electric field. If this is so argued Maxwell then a changing electric field should produce a magnetic field. Maxwell could think of no way to prove this experimentally, but he became more and

Fig. 9.4. Subtraction of vectors—*add the reversed vector.*

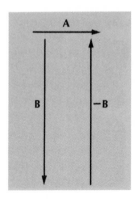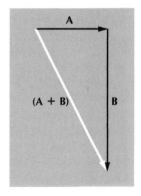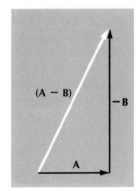

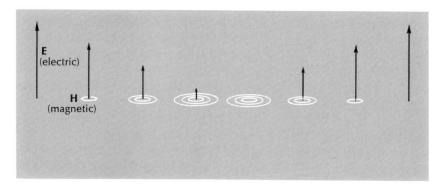

Fig. 9.5. How a dying electric field generates a magnetic field, which as it dies,
in turn generates an electric field: the basis of *electromagnetic waves*.

and more convinced that his theory would be imperfect if it were not
true. So he proposed a set of equations, now very famous, which described all of Faraday's ideas, plus a new one of his own. These are known
as Maxwell's Electromagnetic Equations, and no Ph.D. candidate in
Physics has the smallest chance of passing his oral examination unless he
knows these equations and how to use them. They are a shade beyond
our scope, but only because they introduce mathematical descriptions
which work in three dimensions, not for any other vital reason.

The reader will recall that the relation between a changing magnetic
field and the electric field so produced is of a line and circle type. It is to
be expected that the same kind of relationship would be found between
the changing electric field and the magnetic field, the suggestion put forward by Maxwell. Let us suppose that this is so and see whether we can
get an intuitive feeling of what might happen if we made an electric
field somewhere and then permitted it to die out. To help our thought
we have a representation in Figure 9.5. The original electric field is
shown as a vector upward, and there is no magnetic field at all at the
start, because the electric field is not changing. Now take away the
battery or whatever it is, and let the electric field start to die out. Maxwell's new idea suggests that as it does so, a magnetic field around the
direction of the electric field will begin to appear. We have drawn a
circle to show that. As the electric field goes on dying out the magnetic
field gets stronger and we have used more circles as a way to show this.
Finally the electrical field has wholly gone and there is left the rings
alone, the magnetic field without an electric field at all. Now *this* will
begin to die out and as it does an electric field will appear, according to
what Faraday found, and we can see that as the magnetic field goes away,

an electric field will appear. It is not at all difficult to suppose that *this* field will die out and produce another magnetic field, and that, in turn, this new magnetic field will die out and restore the original electric field. Thus we see that there is a possibility that a continuous alternation of electric and magnetic fields could take place.

Such an alteration is actually familiar: it is the kind of thing we find in a *wave,* where up and down motion alternate in a related way—in a wave on water, for example.

It is not safe to trust our intuition alone in seeking to understand this process, and Maxwell did not do so. He carefully introduced these ideas into mathematical form, and used the logic of mathematics to guide him in what the actual process must be like. His studies led him to the conclusion that such alternation could indeed produce a form of wave motion, and while he could not see how to produce them in the laboratory, he made the suggestion in 1875 that such electromagnetic waves were already commonplace: *light* is electromagnetic waves. We propose to discuss this suggestion in a later paragraph; let us return to electromagnetic waves themselves for the moment.

Maxwell suggested that it should be posible to create electromagnetic waves artifically, though as we have said, he did not propose a successful method. His suggestion was not proved true for ten years, but in a series of experiments between 1885 and 1889, Heinrich Hertz, working under the influence and encouragement of Helmholtz, showed that it was possible to produce the electromagnetic waves predicted by Maxwell.

Hertz used a strange apparatus, resembling in a kind of surrealist way present-day TV apparatus. It is shown in a very schematic form in Figure 9.6. The two plates are connected to two thin rods, which are, in turn, connected to two brass spheres. This contraption, which was the first antenna, was connected to a machine which could produce a very strong electric field across the two spheres. When the field is strong enough, the air, which ordinarily is not prone to show any electrical effects, suddenly changes and a spark passes across the spheres of brass.* This spark in Hertz's experiment caused a rush of electric current across and back in the plates and rods, and this rush of current, of *oscillating* current, is what is necessary to create electromagnetic waves.

This strange rig sufficed for the first transmitter. A much greater problem was the first receiver. Hertz succeeded with a second pair of plates, with a tiny gap between the brass spheres. When a spark passed in the primitive transmitting antenna, a spark also passed in the tiny gap. This in the case where the two were close together was not very exciting:

---

* We will discuss this sudden change which makes the air conducting later in the chapter.

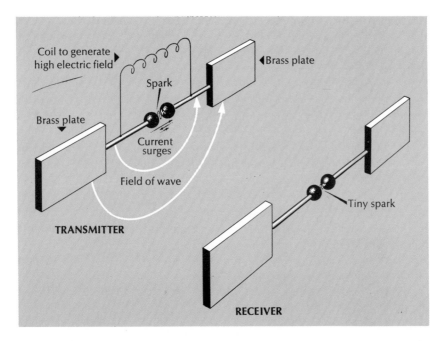

Fig. 9.6. Representation of Hertz's first experiments in which electromagnetic waves were generated and detected. The spark in the transmitter has back and forth surges of current and these generate waves that traverse the receiver, create an electric field in it, and, produce a tiny spark.

effects from one circuit to another are not necessarily waves. But **Hertz** was able to separate the transmitter and the receiver by a distance of some yards, and he was able to show that if he turned the two antennas out of line there would be no second spark. He was also in a position to look into Maxwell's predictions about how electromagnetic waves would behave—for example that the length of the wave is related to the size of the antenna. Hertz thus found agreement with Maxwell's theory. This experiment, the genesis of radio, is one of the greatest experiments of all time.

About 1885 we can see the growth of a new kind of confidence in science. There is very little more convincing to a scientist than a combination of carefully devised theory which makes clear but surprising predictions, which are found to be true. And at this time there was a succession of theory and discovery. Maxwell, simply by using what accurate knowledge there was about electricity and magnetism, by thinking closely about them and stating the thinking in mathematical terms, had been able to see that a further discovery had to be made in the scheme of electricity: that a changing electric field makes a magnetic field. With that new idea he had been able to devise a theory of light and had predicted that it should be possible to make a wholly new form of wave motion: electromagnetic waves, or as we call them today "radio waves." Hertz, by experimenting, proved that Maxwell's prediction was right, and it only remained to exploit the new discovery. It is interesting that this knowledge was not widespread. Probably not more than a thousand men knew much about it, and of those probably not more than twenty understood Maxwell's theory. Nevertheless, those that did were most confident that the means for explanation and understanding of a wide range of natural phenomena were close at hand. If one reads lectures made in the 1890's by eminent men, such as Oliver Lodge or William Crookes, this confidence and indeed exuberance, can easily be sensed. It was also in this era that the journals of science began to be published, notably *Nature* and *Science*.

Before we leave this subject we must call attention to a very important point, not stressed very much at the time, but later to assume tremendous importance. The antenna used by Hertz really used a form of motion of electrical charge which is *accelerated*. The charge, in order to go back and forth, must slow down and speed up again. This is only found where there is acceleration. So it can be seen that there is an inherent relation between acceleration of electric charge and the process of radiation. We want to give the reader a formula which can be derived from Maxwell's theory, which relates the energy radiated per second, U, by an electric charge e, accelerating with an acceleration a. It is

$$U = \frac{2}{3} \frac{e^2 a^2}{c^3}.$$

c stands for the velocity of light. We shall see the importance of this when we come to the structure of the atom.

Maxwell's Theory and Light

Since the success of Maxwell's theories is one of the very great achievements of physical science, it is worth a little more time to elaborate on what happened, and why the advance was so great. Accordingly we add a little more description of Maxwell's theory and its relation to light.

In the years after the middle of the nineteenth century, as Faraday's work was becoming understood, the study of the nature of light was also advancing to great maturity. As early as 1678 Huygens had suggested that light consisted of a form of wave motion, and in 1810, Young had shown that it was possible to produce the phenomenon of *interference*, an alternation of brightness and darkness, with two sources of light. That *two* light sources could ever give darkness obviously needed explanation, and it was easy to do so by looking at the pattern of two waves spreading out and overlapping one another. This idea was developed to a great extent both theoretically and experimentally by Fresnel and Fraunhofer, and the wavelength of light of various colors was very accurately measured, as well as the behavior of light when it encountered various obstacles. The difficult task of measuring the very high velocity of light was tackled by Fizeau and Foucault, and measurements of quite good accuracy began to appear. Thus one could see that the study of light, by 1865, was producing one of the accurate satisfying branches of science. Indeed, it has continued along that development, and is now a science of high precision with many areas of application.

We can contrast the fledgling science of electricity and magnetism, a science of wires, coils, magnets, whose utility was far from apparent, and about which, it is alleged, the passage of words between Faraday and the British Prime Minister, took place. Prime Minister to Faraday, about electromagnetic induction: "That's interesting, Mr. Faraday, but of what possible use is it?" Faraday: "Well, one day, Mr. Prime Minister, you will be able to tax it."

Maxwell set out to bring all of the scheme of Faraday, Henry, Oersted, Ampère, and a few others into a precise science. He was also emotionally convinced that any kind of action at a distance was not possible, so he began by thinking of ways in which the magnetic and electric *fields,* which filled the space around the wires and charges, could really be the responsible factor. He is supposed to have done much of this while an undergraduate at Cambridge, though it was published much later. In any event, he quickly came to a very simple problem which bothered him. He thought of the very simple case shown in Figure 9.7, where two plates, separated by air, are connected by wires to a battery and switch. When the switch is connected currents flow in the wires leading to the plates, currents which last only a moment for the plates will soon charge up and stop the flow of electricity from the battery. In the meantime there has been a magnetic field around the wire, as found by Oersted. *But why has there not been a magnetic field in the space between the plates?*

The more Maxwell thought about this, the less reasonable it seemed to him. The very place into which the charge was going, and where an electric field was building up, was the one place minus a magnetic field. So he postulated that there are two kinds of current: the usual, which is bodily movement of electric charge along a wire, and a new kind, called by him the "displacement current," which occurs when the electric field was changing. By supposing that the displacement current does the same

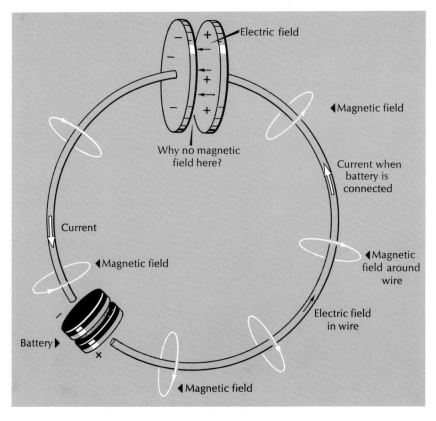

Fig. 9.7. Maxwell's dilemma, which led to his idea that a changing electric field
produces a magnetic field.

as the normal, or conduction, current, that is, it produces a magnetic
field, Maxwell was led to the more general idea that the relationship
between electric and magnetic fields was one in which the change of one
with time created the change of the other with distance. This necessi-
tated some rather stiff-looking equations, involving all three dimensions
and also time, and they are still formidable. Nevertheless, Maxwell believed that he had deduced the final relationship necessary to give a
complete scheme to electricity and magnetism.

Maxwell's electromagnetic equations could be used to solve many
quite interesting problems, some quite artificial as well as interesting.
One of the easiest, once the heavy mathematics had been set on paper,
was the case where one electric field was set up and a magnetic field
around it (as required by the theory) also existed. In not more than a

few lines of mathematics, the theory leads to a relationship between the way in which the fields change, which is well known as the relationship for wave motion. It was thus readily apparent that there should be "electromagnetic waves." However, the state of the art was still so primitive that Maxwell used two ways of measuring electric charge in the equations. He found the velocity of the waves to be the ratio of the two units of measurement of charge. Why these two ways existed needs to be told. One is easy and the reader already knows it: it is the method used in the very simplest statement of Coulomb's Law, the one we have used. This is the measurement of *charge*. The other came from Ampère, who had elaborately and skillfully shown that a loop of current is composed of tiny imaginary magnets. Ampère was measuring *current*. Thus the electric current was thought of in terms of magnetic poles, ultimately, and not electric charges. Moreover, the concepts of magnetism and electricity in their early stages were quite separate. So the measurement of a current was done by Ampère in quite different terms from the measurement of charge by Coulomb's Law. None of this would matter, except that a current is a flow of charge: the rate of passage of charge per second *is* the current. So now Ampère, in measuring current, was also measuring electric charge. By care and skill it is possible to work with these two systems, and it is even done today in many applications. Thus it is not surprising that in working out relationships, Maxwell should often find the relation between the two ways of measuring appearing in his equations. It was easy to show that this relation between a *dynamic* measure (Ampère) and a *static* measure (Coulomb) was of the form of a velocity. Maxwell found that if electromagnetic waves existed, then they must have this velocity.

Now considerable excitement developed. If *light,* the subject of Huygens, Young, Fresnel, Fizeau, and Foucault, was to be interpreted as electromagnetic radiation, then the velocity of light, measured astronomically, or by rotating mirrors, for example, must be *exactly* the same as the ratio of the two electrical units, measured with galvanometers and so on. The effort to prove this is so culminated in two experiments, one by Michelson and Newcomb in the United States, again one of the early ventures of the new nation into the realm of accurate science, and the other by Thomson (of the electron) and Searle, in England. Michelson and Newcomb measured the speed of light, and Thomson and Searle the ratio of the units. Result: both found 2.998×10^8 meters per second. Since that time (1895-1900) no one has questioned the identity of the two numbers.

We cannot let the story rest here. First, we must point out that this kind of unification of sciences is one of the ways in which we can tell that we are on the right track in the interpretation of Nature. As soon as careful work, done by one group of competent people, with their own worries, precautions, ways of thinking, and experimental methods, is found to be sharply, indeed exactly, related to that of a completely different group, we start to feel great confidence in the whole scheme. For centuries science has gone in that direction; now each decade witnesses the telescoping of more and more subject areas together. Sometimes, as we shall see later, the intellectual price paid is high, as in the development of quantum mechanics, where we must think in terms of a constant duality, between waves and particles. Nevertheless the unification is constantly growing.

Second, we should mention the way in which the "barbarous" units used by Maxwell have been civilized. It is done by the subterfuge of introducing two constants in the two primitive equations, one for Coulomb's Law and the other for Ampère's Law. These two constants are to be thought of as measures of electrical (ϵ_0) and magnetic (μ_0) properties of free space. For example, Coulomb's Law is written today in most usages as

$$F = \frac{1}{4\pi\epsilon_0} \frac{q_1 q_2}{r^2}$$

These two constants absorb the inconsistencies; the velocity of light no longer appears as the ratio of two "units of charge," but as $c = \sqrt{\epsilon_0 \mu_0}$. It is more satisfying to some, though it is a little less direct.

ELECTROMAGNETISM

We have just made the point, first made by Maxwell, that if a changing magnetic field produces an electric field, then a changing electric field should produce a magnetic field. It is worth a moment to see how the pictures we have used to describe an electric current fit in with this idea. In Figure 9.8 we draw a picture of a wire, in which, on the whole, a set of electrons are drifting toward the left. If we think of the electron at A moving toward B, then the field produced by the electron at A at the place P somewhere near the wire can be represented by an arrow Pa, while the field due to the electron when it has moved on to B is represented by the arrow Pb. The two are not the same, because their directions are different. In order to make the vector **Pa** into the vector **Pb** we must start at **A** and add vector **ab**. This vector measures the change in the electric field at P due to the electron at A moving to B. Thus the current moving to the left produces a whole set of changing fields, all around the wire; and they all look something like the vector **ab**. According to Maxwell, this changing electric field produces a magnetic field. The direction of the magnetic field is out of the paper, toward the reader,

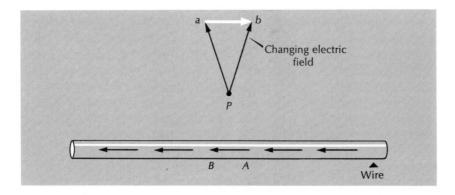

Fig. 9.8. Electrons are moving from right to left in a wire. One such goes from *A* to *B*. The field it produces at *P* is first *Pa* then *Pb*. The difference be-tween them, the *change* of field, is *ab*. This produces Oersted's magnetic field.

at right angles to the electric field change, and forms a set of lines of magnetic field which are rings: they have no starting and stopping point. This feature of a magnetic field sharply discriminates it from an electric field, which is why the two are not really to be compared. The feature is found to be an inherent property of magnetism, related to the fact that *single* magnetic poles are never found to exist.

FORCE ON A CURRENT IN A MAGNETIC FIELD: RELATION TO ELECTRONS

A brief review of our discussion will show that a magnetic field causes a wire to move when a current flows in the wire. It is possible to under-stand this in terms of the idea that an electric current is a flow of electrons along a wire. It is necessary to suppose that each moving electron which finds itself in the magnetic field experiences a force on it. There is a relation for this force which can be understood from Figure 9.9. The

Fig. 9.9. Representation of the way electrons moving in a wire are driven to one side by a magnetic field. The result is a net sideways force on the wire.

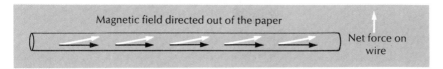

electrons here experience an upward force, which in turn causes them to press against the atoms in the wire and so tend to move the whole wire upward. This force on one electron moving in a magnetic field H with a speed v is of value F, where

$$F = \frac{Hev}{c},$$

e being the charge on each electron, and c a constant, equal to the velocity of light.

The reader may well wonder how it can be that a force which is observed in terms of a wire connected to a battery and a big magnet can be reduced to the description of a force on one electron. And he is right to do so. Since this is concerned with one of the most extraordinary successes of imagination, which is one aspect of scientific hypothesis, it is worth a little time to look at it. An electron, which is a tiny, invisible, highly electrically charged "particle," can hardly be directly observed. We now know it to be 100 million times smaller than the smallest thing we can see—even with the microscope. We know it to be of mass 10^{20} times smaller than the least mass we can readily measure directly. Bear it in mind that one million is 10^6. The factor above is millionths of millionths of millionths—and then some. Such an object, if it is to be conceived at all, has to be imagined. It is the essence of science to permit such imagination freely, but to demand that the imagined thing, or imagined way of behavior, be useful and accurate in predicting behavior which *can* be observed. So it is legal to imagine not only one electron but a whole lot of them. Now if we do, we soon realize that we can call an electric current, the phenomenon discovered by Galvani and Volta, the motion of electric charge due to the charge having speed. It does not take much effort to see, as in Figure 9.10, that if there are a number n of electrons moving with a speed v in any unit volume, then the number which crosses an area A at the end of a wire per second is nvA and the charge they carry is $envA$. So we can call this the current, and denote it by i.

Now the force on the wire is proportional to the current, and also to the size of the magnetic field and the length of the wire. So it is reasonable to think that the force on the whole wire full of electrons will be something like

$$iHl, \quad \text{or} \quad envAHl,$$

where H is the magnetic field and l is the length of the wire.

However the volume of a length l of wire of area A is Al, so that the number of electrons is also quite reasonably nAl and the force on each electron is

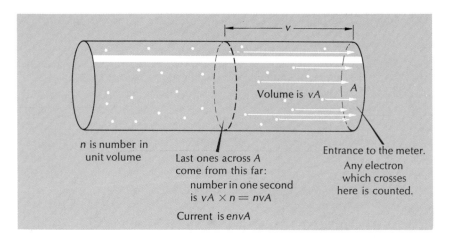

n is number in unit volume

Last ones across A come from this far: number in one second is vA × n = nvA

Current is envA

Entrance to the meter. Any electron which crosses here is counted.

Volume is vA

A

Fig. 9.10. Representation of the electrons moving into a meter at the end of a wire. The number that cross over per second is the current, and this is the number in the volume between the end and the farthest one away. This one is at a distance v, so the volume is vA and the number crossing is nvA. The current is this number times the charge on each electron, or $envA$.

$$\frac{envAHl}{nAl} \quad \text{or} \quad Hev \text{ per electron.}$$

If we just use this expression we have to ask ourselves whether it will also be true that the force F on an electron in an electric field E is

$$F = Ee,$$

as we want it to be. In other words does this force, on the moving electron, agree with the force on a static electron? It turns out that it does not. But if we introduce a factor, which we call c, then it does. So we put the factor in the relation for the magnetic force and write it as

$$F = \frac{Hev}{c}$$

We have already mentioned this factor in connection with Maxwell's theory; it is the velocity of light.

Thus we see that this expression for force is reasonable. We still don't know that there are any electrons. But if there *were*, and if they had a charge e and a velocity v, we could explain Faraday's experiment.

Theory has proved so successful in the last three generations that the reader may wonder why some such idea as Maxwell's didn't occur to Faraday. It may have. But even if it did, two factors would have operated to keep Faraday from talking or writing about it. The first is an innate conservatism of all scientists. The scientist hates to invent just for the occasion, and this sharply distinguishes him from many amateurs, who love to invent all the time. The second is that Faraday, with his equipment and his knowledge, almost certainly could not discover new phenomena which would require the use of electrons in their explanation. So the idea of electrons, while quite applicable to Faraday's experiment, remained as a possible, but unused, idea until discoveries were made which practically forced the use of the electron for their explanation. One such discovery was contained in the electric discharge, which we can consider next.

The reader may have noticed an increased tendency on the part of the authors to employ mathematical reasoning. This is partly deliberate, because they feel that some familiarity with mathematics has been developed by the reader, and partly necessary. We are about to enter on the subject of atomic and nuclear physics, the subject which has developed only within the twentieth century, and which is still making such profound changes in our way of life. It is not possible for us to develop this subject logically and historically as we did for the laws of motion and the conservation laws; instead, we have to tell a story. The story will not convey its true impact if the kind of way in which the new knowledge has been won is not described in some part. In no realm of science, except perhaps the marvelous intellectual structure of molecular genetics, has the use of hypothesis, theory, and experiment combined to give so sharp a knowledge of what can *never be seen,* as in the whole scope of atomic, molecular, and nuclear physics. We have just shown how, by supposing that there are electrons, and that these are the agents by which an electric current experiences a magnetic force, we can deduce the force which *would be on each,* supposing there to be electrons in the first place. This is hypothesis and theory. Now there must be experiment, and we have already suggested that such can be done.

GASEOUS DISCHARGES

The ability to produce a vacuum has been of great influence in the discoveries of modern physics. At the turn of the nineteenth century, producing a vacuum was very laborious; it required the patient raising and lowering of much mercury so as to share the vacuum above the top of a barometer with the space to be evacuated many times, until the vacuum was good enough. It often took all day. Muscles were developed.

One very important set of discoveries resulted from applying a large electric field across a glass tube containing air which was slowly evacuated. In Figure 9.11 we have made a feeble attempt to show the vivid appearances which develop when this most interesting experiment is performed.

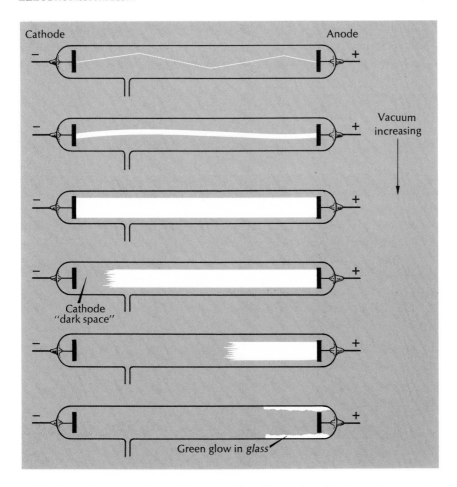

Fig. 9.11. Representation of the events in a glass tube with electrodes carrying a high electric field as the vacuum is increased. At first there is no effect. Then a flickering spark starts, followed by the succession shown.

At first the tube shows no sign of anything: it is as though no electric field were there. Then, as the vacuum develops, a few streaks, not unlike sparks, develop also, as shown at the top, and gradually there forms a continuous glow, which is at first only near the center, but, as the air is pulled out, spreads all the way through the tube. This is very much like a neon sign, and, in fact, except for air in place of neon, that is what it is. Now as the pressure gets lower the luminous discharge leaves the negative end and the cathode dark space forms. The luminous discharge is seen to become less bright and the dark space moves toward the positive end. The next stage sees an uneasy darkness with a green glow in the glass, not in the gas itself. The green glow is at the positive end. A magnet brought near the tube causes the green glow to move upward or downward if the magnet is brought toward the tube from the side, and objects placed in the tube cause shadows. One celebrated experiment, performed by Crookes, involved making such an evacuated tube with a light maltese cross of aluminum in it. The cross could be shaken on a hinge to stand up and intercept the cathode emanation which made the green glow near the positive end. A shadow was cast, and when the cross was shaken down the glow started in the part of the glass where the shadow had been. Finally, when the tube was evacuated as much as it would go, and this was truly laborious, using the pumps of those days, it became lifeless, as it was at the start.

The green glow, which could be deflected by a magnet, was supposed to be due to some kind of "ray." Since the clearing of the tube starts at the negative end, or cathode, and because shadows of objects appear at the other end, the rays were associated with the cathode, and they were called "cathode rays."

Two men, F. Perrin and J. J. Thomson, set out to study these rays to discover their properties, hoping, of course, to find out what the rays themselves were. Perrin's experiment is shown in Figure 9.12. The idea of the experiment is very simple, but it contained one interesting device, which the reader would not expect from the start. This was a light metal can, used to collect the electric charge. The can was hollow, and connected to a very sensitive current detector. The experiment did not take

Fig. 9.12. Perrin's demonstration that the cathode rays are negatively charged. By taking advantage of their deflection by a magnet he sent them into a side tube where they were collected in a metal cup. This was connected to a meter which indicated negative current.

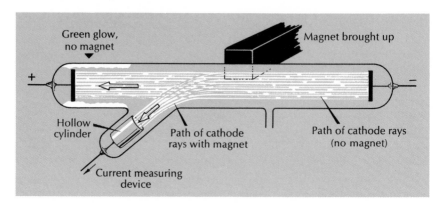

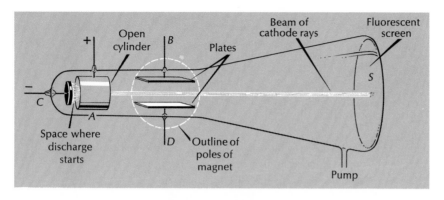

Fig. 9.13. J. J. Thomson's apparatus, which he used to subject cathode rays to deflection by electric and magnetic fields and so to measure their velocity and ratio of charge to mass.

very long, once the whole process of making the glass envelope, sealing in the electrodes and the hollow metal cup, and producing the vacuum was completed. All that was done was to bring up a magnet to deflect the cathode rays from their straight path across the main tube into the side tube with the hollow metal cup at the end of it. Before this was done, the detector showed that the current being collected by the can was very little or nothing, but as soon as the cathode rays were deflected into the side tube the meter began to read—*negative* electricity. Removing the magnetic field removed the current. Thus Perrin showed the rays to be electrically charged, and with negative electricity. This experiment suggested that the best way to make further study was by more electrical investigations. These were done by J. J. Thomson.

J. J. Thomson performed one of the great classical experiments of science in this investigation. His apparatus is shown in Figure 9.13. The space used to make the cathode rays has been shortened markedly and the positive electrode is a hollow cylinder. It was found that the cathode rays formed in the short space CA would mostly go *through* the hollow positive electrode. This hollow cylindrical electrode was found to have the remarkable property of forming a "pencil" beam of rays, now familiar in every TV picture tube, which went on to strike the far end of the glass tube. Painted on the end of this tube was a powder of zinc sulfide, which fluoresces very brightly when hit by cathode rays. Inside the vacuum, between the hollow cylinder and the fluorescent screen, Thomson placed two parallel plates. These were connected through the glass to the outside, at B and D, by special seals, which (in those days) were very hard to make. The tube was kept narrow in this region so that it could be placed between the poles of an electromagnet. These poles are indicated by the dotted circles.

In considering the experiment Thomson made, the reader should remember that an electromagnet allows one to vary the size of the magnetic field by varying the electric current in the coils of the electromagnet.

The first part of Thomson's experiment was to test the effect of an electric field on the cathode rays. To do this, Thomson caused the beam to start by connecting the coil between the plus and the minus; this generates a large electric field and starts the cathode rays into operation. The beam came into existence and a bright spot appeared at S on the fluorescent screen. Then, in the space beyond the plus, between the plates B and D, he produced an electric field by connecting B and D to the poles of a battery. As soon as he did this, the spot moved.

Thomson was able to alter the size of the electric field between the plates by using more batteries or less batteries, and so he could show that the more the field, the more the deflection. He reasoned that the deflection of the spot was caused by an acceleration, which we call a, in the space between plates, an acceleration which is along the electric field, and so, in our diagram, up and down. If E is the electric field, e the electric charge carried by the cathode rays, m the mass of one particle in the rays (assuming them to be particles), then Newton's Second Law tells us that

$$Ee = ma.$$

Now Thomson could easily measure the deflection of the spot at S, and if he had known the speed of the "unknown things" which we call cathode rays could have calculated the acceleration. He certainly knew enough mathematics—indeed, Galileo and the military ballistic experts had long ago done all this sort of calculation for gunfire. But the speed is not to be found this way. So Thomson used a second part to the experiment.

If we remove the electric field, bring up the electromagnet, and turn it on, again the spot moves. If the current in the electromagnet is reversed, the spot moves oppositely. By choosing the appropriate direction for the current in the electromagnet, the spot can be made to move up when the electric field makes it move *down*.

Now if we look back a little, we find that there is a force on a moving charge in a magnetic field and that the force depends on the speed as well as the charge. In fact, in the same units we have used above, the force due to a magnetic field H is

$$\frac{Hev}{c}$$

Thomson then carefully adjusted the magnetic field to give the same deflection. He did this by having both fields on at once and arranging the electromagnet to give no deflection. Then he knew that the magnetic field was exactly countering the effect of the electric field. So he knew that

$$\frac{Hev}{c} = Ee \quad \text{and} \quad v = \frac{cE}{H}$$

which told him the speed. It turned out to be very great—in fact, not far from the speed of light.

Now that he knew v, he could calculate a, as we said, and so he could find the ratio e/m, the ratio of charge to mass for cathode rays. The value found, in the sort of units we have been employing in this book is 10^{17}, which is a number with seventeen zeros after the initial "one." It is big. But it must be realized how big it is. If we take little beads of amber, we can charge them by frictional electricity, and arrange for them to be attracted upward by an electric field. We can then use the equation

$$Ee = ma$$

to measure the ratio of charge to mass for this "man-made" electrified particle. In the same units we find e/m to be about 10, so the ratio for the cathode rays is a million billion times larger. This is why the word "big" which we have used above is truly an understatement. The cathode rays seem to be almost all charge and almost no mass. This suggested to Thomson that the cathode rays were a kind of "new particle" and he pointed out that they must be very electrical and very light. In fact, he believed that he had, almost certainly, found something which had the essential attribute of electricity itself.

Here we find the necessity for another aside. We have slipped into using the phrase, "new particles." This implies that the nature of these particles is new, that before Thomson, they somehow did not exist. Of course, this is not right. The electrons, which we now call the cathode rays, are an essential part of matter: they have been all the time. It is hard to realize that science does not change Nature at all, but only reveals what Nature is like. In physical science we really have a severe problem with society because these revelations seem to make something new and hence different. It used to make trouble for Copernicus and Galileo. These troubles with "newness" seem to be over for physicists, but biologists have not found it so easy, and they are going to have a hard time even in our enlightened era. Man, after Darwin, was just the same as he was before—an evolved creature expressing in his being the marvelous product of two billion years of development, truly the image of his Creator. But to biology fell the task of "revealing" that man has evolved like the animals, and so is to be classed with them: an obvious enough fact. Man never was anything else. But if we insist on using the word "new," as we just did, we hide the fact that a discovery is *not* a creation—only a sharper insight.

To pick up our theme again. This discovery of a very large charge-to-mass ratio spurred effort to measure the ratio for other particles. Within a year or two, Rutherford and (separately) Zeleny, by rather indirect, but adequate, methods, measured e/m for positively charged particles and found a much lower ratio, meaning either that positively charged particles are less charged or much heavier. The ratio is about 10,000 times less. It was strongly suggested that the cathode rays, the negatively charged particles, which are formed so violently, are fragments of atoms, charged fully because one would like to think that charge cannot be fragmented, but having very light mass. Following a suggestion, made very imaginatively and nearly twenty years earlier by Johnstone Stoney, they were called *electrons*. No simple name can be given to the rest of the atom, the positive particles, except positive *ions*. Later we see that it is the nucleus which is positive and also heavy. The task of proving that electric charge exists only in finite, exactly equal units, never divided, fell to R. A. Millikan, who achieved it with a celebrated experiment in which he associated charge with oil drops and measured how they fell, either alone or in an electric field.

This may seem like a complicated story, and indeed it is. Suppose we turn it around and take for granted that there are electrons and that they are tiny, highly charged particles which are part of atoms. We suppose the atom holds them tightly, but not wholly inseparably. Now let us try to understand what goes on in the discharge tube. We use the molecular theory. Figure 9.14 may help the reader.

When the gas in the discharge tube is at high pressure, the atoms in the gas are very close together. Now suppose one electron is somehow liberated near the minus end. This one starting electron may be due to many causes, among them the effect of radiation, which can liberate electrons from atoms. We will discuss this later. This free electron starts toward the plus. But it is soon buffeted by atoms, and the speed gained because of the electrical force is lost before it gets very high. Now lower the pressure. The atoms get farther apart. The electron has a longer free time to move in the electrical field and it accelerates all this time. So it has some speed when it strikes the next atom. It may even get up enough speed to dislodge an electron from the gas atom which it strikes. Each time an electron does this an extra electron is made and this electron can perhaps do the same. So there is a little uncertain flash. Now get the pressure lower still. The electron has a long way to go, has lots of time to get up speed, and *always* causes a dislodgement of

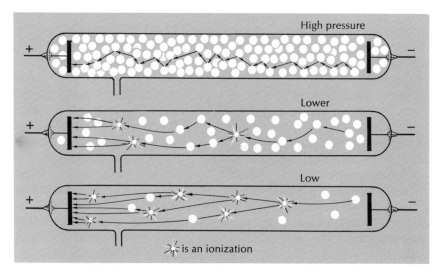

Fig. 9.14. How collisions by electrons can cause a discharge. A chance electron released at the right makes collisions too often to ionize at high pressure. At low pressure the collisions are rare, but at each one every electron has enough energy to ionize, so the number of freed electrons increases to the left and a discharge starts.

an electron when it hits an atom. So does the new electron, and the next, and so on until many electrons are flying through the gas, tearing apart atoms as they go. The torn apart, or *ionized*, atoms recover in time, capturing back electrons, and as they do so, as we shall see later, they give out light.

At still lower pressure, there are very few gas atoms. They offer very little obstruction and the electrons crash into the glass at very high speeds. There they make a green glow, and also, incidentally, some X-rays. Finally, when there is no gas, there are no electrons and no action at all.

ELECTRONS

The discovery that electrons could actually be liberated in a gas "discharge" was rapidly followed by many others. This is a common phenomenon: once a completely new discovery is made, apparently with the greatest difficulty, it is not long before many other aspects of the same discovery are found, often seeming to be very much easier. In the case of the electrons found in discharges, there was a gap of a few years until rather better vacuums could be made, and then, in short order, Richardson discovered that a very hot wire emits electrons (this was the basis of the modern vacuum tube), and Lenard discovered that when violet or ultraviolet light falls on a metal surface, electrons are given off. Thus it became possible to do things with these very light, almost purely electrical "particles," essentially by themselves. Two tremendous developments resulted. The first was the vacuum tube, in which almost unbelievably small electrical effects could be magnified almost to any degree almost instantly. The vacuum tube is so important that taking a moment to look at the principle on which it works is worth while. One of our representative diagrams of a vacuum tube is shown in Figure 9.15. It requires a very high vacuum, and it is one of the miracles of modern technology that cheap ways of getting this vacuum now abound. The electrons which are the basis for the tube are created by heating a wire, in the manner of Richardson, and they are then held back by an open looped or coiled wire, called a "grid," which is held slightly negative. This negative keeps the electrons close to the place where they were produced and causes a "cloud" of them to form, a cloud which has the special name "space charge." The means for dispersing the cloud is provided at the other end of the tube: it is a quite positively charged plate, which would attract the electrons very vigorously were it not for

Fig. 9.15. A schematic picture of a vacuum tube. Very small electrical changes on the grid have a big effect because the grid is right in the midst of a cloud of electrons.

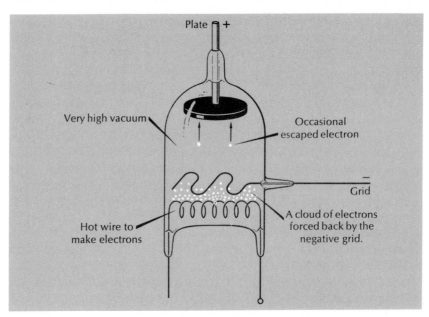

the negative grid which is closer and more intimately mixed with the space charge. Now very small changes toward positive on the grid have a big effect on the cloud of electrons, and release many to go to the positive plate, while a little more negative bottles them up and cuts down even on those which might be getting free anyway. Thus very tiny changes indeed on the confining grid produce big changes in the amount of current which reaches the plate. The electrons, which are almost inertialess, can respond with almost incredible speed to the changes in the vacuum tube: with some care, responses faster than a billion per second can be recorded. The result has been a very large number of previously unthought of applications, ranging from generating tremendous amounts of power in antennas, that are billions of times greater than used by Hertz, to detecting billionths as much as he did, so that it is now possible to transmit signals from Mars to the Earth, as has recently been done. There is no need to elaborate on the importance of the vacuum tube, which has made radio, TV, radar, the "hi-fi," and modern computers possible.

SOCIAL "REVOLUTION" PRODUCED BY THE ELECTRON

It is not always fashionable to attribute social change to scientific discovery. Yet the patterns of life have been greatly changed by discoveries, and that of the electron must be considered to be one such changing influence. One realm of influence is undoubtedly in communications. It is true that fast communication of limited factual knowledge was solved by the telegraph, and when, in 1839, Morse sent the message "What hath God wrought" from Washington to Baltimore, a distance of 40 miles, in little more time than it took to write it by hand, the days of waiting months to hear of deaths and earthquakes were over. But deaths and earthquakes are not the only factors which determine social action. In the years before World War II, when Hitler spoke at the great rallies set up by the Nazi party, his voice and the frightening, fanatic response of the vast crowd could be heard all over the world. More than one person has said that the threat of National Socialism first struck to his heart as he listened to those words. Without the discovery of the electron these harangues could not have been heard outside the audience, and the *feel* of the moment could not have been communicated to the rest of the world. It is said by some that the election of 1960 was decided in favor of Kennedy on television. Again, the ability to see the lines in a man's face and watch his conduct under challenge is something which could not be done without the electron and the technology which ensued from its discovery. That children are different because of the kind of television they watch is not questioned by

many. Differences in children are reflected in adults and differences in
the great majority of children will certainly mean a different society
thirty years from now. It is not our purpose to admire this difference:
rather we are unhappy that this difference is being produced and developed, seemingly with little concern even by those who will be changed
by it. It *is* our purpose to point out one fact: social change results from
invention.

The field of communications is not the only field of influence of the
discovery of detectable inertialess particles. The problem of computation has plagued engineers, economists, administrators, actuaries, and
military technicians, for as long as these lines of endeavor existed. Electronic computers in which each operation takes a billionth of a second
are now in existence. The human mind can perhaps get up to 50 such
operations per second; the computer is ten million times faster. This
means that mathematics of a repeated complexity can now be thought
about: for example, trial-and-error solutions can be sought for complicated situations—one such being a complete city economy, which
can be simulated on a computer without ever putting it into practice.
In full seriousness it has been suggested that wars be fought on computers, entering the strengths of each side and reaching a decision without bloodshed.

This last remark leads to an aspect of the use of computers leading
to social change, and that is the process of decision-making. If the
information we have available cannot lead to a straightforward procedure for action, it may be possible to submit it to computer analysis
and derive a basis for a decision. This has happened in many instances,
so far rather trivial, like choosing names for products, but we have to
remember that methods of use can elaborate themselves, and we may
live to see national policy decided on the electronic computer. This
is another thing we do not wish to approve: again we call attention to
it as a conceivable consequence of a scientific advance.

X-RAYS, OR ROENTGEN RAYS

We have briefly referred to the production of X-rays in a discharge
tube when the pressure is very low and the vacuum is at its best. The
discovery of X-rays is one of the most startling and significant in scientific history. It was made by Roentgen in 1895. The importance of
the discharge tube as a means of revealing new phenomena had been
growing in significance and Roentgen had been wondering whether the
tube, in the condition of the green glow, gave out anything else in the
way of radiation. He coated the tube with black paper, and looked at
a screen of fluorescent material held near the end of the tube. The
screen not only glowed, it glowed so brightly that it could be seen to

glow in the next room. He found that the rays also affected photographic plates: he studied the way they were absorbed, and what conditions were needed for their generation. He did not think he could claim that they were like normal light and so he called them X-rays. In honor of Roentgen they are sometimes called "Roentgen" rays.

X-rays are generated when fast electrons are stopped. It takes only a moment to realize that a light, inertialess electron, traveling at nearly the velocity of light, when stopped within a thickness of a few sheets of paper or less must undergo a very rapid deceleration. A deceleration is the same as an acceleration, only it is negative, and the process by which a charged particle emits radiation when it is accelerated will apply to the electron under these conditions. So the electron radiates, and the radiation is X-rays. Thus we see, that in spite of Roentgen's caution, the X-rays are electromagnetic radiation: they differ from light only in the shortness of their wavelength, or the equivalent, their very great frequency. For now we can postpone further discussion of these radiations and pass on to another similar, but quite unrelated discovery.

RADIOACTIVITY

Becquerel, or rather, Antoine Henri Becquerel, for he was the grandson of a physical scientist and his father was also renowned in that subject, was interested in the phosphorescence of materials. This behavior is usually due to bright light absorbed and given out again slowly. Becquerel found that uranium salts would give out phosphorescence regardless of whether they had been brightly illuminated, and he also found that the kind of radiation that they emitted was very much like that found just one year previously by Roentgen. It had many of the same properties, for example, penetration of opaque material. The new phenomenon was called radioactivity.

Not long after, Pierre and Marie Curie discovered a far more intensely radioactive element—*radium*. This was nearly a million times more active. They showed that three radiations came off: one easily absorbed, in a few thicknesses of paper, the *alpha* rays; one less easily absorbed, the *beta* rays; and one very hard to absorb, the *gamma* rays. They also showed that nothing influenced this radiation—pressure, heat, chemical combination, all had no effect whatsoever. The new powerful radiation had a way which was all its own.

In the next chapter we take up radioactivity, and we will trace it to its source—the nucleus of the atom. Clearly we are now embarked firmly on a description of what is called "modern physics," which is characterized by the discovery of the nature of the atom and its structure, and the way in which atoms join to make up the whole of matter as we know it.

Before we examine the atom and its nucleus, a moment of comment on the last decade of the nineteenth century may show something of interest. At the end of the eighteenth century we saw with Galvani and Volta the arrival of a discovery of something quite unexpected: current electricity. Almost surely someone had seen freshly prepared frog's legs react to two dissimilar metals but had thought no more of it. The mood of the end of the eighteenth century was such that it was ready for this kind of discovery and accordingly the follow-up took place and a major new aspect of Nature was revealed. The end of the nineteenth century saw a whole set of these discoveries: X-rays, the electron, radioactivity, the realization of the possibility of transmission of radio over great distances, to name only some of them. We feel like including the rediscovery of the work of Mendel by DeVries almost a few hours before the turn of the century. Almost no era has ever produced so much of scientific promise as this decade. To look back over the newspapers and magazines of that time is to see a mixture of amazement and confidence in science. It is also interesting that this is a time of reaction in literature. The mood of Dickens, Thackeray and Trollope had given way to Henry James and Oscar Wilde. It is possible that this great and almost formidable surge forward in science, coming at a time of experimentation in art caused the beginnings of the separation between scientific thought and artistic thought. In any event, we do think that we must give the final decade of the nineteenth century more than a passing remark as we go on to the subject of the atom.

Suggestions for Further Thought

1. Describe the principal contributions made by Maxwell. Include an account of the use of theory and the way he related his ideas to light. What role did Hertz play in establishing Maxwell's electromagnetic wave theory?
2. Outline the discovery of the electron. Include a description of Millikan's oil drop experiment.
3. Compare the revolution in society produced by the discovery of the electron with that produced by the invention of the steam engine.
4. Write a short account of vectors. Explain the operation of vector subtraction. Use it to indicate how an acceleration can develop.

References

Guy C. Omer., Jr., H. L. Knowles, B. L. Mundy, and W. H. Yoho, *Physical Science: Men and Concepts* (Boston: D. C. Heath, 1962).

George Gamow, *Matter, Earth and Sky*, 2nd ed. (Englewood Cliffs, N.J.: Prentice-Hall, 1965).

Science and the Taxpayer

No matter how much science and technology may add to the quality of life, no matter how brilliant and meritorious are its practitioners, and no matter how many individual results that have been of social and economic significance are pointed to with pride, the fact remains that public support of the overall enterprise on the present scale eventually demands satisfactory economic measures of benefit. The question is not whether such measures should be made, it is only how to make them.

C. W. Sherwin and R. S. Isenson
Project Hindsight

INTRODUCTION

Scientific research in the past 150 years has unquestionably been expensive. In order to find funds to carry out this research, various sources have been tapped and of late the vast majority of funding for research has begun to come from the various governments.

If we go back to research in the United States, then we can see the beginning of it picking up in an organized way with Joseph Henry, the Smithsonian Institution, and the start of the National Academy of Sciences. Nevertheless, even at this time, approximately 100 years ago, the money for scientific research was expected to come from private funds, or for some profit-making purpose. Occasionally large enterprises were started. One of these was the first large ocean-going ship, the "Great Eastern" (1850-70) which was far ahead of its kind in size, and which occupied almost a standard taxpayer's burden in Great Britain. It was chartered for various purposes, among them the laying of the first Atlantic cable. Until 1900 there was only private support for scientific investigation, which was most extensive in medical research, except for a certain amount of military research for special instrumentation for the Army and Navy. In the years 1800 to 1900 the number of first-class laboratories in the United States probably did not exceed twenty-five. In Great Britain the number was even less and the same was true of France and Germany. On the other hand, in 1966, large first-class laboratories exist in all these nations and can be found in excess of 100 in all of them. Thus there has been a large expansion in recent years, and this is a phenomenon which has been associated with the introduction of government support for laboratories.

The growth curve of federal support for scientific research and development in the United States of America has actually been rising so steeply since World War II that its projection starts to move into the zone of the gross national product. Indeed, there have been some almost straight-faced discussions of what could be done if the whole of the gross national product were spent on scientific research. It is interesting to note that we are today at this phase in expansion, because it is the stage at which experience has shown that something starts to modify the growth process of a living system. We are living in the years when this will occur, and since about the only way to interrupt the growth of government-sponsored expenditures is by action of the people, we are going to see the intervention of the citizen in scientific research very much more than we have in the past.

THE DEVELOPMENT OF THE REGULATION OF RESEARCH BY FUNDING

Since the time of World War I it has been quite clear that the governments have an interest in scientific research. It was of importance to both Germany and England in World War I. Germany could not have fought World War I more than six months without the discovery of the Haber process for the fixation of nitrogen, which gave them their explosives. England made considerable use of underwater sound detection for submarines and also of sound ranging for gunfire at that time. As a result there emerged from World War I organized methods of supporting scientific research. In England these took the form of the Department of Scientific and Industrial Research which gave grants for study and research, and in the United States the National Research Council was appended to the National Academy of Sciences and fulfilled somewhat the same function.

It is interesting to notice how some quite enterprising pieces of research were achieved in this period. The operations of Ernest Lawrence in the construction of his sequence of cyclotrons is of great interest. If one looks at the development of this very interesting device, one sees in 1933 the original design of Lawrence and Edlefsen in which the mechanism was contained in a glass envelope, quite small and requiring only a small magnet. Following this, funds were made available at the University of California to build a larger magnet and put together a small instrument which reached the very modest energy of 1,000,000 volts. The cost of this machine was probably not much more than the cost of a machine shop and the brawn of the individuals that made it go. It was soon realized that with such small instruments the potential of this atom smasher could not be exploited. Lawrence discovered that the Federal Telegraph Company had some electrical magnets which had been built for radio transmissions prior to the discovery of the vacuum tube. He obtained permission to move one of these to Berkeley, and found enough money to construct a cyclotron that would fit within the gap of the pole pieces and produce the first really useful energy of 6,000,000 volts. This was designed by Lawrence and Livingston and later Lawrence and Cooksey. The whole construction was essentially done by amateurs, even the machine work and the construction of the quite large radio transmitting tubes that were necessary. The total cost of this cyclotron, really the first demonstration of the value of the method, perhaps amounted to $20,000.

I recall that at Yale University we started the construction of a cyclotron somewhat smaller than this one, with an initial grant of $1,200. For less than $4,000 the whole machine was put into operation, not functioning very well but nevertheless functioning. Building it took an immense amount of strength—among other things, we had graduate-student laborers pushing 700-lb. pieces of iron around—and it took something like two years in building. One didn't dream of really sizable funds, which would, in any event, have been at the most in the order of $50,000. Actually the machine was put into operation because Lawrence generously donated an early version of his cyclotron to me, which we at Yale were able to install within our magnet and make it function. This was the kind of assistance one scientific group gave to others in this period of lean funds.

The situation totally changed with World War II. Whereas in World War I science had proved to be useful, in World War II scientific research proved to be decisive. This was recognized very early, in fact *prior* to World War II, by the British. It was recognized in a somewhat different way by the Germans (who used research *prior* to the war, but did not encourage it *during* the war) and a little later also by the United States. The result of this realization was the organization of really large teams of scientists. These teams were large even in today's terms and they compounded such endeavors as the development of radar, the development of a proximity fuse which exploded in the vicinity of a target without having actually having to hit it, development of methods of combatting magnetic mines, and, ultimately, the development of the atom bomb. With these weapons went also the development of systems for operations research which would be a guide in strategy.

The weapons that came out of this organized scientific research were so potent and the power of such laboratories so great that no one felt that an end to this kind of work should come abruptly. The development of the atom bomb was followed by the formation of large national laboratories, for example, Oak Ridge, Tennessee, the Argonne National Laboratory in Chicago, and the Brookhaven National Laboratory on Long Island. Each of these is a laboratory with over 3,000 scientists, and each has a budget in the tens of millions of dollars per year. While this kind of development was accepted as necessary for breakthroughs like the discovery of nuclear power, it was felt that the support of fundamental research in the universities was also desirable. Some method of supporting this was accordingly devised, and the Office of Naval Research gave the first grants from the federal government to universities for research in areas such as nuclear physics within their own physics and chemistry departments. This was followed by support by the Atomic Energy Commission, the formation of the National Science Foundation, and the extensive support of the Public Health Service by Congress, and more recently the formation of the National Aeronautics and Space Administration. All of these agencies began putting considerable funds into scientific laboratories. This created industries which supplanted the need for scientists to make their own equipment. At the time I did most of my nuclear physics research it was quite standard for us to make our own Geiger counters, and, indeed, all of our detecting equipment including amplifiers were hand-constructed by ourselves. Today this is a multi-million dollar industry and almost no scientist even thinks of making his own Geiger counter unless he has a special purpose in research.

RESEARCH VERSUS DEVELOPMENT

Research and development, both of which involve laboratories, are really quite different. There are items of pure research which have not been followed by what has often been called "development," among them the discovery that right- and left-handedness in nuclear reactions are not separate and that it is possible to convert from one to the other. This is often called the "overthrow of parity." Much of the work in very high energy nuclear physics which bears on cosmology is not being followed by a development. Some of the discoveries in molecular biology in which virus genetics and biochemistry form a great part have not yet been followed by any further development. Against this we can contrast work which will make a space craft reliable. This involves a great deal of research on components which will stand high stresses and temperatures, and such work does have to be done in laboratories but does not always have the same intellectual stimulus that goes with fundamental discovery. Another illustration is the production of radar. In crude laboratory lashups it was possible to observe the first echoes from the transmission of radar to prove that it could be used. Even with the strong impetus of war it took something like an additional year to produce the first usable machine. This intense effort for a year was in what we call development.

Some of the achievements of World War II were indeed staggering. Thus the step from the discovery of plutonium to a large-scale production unit for it, was achieved with almost none of the intermediate development at all. This was one of the greatest successful gambles in all of science; it is not the normal way things are done.

The development of vaccines and drugs has gone far beyond the early days when Pasteur could use the dried spinal cord of a rabbit to prevent rabies. Extensive research on cells in "tissue culture" and on animals, all costly, is now required before a valuable drug can be used. Here, too, development goes along with research.

AGENCIES AND THE FUNDING OF RESEARCH

There are two ways by which a scientific project is given monetary support. It may be done in what is often called an "in-house" laboratory. Thus the laboratories of the Atomic Energy Commission might have in them individuals who are interested in undertaking a certain broad line of research. The director and the individuals responsible for the branches within the laboratory would then decide to make this part of the program of the laboratory, and essentially the money would come from the budget provided to the whole laboratory for its operations.

Another class of operation is the contract type. Here the decision is made that something is needed and then contracts to perform it are provided by a national agency. Much of the work of the National Aeronautics and Space Administration is of this type. Over and above this, and perhaps most exciting in terms of the research yield, are the projects for which universities and non-profit laboratories make spontaneous requests for grants. An investigator, more usually a group of investigators, decide that they would like to try a branch of research. They make a proposal, usually on some kind of standard form, which they back up by their own past publications and by a clear statement of what it is they hope to do, with a description of the relationship of this work to the work that has been previously done in their field. They propose a budget and list the people that are needed. They send applications to one or more agencies, where some kind of a review is made. In the Public Health Service an elaborate system of "study sections" exists, something like a hundred in number and these are groups of a dozen or so individuals chosen for scientific ability and reputation who have competence in all areas of interest to the Public Health Service. The request is sent to them and usually handled by a small committee, which presents it to the whole study section. The small committee gives its opinion and the whole study section then rates the project. If the study section decides the project is worth while, it then goes before a council which is a separate group only partly composed of scientists. They make decisions regarding the allocation of funds. The other agencies handle the process somewhat differently, with the essential principle that a group of scientists is called on to give a kind of group opinion. In the case of NASA there is both the problem of the review for scientific merit and the fitting of the work into a space mission. This sharpens and complicates the problem.

REWARDS TO SCIENTISTS

Various methods of rewarding scientists exist. The most famous of these are the Nobel prizes, which are given to the areas of physics, chemistry, and medicine. They are intended to be given for new discoveries of a special, and perhaps, to use a trite word, breakthrough type, and not necessarily for long solid years of study. There are an increasing number of national scientific awards, and there are also awards given by societies. Most of the societies have a category called "fellowship," which is intended to give a certain recognition to members of the society; the national academies and the royal societies elect fellows and usually election to such a fellowship is regarded as a considerable honor. The rewards are not normally financial, although the Nobel prize award definitely is, but the honor is regarded very highly by scientists and their colleagues.

COMPARISON OF SUPPORT IN ENGLAND AND THE USSR

The method of supporting research in England is not greatly different from that in the United States except that the number of agencies is somewhat more limited and that there is a tendency for a support of "research units," which have a continuity and which can plan on a budget rather than the support of individuals on separate contracts or grants. In the USSR research is strongly influenced by the National Academy of Sciences, which essentially lays out a master plan for research throughout the nation. The United States does not have such a master planning agency and perhaps is fortunate not to have one.

THE CITIZEN

In the United States the relationship between science and the citizen is very loose. It was almost non-existent until 1950 or so. During that time scientists who had worked in wartime laboratories and had learned the tricks (and these included the high energy physicists) were able to induce the granting agencies to provide large sums of money for their work. Laboratories which had budgets exceeding the budgets of the university became fairly common. Since 1950 there has been a somewhat more severe attitude toward the situation and in the past five years there has been a strong tendency for both the Administration and the Congress to look a little more sharply at the way money is expended. One important agency which exerts a strong influence today is the President's scientific advisory committee, which came into existence after the Russians launched Sputnick. This committee has not only concerned themselves with support of scientific research, but has also encouraged scientific education. In addition, several congressional committees now exist for examining various branches of research. Recently we have seen large projects involved in sharp congressional lobbying for sites.

With this stern controversy over what to do with money for science, we begin to see the existence of scientific prejudice and scientific debate. A fine example of this is to be found in the conflict between Tizard and Lindemann, mentioned by C. P. Snow in his essay on "Science and Government." This was essentially the battle of the minds between the proponents of heavy bombing of cities and the proponents of support for the armies. This conflict extended even into the United States and I well remember emotional debates in which the pros and cons of supporting the Strategic Air Force with radar equipment, and using radar equipment to assist in the close support of armies, were brought into sharp conflict and were debated vigorously by scientists. Where such situations occur there is inevitably a danger that scientific judgment may be confused with scientific polemics and, indeed, scientific objectivity may be lost. This is not a trivial danger and it is one that the citizen is going to need to recognize and understand.

INFLUENCE ON PROGRAMS OF RESEARCH

In the future we are going to see an influence of the granting agencies on programs of research. For example, the subject of physics has developed sharply since World War II in spite of a professional lack of acumen about building it up. It has always been traditional with physicists in every nation to cast off an application as soon as it ceases to be fundamentally physical in nature. Thus, we have seen branches of physics move over into chemistry or biology or engineering, one by one. In spite of this, the support by federal funds has been so great since World War II that most university physics departments have doubled or tripled their size. This strong impact of research money is something to be noted.

We can see that in the future there will be new procedures. Scientific societies will have to take a stand of what they believe is important research, and they will have to move closer to the sources of influence. There will be a much greater role for the National Academy-National

Research Council, to the extent that the decision-making role of this group may actually alter the very character of the group itself. It may be necessary to widen its membership and make it closer to the whole scientific community, rather than close to a few strong laboratories as it is at present.

It is possible that differences in national philosophy may cause differences in attitudes toward scientific support. Thus the national philosophy in Russia is probably closer to a genuine faith in science than that in the United States. This may mean that Soviet science may become stronger than American science, though it is not so at present. If this should happen then there well may be an influence on the national character by this scientific faith. Thus, in the future, the relationship between the citizen, the taxpayer, and scientific research is going to be closer, and this will be an interesting time.

Deliberate studies to find the optimum way to spend funds are now being made. One of these, called "Project Hindsight," * examines the effectiveness of various kinds of research in developing equipment for the armed services. The findings are surprising in several ways. The first is that "many innovations are needed." This means that advances are made in terms of multiple use of new discoveries rather than in terms of "breakthroughs." The second is that directed effort pays off. The third is that recent random scraps of knowledge are not of much use. "Well organized, thoroughly understood and carefully taught science" has the impact. All these ideas run somewhat contrary to some widely held positions, notably the notion that the individual experimenter, the one who makes the "breakthrough," is the important man. It is clear that if even the scientific director, in making evaluations of how to act, finds himself changing his concepts of how to use science, the citizen, as represented by congressional committees, is also going to be willing to change his concepts. Again, this suggests an interesting future for science, particularly in universities.

ERNEST C. POLLARD, 1967

* "A Study of the Role of Research Made by the Department of Defense," *Science, 156,* 1571-7 (1967).

10

Radioactivity and the Atomic Nucleus

It cannot be denied that, so far as the future is concerned, an entirely new prospect has been opened up. By these achievements of experimental science Man's inheritance has increased, his aspirations have been uplifted, and his destiny has been ennobled to an extent beyond our present power to foretell. The real wealth of the world is its energy, and by these discoveries it, for the first time, transpires that the hard struggle for existence on the bare leavings of natural energy in which the race has evolved is no longer the only possible or enduring lot of Man. It is a legitimate aspiration to believe that one day he will attain the power to regulate for his own purpose the primary fountains of energy which now Nature so jealously conserves for the future. The fulfilment of the aspiration is, no doubt, far off, but the possibility alters somewhat the relation of man to his environment, and adds a dignity of its own to the actualities of existence.

Frederick Soddy
The Interpretation of Radium, 1909

THE ELECTRICAL CONDUCTIVITY OF GASES

It may seem strange, even oblique, to begin a chapter about radioactivity by discussing gases, yet no account of the historical development of the subject would be faithful if this whole broad preoccupation of science were not mentioned. Gases were known to avoid the conduction of electricity: not so solids, not so liquids. Why the obstinacy of gases? Since something special could happen in solids and in liquids to make them conduct, why not in gases? This intriguing question was behind a great deal of the work done between 1885 and 1910. Roentgen was seeking the answer, so were Perrin and Thomson, so were many others.

Roentgen found X-rays; Thomson found the electron; but still the whole question was open.

In 1885 two ways to make gases able to conduct electricity were known: the electric discharge, and the heating of a flame. Both are different in outward appearance and both are really quite violent. In the years 1895 to 1915 great attention was paid to the extent to which, under normal conditions, gases will not *conduct at all*. These studies, made by many now famous men, such as Rutherford, C. T. R. Wilson, Elster, Hess, and Kohlhorster, used methods of great sensitivity, and they revealed three very important new ways of making air, or any gas, conduct: X-rays, radioactivity, and radiation from outside the earth in origin, called, later, "cosmic rays." All three are interesting: in this chapter we are mostly concerned with radioactivity.

THE "STRING AND SEALING WAX ERA"; THE ELECTROSCOPE

Today, if one wants to do research in nuclear physics, it is necessary to join some "team" where an expensive instrument is available. The word "expensive" is quite in order; one such instrument presently under construction at Stanford costs $106,000,000. The new accelerator at Weston, Ill., was negotiated with considerable pressure from states and various interested localities, to try to get the facility assigned in their area, and is to cost about $500,000,000. In 1909, on the other hand, when Rutherford moved from Montreal to Manchester, or later, in 1919 when he moved to Cambridge, he needed little more than a suit-case to move his equipment. That era, when the design of experiments needed much ingenuity and little equipment is often referred to as the string and sealing wax era: not that string played much part, but sealing wax certainly did.

The favorite instrument of that period was the gold leaf electroscope, and one such is illustrated in Figure 10.1. Imagine a square metal can, the size that is made to hold one pound of tea. A set of holes are punched in the bottom, two holes are hacked out of the front and back, and a hole is drilled in the top. Through the top the operating part is inserted. It consists of a metal rod, flattened on one side, to which a thin gold leaf is stuck, usually by simply licking the rod and then rolling it onto the gold leaf. The rod is electrically insulated from the can by holding it in place and running hot sealing wax around it, taking care the rod does not touch the metal of the can. Two pieces of glass are set as windows at the front and back, so that the gold leaf can be watched. The gold leaf assembly can be seen in insert B of the figure, and the operation of the whole outfit can be grasped from insert C. If no agent such as radioactivity, or X-rays is present, then a positive charg-

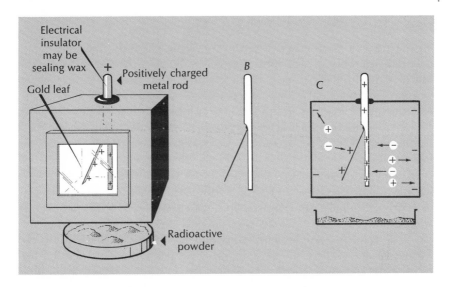

Fig. 10.1. The gold leaf electroscope: charging the rod and leaf causes repulsion and the leaf stands away from the rod. Radioactivity steadily ionizes the air and causes the leaf to fall at a steady rate as the negative ions neutralize the positive on the rod and leaf.

ing of the rod and gold leaf (which is done separately with a rubbed glass rod) will produce sideways deflection of the gold leaf as the + seeks to get away from the other +. This deflection will remain steady. An agent which can render the air conducting will produce + and − charged atoms known as *ions*: they move as shown by the arrows and they act to neutralize any charge which is there. The negatives will neutralize the positives on the rod and leaf, while the positives move over to the can. The can has negatives pulled on to it by the attraction of the positives on the rod and leaf and these are now neutralized by the positive ions. The result is that the leaf finds itself with less positive and so tends to stand out less, i.e., it begin to fall. It only falls while there is a supply of ions, that is to say, while there is some agent producing the ions. By devising some means of accurately measuring the position of the gold leaf (a cheap microscope with a scale in the eyepiece was often used) the number of "divisions" changed per minute or hour can be counted. This is called the "activity." A very large amount of study was done with this instrument, in almost precisely the terms described, including the tea can and the sealing wax and the primitive adhesive.

RADIOACTIVITY AND ITS RADIATIONS

At the turn of the twentieth century a small vigorous group of young
scientists, notably Rutherford (physicist), Soddy (chemist), Pierre and
Marie Curie (physicist and chemist), and Boltwood, (chemist) began
working in this field. Two major classes of experiments were done:
one a physical study of the radiations, and one a study of the chemistry
of the substances which were radioactive. We will take the physical
studies first. Let us act as though we ourselves were doing them in the
laboratory.

Imagine our electroscope with the holes in the bottom, and suppose
we have some powder which is radioactive. We put this in a tray
and place it under the electroscope, which we have just charged up.
Immediately we see the gold leaf moving down, probably quite fast.
We time it with a watch, with some difficulty, for it is very active, and
we record the activity in divisions dropped per minute: it will be big.
Now we introduce something to absorb the radiation, for example some
paper—why not? We find that putting in just a few sheets of paper
changes the whole behavior of the electroscope, it goes from being very
active to having a comfortable steady rate of drop, and the rate is perhaps ten times less fast than it was. We might conclude that all the
activity is gone and is stopped by the paper, but no, the electroscope
is by no means passive: there is clearly still something making the air
conduct. So we go on adding paper, and the effect is very little. We
get restless and look around for something denser than paper and find
some sheets of copper or brass. Putting these in is more dramatic: the
activity goes down each time we insert a copper sheet, and after a
while we feel that the activity has been lost entirely. About a tenth
of an inch of copper is in place. However, we are good experimenters,
so we keep the powder there and see if there is even a weak activity.
There is: we need to measure it in divisions per hour rather than per
minute, but we can nevertheless always tell that the powder is there,
with its copper covering, as contrasted with taking it away. Now we
start the laborious part of the experiment. We hunt about for the
densest material we can readily find, sheets of lead, and having found
these, we begin to put them in. As thicknesses of an inch or more go in,
the weak activity goes down. It does so very tantalizingly, for whereas
we felt we had produced a definite cessation before with the paper and
copper, now we never do. We always seem to be able to make the
activity less, but we never seem to stop it altogether.

Being scientists, we make a graph of our data. It looks like Figure 10.2.
To us it seems as though three separate agents are present: the paper-
absorbable agent, the copper-absorbable agent, and the remainder, cut

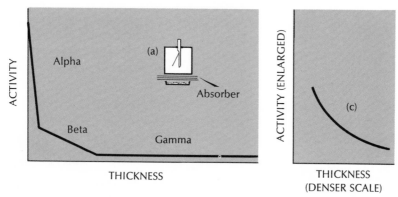

Fig. 10.2. The absorption of radiations as measured with the electroscope. Three kinds of radiation are seen. The least easily absorbed is gradually diminished by considerable thicknesses of dense material like lead. The most easily absorbed is removed by a few sheets of paper.

down but not stopped by lead. We are dealing with something which radiated from the powder, so we call these three agents "rays," and they become *alpha* rays, *beta* rays, and *gamma* rays. To try to make the figure more clear, the insert (a) shows the way the absorber, powder, and electroscope are related in the experiment, and the insert (c) shows the absorption of the gamma rays with the activity scale enlarged and the thickness scale compressed. The slow falling off, but never ceasing, aspect can be seen more clearly. Now, what more can we find out about these rays?

Using absorbers is a very easy first start, but perhaps a bit unimaginative. By now we know that magnetic and electric fields produce forces on moving particles, and if there are any such particles among these rays, we could tell rather quickly by showing that a magnetic field affected them. So we move the powder back a little (not far, for the increased thickness of air might absorb our alpha rays) and put in a simple set of channels above the powder. A plate of brass with holes drilled in it, like a thick meat grinder, would do very well. The activity can still be measured, and it is only reduced by perhaps three times, so we can still easily study the electroscope. Now we bring up a magnet so as to put a good-sized magnetic field right by the powder. We see a drop in activity, but rather disappointingly only about a third or less dies out when we introduce the magnetic field. So we do our absorber experiment again, and this time we are most happy, for we find that although there is almost no effect on the alpha rays, there is a complete *removal* of the beta rays, and no effect at all on the gamma rays. Our graph now looks like Figure 10.3. We promptly conclude that the beta rays *are* electrical, we reserve judgment on the alpha rays, and we feel sure that the gamma rays are *not*.

To go on with this imagined laboratory exercise is no longer profitable; the reader can sense that we have reached a stage, familiar to all who do research, where the way to proceed next has become clear, and where more special and elaborate ways to study will be a necessity. Let us describe the end of these, and not go through all the processes. The beta rays are found to be electrons. They are remarkable because the electrons emitted from the powder have all kinds of energies, up to a highest energy, each depending on the chemical element which is radio-active. The energy is more significant than the speed, for the speeds of the electrons are very great, coming very close to the velocity of light. The charge to mass ratio for the slower ones is the same as expected for electrons, but for the faster one it is smaller, meaning that either the charge is less or the mass greater. Since Einstein had suggested that, according to the theory of relativity, the mass of a particle moving nearly as fast as light should be greater than that of one moving slowly, the explanation given is that the faster particles have the same charge, but their motion makes them heavier.

INCREASE OF MASS WITH VELOCITY: "SPECIAL RELATIVITY"

In its motion around the sun the earth travels at a very high speed. This speed, about 18 miles per second, is still very much less than the

Fig. 10.3. A magnetic field bends the beta rays completely away from the electroscope and into the metal plates. The alpha and gamma rays are not so affected.

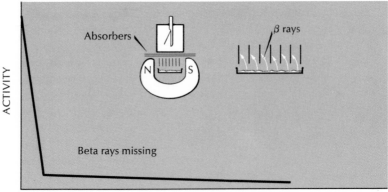

speed of light, which is 186,000 miles per second, but they still can be compared, especially if one has very sensitive instrumentation. In 1898 Michelson and Morley devised an experiment to see whether a light beam going *with* the earth actually went faster than one which went *across the direction of* the earth. They found *no difference:* a strange result, for we might suppose that the motion of the earth should be added to that of light in one case and not the other. On the other hand, the apparent position of a star does change as the earth goes around the sun, which would imply that somehow light is affected by the motion of the earth.

To try to reconcile these findings, Fitzgerald and Lorentz suggested that, for light, the value of distance changes as the speed increases, getting less at higher speeds—thus the light going with the earth did not get as far as was expected.

These ideas were taken by Einstein and developed into a complete theory of *"relativity."* Actually Einstein developed two theories: "special" relativity, which expressly covered the kind of experiment we have just discussed, and "general" relativity, which went further and made more predictions, some of which are now being verified. "Special" relativity makes more of the requirement that the velocity of light in vacuum is a maximum velocity, and, in free space is always the same. The theory predicted that mass will change as the velocity increases according to the relation

$$m = \frac{m_0}{\sqrt{1 - \dfrac{v^2}{c^2}}},$$

where m is the mass at a speed v, m_0 is the "rest mass," which is the mass measured at very low speeds, and c is the velocity of light.

The discovery of beta rays, in which a whole variety of velocities were possessed by electrons, enabled a check to be made on this formula. It works.

The same ideas also lead to the concept that mass has energy, with the famous relation

$$E = m_0 c^2,$$

where E is the energy associated with a rest mass m_0. This relation, which was most startling when first suggested, has also been quantitively verified by accurate studies in nuclear physics.

We have wandered away from our three kinds of radiation. A study similar to that made on beta rays, but actually taking rather longer, showed the alpha rays to be much heavier, slower, and positively charged. They were shown, to a large extent by Rutherford, to be helium atoms with two positive charges. He himself always referred to them as alpha *particles*. We shall discuss them more later.

The gamma rays prove to be very similar to X-rays. In general they are more penetrating, but the difference from X-rays is one of degree and not of nature.

CHEMICAL ELEMENTS AND RADIOACTIVITY

Now while the physicist was using the electroscope to establish the physical nature of radiations, the chemist was also busy. He was able to conduct a set of experiments, back in the tradition of the early work which established the nature of the chemical elements, and each time he conducted an operation—formed a precipitate, or filtered, or heated with acid, and so on—he could check whether the activity followed his procedures or not with the electroscope.

These studies were made on every kind of mineral containing radio-activity, and they revealed two primary chemical elements which are responsible for the radioactivity that naturally occurs terrestrially. These are uranium and thorium. But, as we shall see later, it is not very sensible to discuss "elements," because the nucleus of the atom, with which we are dealing, has variety *within* elements. We do not want to enter into thes complexities until some of the more simple aspects of the process of radioactivity have become apparent. For that reason we prefer to show what can be found if the chemistry of *radium* and its products is studied.

By looking at Table 10.1 we can see the kind of findings that were made quite quickly. We ask the reader to reserve thought about the last entry in the table for a moment. Consider the first two. What

Table 10.1   Transformations Observed from Radium

Name of Active Substance	Kind of Radiation Emitted	Half-life	
Radium	alpha	1600	years
Radon or radium emanation	alpha	3.8	days
Radium A	alpha	3	minutes
Radium B*	beta	27	minutes
Radium C	alpha	20	minutes
Radium C'	beta	1.32	minutes
Radium D*	beta	22	years
Radium E	beta	5	days
Radium F	alpha	138	days

* Examples of isotopes.

are given are the early names for the radioactive substances which were found in conjunction with radium. The two easiest to discuss are the first two. Freshly made radium was found to give off an alpha particle, and at the same time a gas slowly collected, known as the "radium emanation." This gas proved to be quite inert chemically, though intensely active radioactively. By pumping off the gas, after a week or ten days time of collection, almost all the activity of the radium preparation was found to be in the gas. This activity did not stay in the gas, for if one pumped off the gas and quickly looked at the activity of the glass vessel which had held it, the activity of the glass itself was found to be quite high, though it did not last. Patient work showed that a set of transitions was taking place, as indicated, and that each transition involved the emission of *either* alpha rays *or* beta rays, with gamma rays sometimes accompanying either one.

It was also realized, actually quite early by Boltwood, that some of these elements—for example, radium B and radium D—though very easy indeed to distinguish by their radiations, could not be distinguished at all by chemical means. These physically distinct but chemically indistinguishable elements were called *isotopes* and we shall have more to say about them as the chapter develops.

From this work, then, the idea of radioactive transformation emerges. Radioactivity involves the change of one element into another and then on to a third and so on. The manner of change is characterized by the kind of radiation emitted.

RADIOACTIVE DECAY

We can now turn to the third column in the table. It was found that the change from one element to another, which we call radioactive decay, is quite uninfluenced by any agent at all. High temperatures, extreme cold, high pressures, vast electrical fields, various states of chemical combination, all showed no effect. It can best be described by saying that for any one element there is a fixed chance of decay, proportional only to time and not dependent on anything else. Each rapidly decaying element is always rapid in the same way, and a slow element always slow. We can write an equation for this known as the *law of radioactive decay*. It is

$$\frac{dn}{n} = -\lambda dt$$

where dn is the number of atoms decaying in a time dt, n is the number of atoms present, λ is a constant, called the decay constant, and the minus sign expresses the fact the atoms of one element are becoming less in number.

We can make a graph of the above law. It looks as drawn in Figure 10.4. We find one very interesting fact—that the time to go to half any activity is always the same. This is a useful fact, and we therefore designate an element by its half-life, which is the time it takes for the activity to drop by half. The decay constant is large if the half-life (T_H) is short: The two are related by the formula

$$T_H = \frac{0.69}{\lambda}.$$

AGE OF THE EARTH

Uranium has a very long half-life. So long is it that we must measure it by referring to the equation of radioactive decay and directly measure the number of atoms decaying in a known time. Then if we know the number of atoms present we can find the decay constant and also the half-life. It turns out to be 4,500,000,000 years. Now ultimately uranium decays into lead, but the lead from uranium is distinguished from "ordinary" lead, for it has a different atomic weight. Then if we take a rock which contains both uranium and this kind of lead, we can measure both lead and uranium and figure out how long it would have taken for the uranium to decay to make the lead. The result is the measure of the age of the rock, and by studying many rocks and finding the oldest, we can estimate the age of the earth. It is in the vicinity of 4 to 5 billion years.

Fig. 10.4. A radioactive element loses activity as time advances. It constantly loses activity, and the time it takes to become half as active is always the same. This time is called the "half-life."

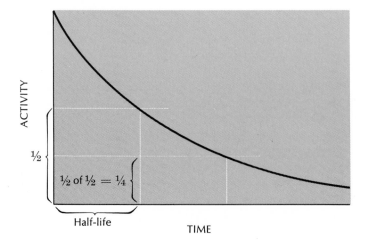

Another quite different way to measure the age of a rock is by means of "pleochroic haloes." These are caused by the inclusion of a little piece of uranium in a piece of mica. All the various alpha rays from any radioactive element have exact energies, the energy appropriate to the element. The massiveness of the alpha particle means that although the energy of a particle is large, its speed may be low. This relatively low speed, far less than beta rays, means that alpha particles lose energy very rapidly, and this carries with it the interesting consequence that each alpha particle from one of the elements in the series can travel a precise distance. A small piece of uranium which is trapped in mica then goes through all the decay processes of the kind we have described, and a whole set of alpha particles are emitted. Each kind travels just so far in the mica, and causes a spherical zone of darkening. In the pleochroic haloes these zones of darkening are visible, and their distance can be correlated with the different energies of alpha particles given off by the whole decay of uranium through all the series. Now radium is one million times more potent than uranium, so it is not hard to make our own haloes with radium in the same piece of mica, and find out how many alpha particles are needed to make the blackening the same. In this way the age of the uranium inclusion in the mica can be found. The result is again, a time reaching into the billions of years.

THE DETECTION OF SINGLE PARTICLES

If an alpha particle is indeed a charged helium atom moving at one-tenth the velocity of light, then it must be very energetic. It turns out to be sufficiently energetic to produce a flash of light in a small crystal of zinc sulfide, a very tiny flash, but one which can be seen with a microscope and with the eye when it has become well adapted to darkness. Such flashes are called scintillations and they are made by single particles.

With the discovery of this method of detecting single particles, a variety of new experiments became possible. One of the most important, done in Rutherford's laboratory in Manchester, led to the idea that the atoms must have a very dense, very tiny, positively charged nucleus, which is somehow surrounded by electrons.

To understand the nature of these most important experiments, it is necessary to know something of their background, of atomic theory as it was in 1908, when they began. All the early ideas of atoms were purely speculative, by which we mean that the existence of atoms was known but their size and even most rudimentary properties were not known at all. One very important lack in knowledge was that of *how many* of these tiny indivisible identical "atoms" were to be found in something we could actually weigh. Between 1895 and 1908 several lines of work had begun to show something about the numbers of atoms— for example in one gram of hydrogen, or 16 grams of oxygen—and from these figures, many of which were derived from experiments by Perrin, it was realized that the atom was small, roughly 1/100,000,000 centimeter across. If it were supposed that the electrons in such an atom moved like the moon around the earth, with a heavy nucleus in the atom, then it was easy to calculate how fast the electrons must be moving, and since they are moving in *orbits,* how much they must be accelerating. This is discussed more fully in the next chapter. We can say here that the acceleration is very big, and so, as J. J. Thomson knew, the electrons must radiate a lot of energy and therefore come to rest having lost their energy. So he dismissed this kind of atom, and so did every one else. The structure of the atom then tentatively accepted was the so-called "plum pudding" atom, in which the majority of the structure was a heavy positive part, with electrons imbedded in it. These electrons were still, not accelerated, and so would not radiate. In Figure 10.5 we show the kind of atom thought of by everyone in 1908, and we also show, in an imaginative way, what a thin gold foil looked like, using these atoms as a basis for our imagination. In the upper part of the figure we show an atom of carbon, supposed to have six electrons. The "dry wall" of atoms at the left is a small part of a thin gold foil. The units of the wall are gold atoms, and each one is positive and dense. Each one has many more electrons, which are negative and so is really much more complicated than the carbon.

Fig. 10.5. The "plum pudding" concept of an atom of carbon and a sketch of a gold foil on the same idea. The atoms form a kind of "dry wall" and are in contact with each other.

Atom of carbon
(old idea)

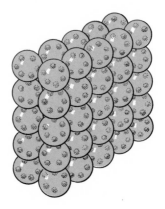

In 1908 Geiger, in Rutherford's new laboratory at Manchester, following up an observation made by Rutherford, showed that alpha particles could go through a gold foil, and that when they did they were hardly deflected at all from their path. There were deflections, as suggested by Rutherford's earlier work, but the angles of deflection were very small. Looking at Figure 10.5, we see that this experiment is very hard to understand. Why should the alpha particle, which is in essence a helium atom, go *through* all those gold atoms without any alteration of its path? Ways around this difficulty can be devised by supposing the alpha particle to be very energetic and the gold atoms to have some spaces between them. But all the ways around the difficulty must follow the observation: they must suppose that an alpha particle is not very much deflected by a gold atom.

One year later, Geiger and Marsden, in the same laboratory, found that, while it is true that alpha particles are not deflected very much by gold atoms, once in a while, one in 8,000 times was their estimate, an alpha particle is *reversed* in direction, meaning that it *is* greatly deflected by a gold atom. This set Rutherford to think about a completely different theory of an atom. His atom had a tiny, extremely dense nucleus, with all the positive charge there, and electrons in orbits at a distance from the nucleus. He is supposed to have gone home, taught himself enough analytical geometry to tackle a hyperbolic trajectory, and worked out his theory in three days. In 1910 the theory was truly bizarre, and it is a bit of a surprise to many students today. He predicted that the number of alpha particles deflected through an angle would depend on an odd trigonometric function of *half* the angle, *raised to the fourth power.* The number deflected, he predicted, would be *less,* the more the energy of the alpha particle, and again this went as the inverse square of the energy. He promptly set Geiger and Marsden to see if this outlandish behavior was found in reality. The apparatus they used is shown, schematically only, in Figure 10.6.

The "source" of alpha particles was a very thin glass tube into which radon gas had been compressed. The glass was thin enough to let the alpha particles through, and a selection of these particles which would go through two holes was made, to give a *beam* of particles, as shown. The beam was directed at a thin gold foil, and as we know, most of the particles went right through as we have shown. They were observed with a scintillation screen and microscope and the dark-adapted eye, and the number of alpha particles deflected from the beam (the technical word is "scattered") counted at various places, A, B, C, D, and so on. Because Rutherford obviously took so much satisfaction in the results which emerged, we reproduce a part of the findings. See Table 10.2. We ask the reader to overlook the odd trigonometric function—

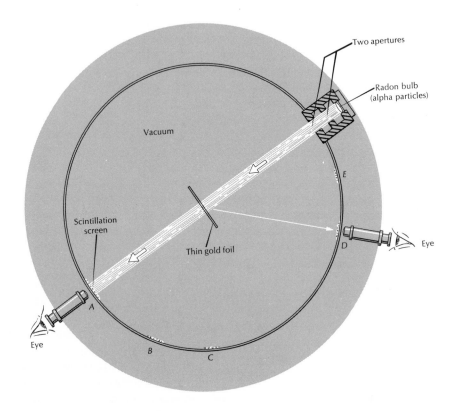

Fig. 10.6. Schematic representation of the scattering experiment made by Rutherford, Geiger, and Marsden. The number of alpha particles in the various directions can be counted by counting the light flashes in the microscope.

like Rutherford, we have given its value anyway—and concentrate attention instead on the way the number of alpha particles faithfully follows the dictates of that strange function: as Rutherford proudly remarks, over a range of 250,000!

We can point out one feature of this table. It shows the data to be found in a pioneer experiment. The agreement is *not* perfect: even a semiskilled scientist can see that there is a systematic increase in the ratio in the last column, except at the very small angle. Nevertheless, the agreement satisfied Rutherford. In his own laboratory he set about other experiments—for example, verifying the relationship for energy, and seeing how different elements behaved. In this lack of perfectionism we see the truly great scientist. Rutherford knew enough to know that his students' data showed a new atomic model to be highly probable. He

Table 10.2

Angle of Deflection	$\operatorname{cosec}\frac{4_\phi}{2}$	Number of Scintillations, N	$\dfrac{N}{\operatorname{cosec}\frac{4_\phi}{2}}$
150	1.15	33.1	28.8
135	1.38	43.0	31.2
120	1.75	51.9	29.0
105	2.53	69.5	27.5
75	7.25	211	29.1
45	46.6	1,435	30.8
30	223	7,800	35.0
15	3,445	122,000	35.4
5	276,300	8,400,000	30.5

knew for absolute certainty that some other totally different lines of work would be desirable: any *one* experiment can often be interpreted in more than one way, but a set of several quite different experiments which all lead to the same conclusion give the feeling of certainty. Our knowledge of the atom is of the latter kind. It can be claimed that in the whole realm of atomic physics there is not one single *definitive* experiment—not one—which, alone, leads to only one possible conclusion. Rutherford might not have agreed with that statement, yet it is true that today we give a totally different analysis of this very experiment, in terms we will discuss in the next chapter. The conclusions do not differ for Rutherford's experiment. But for modern work, with more energetic particles, they do differ.

Perhaps this aside only serves to make the reader insecure. It should not. As soon as the structure of the invisible atom comes under question, there is only one way to elucidate it, the way we have already described—by hypothesis, theory, and experiment. Modern knowledge of the atom involves the convergence on the same structure of several widely different approaches. Rutherford's scattering work we have just described is one, and one which caused a radical change in the thinking about atoms: it is not the only one.

We can now briefly summarize the thinking in Rutherford's laboratory in Manchester in 1910 to 1912. The atom—for example, gold—has a very tiny, highly positively charged nucleus. All the positive charge is there. The electrons are somehow outside, presumably in orbits like those of the planets around the sun. The nucleus is dense; the electrons are very light. The alpha particle is a free nucleus, of helium. It is itself very tiny. So it is no surprise that it goes between the gold atoms, and it constantly encounters the electrons in their orbits, but the light electrons do not deflect the massive alpha particles at all. Rarely, very rarely, the tiny nucleus of the alpha particle comes near the tiny nucleus of a gold atom, and when that happens, the massive gold nucleus exerts a strong repulsion on the helium nucleus and turns it back: this is the scattering which was studied.

THE NUCLEUS OF THE ATOM

At the close of the last paragraph we showed the reason why Rutherford was led to suggest the idea of an atom having a tiny nucleus which is positively charged, very small, and very massive. We shall later see that this atom, and particularly the planetary electrons, posed some extremely knotty problems. Let us enjoy the easy side for the moment, and think about the nucleus.

It is very small. It is so small that if all the nuclei of the earth were allowed to fall into contact with one another the whole earth could be pushed under a card table. It would be tough to push, for its whole mass would be there. Some dense stars are something like this. The nuclear radius can be roughly estimated as follows: if A is the atomic weight of an element (as for example hydrogen $= 1$, oxygen 16, and uranium 238) and if R is the radius of the nucleus of an element, we have

$$R = 1.4 \times 10^{-13} A^{1/3} \text{cm}.$$

This means the radius depends on the cube root of the atomic weight. Thus for hydrogen ($A = 1$) the radius is a number reading twelve zeros after the decimal point and then 14. .00000000000014. It is *small*. Measuring this radius formed part of the early work of one of the authors and perhaps that is why we include the formula.

Because it is small it is hard to get at. If we suppose that radioactivity is in the nucleus and is a property of it, it is easy to see why it cannot be influenced by such trivia as pressure and temperature.

One of Rutherford's students—Chadwick—was able to extend the original experiment of the "scattering" of alpha particles by gold to several elements, and to measure the charge carried by their nuclei. In terms of a unit charge like that of the electron, only positive, he found that helium was 2, copper 28, silver 47, and platinum 78. In the meantime, Moseley, working at Manchester, had shown, by a completely different method, involving the observation of the X-rays given off by different elements when they were used as the positive electrode in discharge tubes, that to each chemical element there could be assigned an integer number, which he called the "atomic number." When the elements were arranged in the order of these numbers, there resulted a table which closely resembled the "periodic table" already discovered by chemists, notably by Mendeleef. The atomic numbers and Chadwick's nuclear charge were the same, and we now recognize that each atomic nucleus contains a definite number of positively charged particles and that that number also characterizes the nature of the chemical element.

To a great extent the subjects of physics and chemistry have had a separate growth. Now we see them begin to converge. Almost everything about the work in Rutherford's laboratory was physical, and almost all the reasoning we have just described is in terms of flashes of light, the repulsion of charged nuclei, and the behavior of alpha particles— not in the terms of chemical reactions. Yet we have just made a startling generalization which clearly applies to chemistry. We have said that each chemical element has a characteristic nuclear charge, and that these charges can be designated by simple numbers, 1 for hydrogen, 2 for helium, 29 for copper, and so on. We shall soon see an even more satisfying relation between the nature of the atomic nucleus and the atomic weights found by the chemist.

RADIOACTIVE TRANSFORMATIONS AS REACTIONS

We can now see that radioactive decay is a form of nuclear reaction. The process takes place in the inner realm of the tiny nucleus, but it is nevertheless a part of an atomic process. For example, the way we write the decay of radium by emitting an alpha particle is as follows:

$$^{226}_{88}\text{Ra} \rightarrow ^{222}_{86}\text{Rn} + ^{4}_{2}\text{He} + \text{much energy}$$

Here we use the convention that the bottom number is the number of nuclear charges and the top number is the atomic weight found by the chemist, or a number very close to it.

For a beta ray decay it would be, for example

$$^{210}_{83}\text{Bi} \rightarrow ^{210}_{84}\text{Po} + \text{electron} (-) + \text{also much energy}$$

Here the old nomenclature was RaE for ^{210}Bi and RaF for ^{210}Po.

Nuclear Reactions and the Nuclear Age

THE FIRST MAN-MADE NUCLEAR REACTION

It is hard to start this subject without going back to alchemy. For centuries the early chemist struggled to change "base" metals to "noble" metals. Chadwick, in starting his chapter on "The Artificial Disintegration of the Elements," in the classic work by Rutherford, Chadwick, and Ellis, spends a page on this subject. According to Aristotle's views, that all matter was made of earth, air, fire, or water, why should not one element change into another? Sometimes it did, or at least they thought so; for example, iron vessels immersed in springs containing copper in the water seemed to become copper. Only the outside was copper, but that was not so easy to prove in those days. The truly staggering amount of effort which went into this pursuit sobers a modern scientist. It is interesting to follow the more recent history of this subject of *transmutation*. As the science of chemistry became established, the firm nature of the elements was recognized, and it is practically impossible to conceive of a nineteenth-century chemist giving more than an idle thought to changing one element into another. When Rutherford achieved the first nuclear reaction, he did indeed change a few atoms of one element into another, and as a curiosity he referred to the older work, and the "philosopher's stone," the agent which would do the job if one could only discover it. Today we have nuclear "reactors" and maybe *they* are the philosopher's stone.

We cannot resist an aside here. Some lines of thought seem to attract humanity out of all proportion to their return to the intellect. Newton spent many years of his life in this kind of alchemy, deflecting that magnificent penetrating mind to the study of unrewarding trivia. We see the same today in the strange interest in "unidentified flying objects." That there are goings-on by groups of earthlings involved with one or other secret projects is quite possible, but some of the interest comes of the belief that these "objects" are visitors from other planets, swooping by our earth. That such visitors would have to encounter the earth's gravitational field, descend through the atmosphere, and then fly by aerodynamically possible means, can hardly be denied, and when viewed in that light the suggestion that these "objects" are such visitors reminds us of the years wasted on alchemy. The process of interplanetary travel is now one we can contemplate with reality, just as we can use a reactor to convert one element into another, and the process does not lend us to believe in silent, oyster-shaped objects, floating in our atmosphere with no regard to the laws of Nature.

To return to the first man-made nuclear reactions. This was achieved by Rutherford with a startlingly simple apparatus. It is shown in Figure 10.7.

Rutherford employed his favorite alpha particles as the agent to produce the reaction. He detected the product of the reaction with a scintillation screen, and the long tedious hours of looking for "particles" he shared with a very good laboratory assistant, G. F. Crowe. The alpha

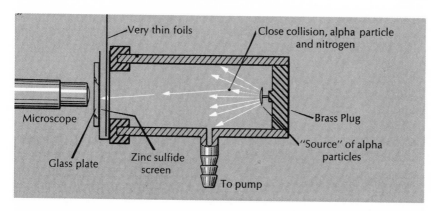

Fig. 10.7. The first man-made nuclear reaction. Very faint scintillations were seen when nitrogen—and not oxygen—was present in the space in front of the alpha particles. Measuring the penetration of the particles that made these scintillations showed they were hydrogen, generated from nitrogen and helium.

particles were produced by exposing a small thumbtack-like piece of brass to radon gas generated from radium. The activity deposited, which is mostly RaB, does not last very long, but then one cannot stay in a dark room with one's eyes glued to a microscope very long either.

The space just in front of the alpha-particle source was filled with nitrogen. This stopped all the alpha particles, and no scintillations should have appeared on the screen. With oxygen in place of nitrogen this was true. But with nitrogen, a few, perhaps ten a minute, appeared. They could be absorbed completely by putting in very thin foils, but these needed to be four to five times as thick as used to absorb the alpha particles. The scintillations were faint and could only just be seen after half an hours adaptation in the pitch dark. After a set of check experiments Rutherford concluded he had altered the nitrogen nucleus and he finally described the nuclear reaction as

$$^{14}_{7}N + ^{4}_{2}He \rightarrow ^{17}_{8}O + ^{1}_{1}H$$

Here was a transmutation: nitrogen and helium had become oxygen and hydrogen. The long-sought "philosopher's stone" had been found; the alchemist's dream realized.

Rutherford showed other reactions also occurred. Examples are:

$$^{10}_{5}B + ^{4}_{2}He \rightarrow ^{13}_{6}C + ^{1}_{1}H$$
$$^{27}_{13}Al + ^{4}_{2}He \rightarrow ^{30}_{14}Si + ^{1}_{1}H$$

It is interesting that in these reactions energy is *released*. In Rutherford's very first reaction a small amount is *absorbed*.

THE NEUTRON

We have already seen that to each kind of element there is an appropriate nuclear charge and that these are in units which are the same
as the electron charge, only positive. Thus if we call the electron − 1,
then we have hydrogen + 1, helium + 2, lithium + 3, beryllium + 4, and
so on.

Now the atomic weights are different. If we list them, as below, with
hydrogen taken as unity—that is, one—both for charge and weight, we
have:

Element	Charge	Weight
Hydrogen	1	1
Helium	2	4
Lithium	3	7
Oxygen	8	16
Uranium	92	238

There is thus an excess of matter over charge in all elements—except
hydrogen. This led Rutherford to suggest, in 1922, that there ought
to be a new kind of particle, a *neutral* particle, like a hydrogen nucleus
but uncharged. He even gave the undiscovered particle a name—the
neutron. The hydrogen nucleus, the elementary positive particle, is
called a *proton*.

In 1932 Chadwick proved the existence of neutrons. For two or three
years it had been noticed that a reaction like Rutherford's did not
take place when the light element beryllium was exposed to alpha particles, but that some very penetrating radiation with strange properties
appeared. By studying the operation of the principle of conservation
of momentum, Chadwick showed that the strange radiation was made
of particles, equal in size to hydrogen nuclei, or protons, but lacking
charge. These were neutrons, and the reaction is

$$\frac{9}{4}\text{Be} + \frac{4}{2}\text{He} \rightarrow \frac{12}{6}\text{C} + \frac{1}{0}n$$

Where $_{0}^{1}n$ stands for the neutron.

The neutron accounts for the fact that atomic weight is nearly always
greater than the nuclear charge. Thus helium has a nucleus made of
two protons and two neutrons; uranium, one of 92 protons and 146
neutrons. The nuclei of atoms are thus composed of *two* kinds of particles, the proton, which is charged, and the neutron. The neutron,
being neutral, has no influence on anything electrical, and the electrons
in the orbits around the nucleus are electrical. So the external part of
the atom is governed in some measure by only *one* of the two constituents

of the nucleus, the proton. Thus the *kind* of the element, in the chemical sense, depends only on the protons and hence the electrons, but not on the neutrons. It is found that atoms of the same element can have different numbers of neutrons in their nuclei. Such variant atoms are called *isotopes*.

We have no right to draw our impression of nuclei, because there is no real certainty about their structure, and besides, in the next chapter we will talk about the "uncertainty principle," which restricts our knowledge of both position and momentum and really prevents us from any detailed drawing. Nevertheless, we think we can convey the legitimate ideas about the atomic nucleus quicker by sketch than by word, so in Figure 10.8 we show an impression of five nuclei. The figure shows four important factors which concern nuclei. The blackened circles are protons, the open circles are neutrons. The range over which the nuclear forces act is shown lightly shaded and the electric field of the protons is shown as lines of force. The nuclear components, sometimes called "nucleons" are certainly in rapid motion, but *how* is not legal to draw. We have shown the existence of motion by arrows, but we make no more claim for the arrows than just that.

Hydrogen is clearly very simple. It can exist in a more complex form, indeed, in *two* more complex forms, one of which is shown. The more complex form we show here has a neutron as well as a proton. The lines of force are the same, and so an electron will not experience any special difference between this form of hydrogen and the ordinary form. The second form is called an isotope: strictly speaking, each nucleus is an isotope; each is a certain form of one element. Carbon is more complicated, having six protons (which is the requirement for being carbon), and six, seven, or eight neutrons. These are denoted as ^{12}C, ^{13}C, or ^{14}C, the superscript being the total of neutrons and protons. The first two of these isotopes are stable: the third is not. Carbon^{14} is radioactive; it emits a beta ray, and when it does, the carbon at once becomes a nitrogen atom.

We see no point in listing vast tables of nuclei. Something like 1,000 different ones are known. Most are radioactive, and this opens a subject we must consider next.

ARTIFICIAL RADIOACTIVITY

In 1934, Irene Curie (the daughter of Madame Curie, of radium fame), and Frederic Joliot, her husband, discovered that bombarding boron with alpha particles produced a radioactive element, with a half-life of ten minutes. Not long after, it was found that neutrons would react with atomic nuclei and produce new forms of radioactive elements. All

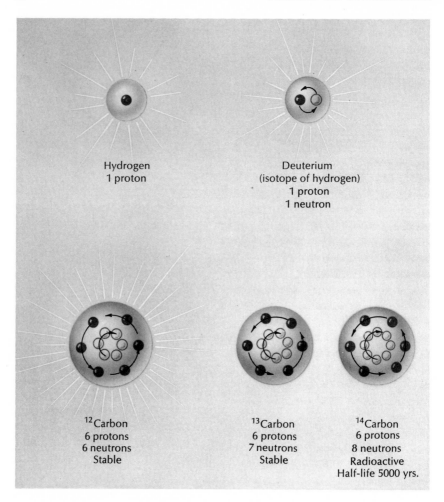

Hydrogen
1 proton

Deuterium
(isotope of hydrogen)
1 proton
1 neutron

^{12}Carbon
6 protons
6 neutrons
Stable

^{13}Carbon
6 protons
7 neutrons
Stable

^{14}Carbon
6 protons
8 neutrons
Radioactive
Half-life 5000 yrs.

Fig. 10.8. Imaginative pictures of some nuclei. The two particles, protons and neutrons, exert forces on each other over a very short range, which is shown as having a spherical boundary. The protons produce an electric field, shown by lines of force. The structure may have various degrees of stability and can be radioactive if unstable.

these forms of radioactivity were strongly related to beta ray decay; they were not all quite the same, but they were definitely not of the class of alpha ray decay. It was found that two light, charged particles were emitted in the great majority of these cases of man-made radio-activity: one the familiar electron, and one a positively charged particle, very much like the electron, except in one literally devastating way, of which more later.

The studies of these new elements, which have gone on intensively since 1934, have yielded the following major concepts. A nucleus shows a very intense binding between its constituent particles. This force which binds the neutrons and protons together is the truly great force in Nature, and the energy which can result from the operation of this force is huge, the only appropriate word for it. At the same time, a far weaker "interaction," a word which disguises some lack of knowledge, acts to convert neutrons into protons or protons into neutrons. The conversion is more than that: it also involves *two other particles,* an electron and a *neutrino* (Fermi's delightful name for the "little neutral one") in the neutron-to-proton case, and a *positron* and an *antineutrino* in the proton-to-neutron case. Leaving aside this sudden spawning of particles and words, at least for the moment, we see a way in which a nucleus that is not as stable as it might be can interconvert its structural elements and gain stability. Radioactivity is that process. Below we write the two essential reactions (n for neutron, p for proton, e^+ and e^- for positron and electron):

$$n \rightarrow p + e^- + \text{neutrino}$$

$$p \rightarrow n + e^+ + \text{antineutrino}.$$

If one of these reactions takes place in the milieu of a nucleus, and the nucleus gains stability by so doing, there will be emitted the two light particles, and we say that *beta decay* has taken place.

The existence of the *neutrino* was deduced by Fermi. It is in some ways the strangest thing in nature, for it has only the mass which is conferred on it by having energy, and it reacts so seldom with anything that in going through the entire earth it has less than a 50 per cent chance of being absorbed and lost. In spite of this elusiveness, direct experiments to detect neutrinos have been made successfully.

An example of a radioactive process is

$$^{14}C \rightarrow {}^{14}N + e^- + \text{neutrino}.$$

We should say something about the positron and antineutrino. These are examples of "antimatter," a theoretical concept first deduced by Dirac. The positron is the "antiparticle" of the electron, and one of the predictions of Dirac's theory is the almost incredible prediction that if a particle and its antipartner meet, they will annihilate one another. When they do, the energy of their mass is released in some form, generally as gamma radiation. This prediction has been verified many times. Antiparticles to the neutrino, the neutron, and proton are now known. They are costly to produce, for the energy given up in their annihilations must be supplied to restore them to our observation. For a proton, this is considerable.

Neutrons, in their way, are as revolutionary as electrons in their potential for exploitation by the inventive mind of man. While electrons interact only with electrical things, neutrons interact only with nuclei. Since, as we have said, the nucleus is the region of Nature where great energy effects take place, we can think of the neutron as the key which unlocks the source of energy. Thus while the scientific revolution occasioned by the discovery of the electron in 1896 has resulted in many devices which extend our intellectual capacity, such as communication, recording, amplifying, television and computing, the discovery of the neutron has extended our capacity in power. The electron has been "around" for about sixty years: the neutron for only thirty. Perhaps the full understanding of the change introduced by the neutron will only become apparent after another thirty years.

While neutrons react only with nuclei, they do so very vigorously. The commonest result of a collision between a neutron and a nucleus is the capture of the neutron. After this has happened the new nucleus is probably not a typical nucleus, and so it may be unstable. The instability can correct itself in two ways—that which we have just discussed, which is the process of radioactivity, and another, the prompt splitting of the new nucleus. This process, which is less likely, is called *fission* and is interesting because it is a relatively violent nuclear change and hence is liable to be closely involved with energy release. Examples of this fission are:

$$\,^6_3\text{Li} + \text{n} \rightarrow \,^4_2\text{He} + \,^3_1\text{H} + \text{Energy}$$

$$\,^{10}_5\text{B} + \text{n} \rightarrow \,^4_2\text{He} + \,^7_3\text{Li} + \text{Energy}$$

$$\,^{235}_{92}\text{U} + \text{n} \rightarrow \,^{140}_{56}\text{Ba} + \,^{92}_{30}\text{Kr} + 3\text{n} + \text{much energy.}$$

It is worth a moment to consider why these two different groupings of reactions, some involving nuclei of the very light part of the table of elements, and the others involving complex nuclei, take place. Among the light nuclei there is one of great stability and unusual character, the nucleus of helium, the alpha particle. Forming this nucleus results in a very favorable arrangement of nuclear particles because the alpha particle itself is favorable. The incoming neutron alters the nucleus and offers the chance of forming an alpha particle. The chance is taken and we can see that in the light elements the two reactions both have alpha particles among their products. Among the heavy elements something else occurs, which perhaps shows well if we look at Figure 10.9.

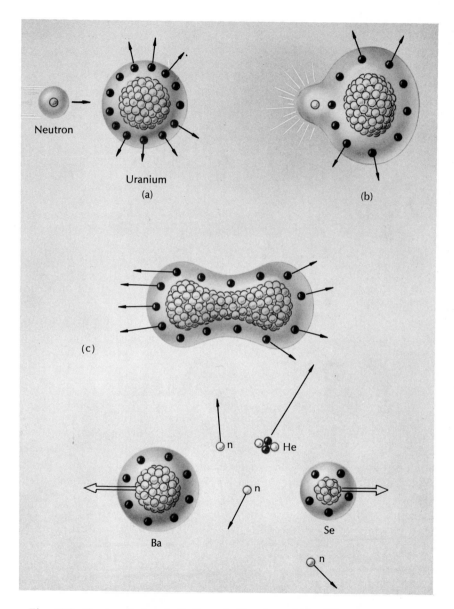

Fig. 10.9. Neutron-induced fission of Uranium 235. The neutron enters (upper left) and starts a distortion of the new nucleus, which goes into an unstable state resulting in a breaking apart.

Here we have tried to indicate the very complicated nucleus of uranium 235. This element has 92 positive charges in the nucleus, a strongly mutually repulsive group. We have tried to show this by the arrows. The neutron approaches from the left, and we have represented it as sticking to the uranium. It will alter the relationships of the nuclear particles when it is captured and there will be a local readjustment, which we have tried to represent. This local readjustment is followed by a distortion of the whole nucleus, which goes into a shape as drawn, and now the repulsive forces between the protons cause the whole to fly apart. This happens in many different ways, and in one of them an alpha particle is formed. (Or at least, as is often the case, we have *supposed* it has.) The two smaller nuclei that result from this flying apart are more stable than the heavy nucleus, and the result is that the reaction takes place with great energy release. The stable products are found to have less mass than the original neutron and uranium, and this loss of mass can be correlated with the energy given off.

In all this adjustment and explosion are there any surplus neutrons? It might be that the forces of nuclear binding would hold them all: *almost,* that is true, but on the average something like three neutrons are found separately from the other 144, two more free neutrons than we began with. It is this generation of both energy and surplus neutrons which has made it possible to develop nuclear reactors and nuclear (misnamed atomic) bombs. Much time is often spent explaining a chain reaction, which is the process going on here, in both the light elements and the heavy. No profound mental gymnastics are necessary. If the *only* nuclei present are uranium 235, then each new neutron can only find uranium to encounter and every time this happens lots of energy and two more neutrons are produced. Since nuclear reactions in a solid take only $1/100,000,000,000,000$ of a second to occur, it does not take long to produce a great many neutrons and convert a great deal of uranium into lighter products. So a big enough piece of uranium, big enough so that the *only* place for a neutron to go is into more uranium, will be very dangerous, as the first neutron will set it off. In the radiation we have described as cosmic rays there are a few neutrons so that such a piece of uranium would receive its first neutron in a matter of seconds. It is, in effect, an armed bomb. This size is what we are talking about when we speak of the *critical mass.* If the size of the piece of uranium is small, then the neutrons near the edge go away from the uranium and do not make the reaction go: they are lost. Below a certain size the uranium is harmless. To set off an atomic bomb a large piece of uranium must be assembled very rapidly out of smaller pieces: in the first weapon this was done by firing two subcritical masses of uranium into each other using TNT in a closed cannon. It was primitive. Much better ways doubtless now exist.

Considerably more interesting than the "atom" bomb is the nuclear reactor. This is much more ingenious and is a very beautiful instrument. Its safety and convenience turn on two elaborations of the above: the first is the discovery by Fermi that neutrons which have made many collisions in material with which they do not readily combine, hydrogen or carbon, for instance, are very effective in causing the fission of uranium. The second is that there exist a very small, but useful, number of neutrons which are delayed a little: they are a freak product of the radioactivity so generously made by the reaction of uranium fission in the reactor. These two discoveries make it possible to design a large reactor, well spread out, with uranium always comfortably below the critical mass, and with space to put in absorbers of neutrons as control devices. Such a reactor is among the safest of all large energy sources. If one "runs away," it usually takes something like hours to do it. Considering the pressure of wartime development, the nuclear industry has one of the very best industrial safety records of all. Many nuclear reactors for generation of electric power now exist. By about 1970 nuclear power should be competitive with coal and oil even in an industralized nation as rich in those products as the United States.

MORE DEADLY WEAPONS: THE CONTROL OF NUCLEAR BOMBS

The temperatures developed in a uranium bomb are up in the billions of degrees. At these temperatures reactions between lighter elements, such as hydrogen or lithium, can be made to go, and when they do the temperature rises still more and more reaction can go. This process— called "fusion," though not for very good reasons—does not have a critical mass, and can take place on any desired scale. Such weapons, often called hydrogen bombs, are fearsome even when compared to the already fearsome uranium bomb. One of these bombs, with fifty times the explosive power of the Hiroshima bomb, capable of devastating a city of 4,000,000, costs about $500,000. This is considerably less than the cost of a single fighter airplane, and probably technology is driving the cost down still further. For the first time in history, mass destruction is far less expensive than construction. The harnessing of the nuclear force for destruction introduces a wholly new element into the use of weapons. This "advance" is not to be compared with past advances. For example, an archer can put an arrow completely through a human body: a bullet does no more. Gunpowder may have made a difference of a factor of five or ten, and perhaps needs less skill. Nuclear weapons involve a factor of *ten million*. No one should contemplate this tremendous scaling up as though it were of the normal type previously digested by humanity: the majestic power of the sun is liberated in the hydrogen bomb, not the skillfully used power of the same kind of chemical reactions we use when we eat our food. It seems to us that the essential element to obtain international control of weapons is already present: the element that *all* parties to the agreement genuinely gain security by making the agreement. Not every one is convinced of the truth of this statement, and this is, to the authors, a genuinely frightening situation.

The Early Moments of the Universe

THE FORMATION OF THE ELEMENTS

We would like to conclude this chapter with something partly speculative and partly sensible. We do not really know how the universe began: some lines of evidence suggest that it started in a narrow region about ten billion years ago. We do not know from whence it came, or of what it was composed in the first few instants. But if we suppose that it began with all the great energy of the present universe in a small region and all the void outside, we can guess that it exploded vigorously into existence. We can also picture the first instants. This is an interesting exercise, and quite rewarding in the conclusions we reach.

The universe must have exploded, or expanded at something like the velocity of light. In a few seconds it would have reached a size as extensive as the orbit of the moon around the earth. In 500 seconds it would have filled the whole space between the earth and the sun. Let us think about it at that time. It will have cooled greatly from the original immense heat it had at the origin, and perhaps by that time the particles which form the precursors of those we now know will have given place to our neutrons and protons. Let us suppose this. At the still enormous temperatures the nuclear particles will freely collide and combine, and as they come within the range of each other's action, all sorts of combinations will have been made. Let us see what will happen to all these. First, those combinations in which large numbers of particles aggregate: wild elements, of nuclear charge in the thousands, will not last long. The repulsion between the positive particles will be so great that the nucleus so formed will be blown apart and cut into pieces by the mechanism we have already seen: fission. This fast adjustment can be thought of as reducing the number of complex nuclei rapidly to the kinds of elements we know of today. Now the second process of "evolution" starts to be seen: the interchange of neutron for proton and vice versa, always seeking the greatest stability. This is the time of intense radioactivity, and billions of years ago the radiation from this must have been impressive.

The final result, or rather the present result, for we are not yet at the end of time, is our set of elements, mostly stable, with a few "holdouts," the naturally radioactive elements. One can draw an analogy: just as coal and oil represent the stored energy captured by life may thousands of years ago, derived in the end from the sun and buried in geological events, so the nuclear fuel we use in uranium and thorium represent the energy left over from the heat and fury of the origin of the universe.

The reader may like to go a little further. As time goes on, the weak aggregative forces of gravity begin to show, and the stars begin to form. He can thus see the following sequence: Creation; then nuclear forces, the strongest, forming the nuclei; the weaker forces of radioactivity evolving them into the present elements; and the weakest force of all, gravity, forming matter into the aggregates we call stars and planets. It has a satisfying sweep to it. Some of it might be right.

Suggestions for Further Thought.

1. Write an essay on Ernest Rutherford.
2. Describe the electroscope. Indicate how it was used (a) to study alpha, beta and gamma rays, and (b) to determine the chemistry of radioactivity.
3. State and discuss the law of radioactive decay. What is meant by (a) half-life, and (b) isotope? Describe two methods by which radioactivity has been used to measure age.
4. Describe two lines of evidence which show that the atom has a nucleus.
5. Write an essay on man-made nuclear reactions.
6. Discuss (a) the discovery of the neutron, and (b) the uncertainty principle.
7. Discuss the problems posed to society by the use of the electron for rapid communication and computation and of neutrons to generate power.

References

Laura Fermi, *Atoms in the Family: My Life with Enrico Fermi* (Chicago: University of Chicago Press, 1954).

George Gamow, *The Atom and Its Nucleus* (Englewood Cliffs, N.J.: Prentice-Hall, 1961).

Ernest Pollard and W. L. Davidson, *Applied Nuclear Physics*, 2nd ed. (New York: John Wiley & Sons, 1951).

Ernest Rutherford, *The Newer Alchemy* (New York: Macmillan, 1937).

*Selections from an Eye-Witness Account of the First Atomic Pile**

An outsider looking into the squash court where Fermi was working would have been greeted by a strange sight. In the center of the 30 by 60 foot room, shrouded on all but one side by a gray balloon-cloth envelope, was a pile of black bricks and wooden timbers, square at the bottom and a flattened sphere on top. Up to half of its height, its sides were straight. The top half was domed, like a beehive. During the construction of this crude-appearing but complex pile (the name which has since been applied to all such devices) the standing joke among the scientists working on it was: "If people could see what we're doing with a million and a half of their dollars, they'd think we are crazy. If they knew why we were doing it, they'd be sure we are."

At Chicago during the early afternoon of December 1, [1942,] tests indicated that critical size was rapidly being approached. At 4 P.M. [Walter] Zinn's group was relieved by the men working under [Herbert L.] Anderson. Shortly afterward the last layer of graphite and uranium bricks was placed on the pile. Zinn, who remained, and Anderson made several measurements of the activity within the pile. They were certain that when the control rods were withdrawn, the pile would become self-sustaining. Both had agreed, however, that should measurements indicate the reaction would become self-sustaining when the rods were withdrawn, they would not start the pile operating until Fermi and the rest of the group could be present. Consequently, the control rods were locked and further work was postponed until the following day.

That night the word was passed to the men who had worked on the pile that the trial run was due the next morning.

About 8:30 on the morning of Wednesday, December 2, the group began to assemble in the squash court.

At the north end of the squash court was a balcony about ten feet above the floor of the court. Fermi, Zinn, Anderson, and [Arthur] Compton were grouped around instruments at the east end of the balcony. The remainder of the observers crowded the little balcony. R. G. Noble, one of the young scientists who worked on the pile, put it this way: "The control cabinet was surrounded by the 'big wheels'; the 'little wheels' had to stand back."

On the floor of the squash court, just beneath the balcony, stood George Weil, whose duty it was to handle the final control rod. In the pile were three sets of control rods. One set was automatic and could be controlled from the balcony. Another was an emergency safety rod. Attached to

---

* From "The First Atomic Pile: An Eye-Witness Account Revealed by Some of the Participants and Narratively Recorded by Corbin Allardice and Edward R. Trapnell" (1946, published 1949 by the United States Atomic Energy Commission).

one end of this rod was a rope running through the pile and weighted heavily on the opposite end. The rod was withdrawn from the pile and tied by another rope to the balcony. Hilberry was ready to cut this rope with an ax should something unexpected happen, or in case the automatic safety rods failed. The third rod, operated by Weil, was the one which actually held the reaction in check until withdrawn the proper distance.

Since this demonstration was new and different from anything ever done before, complete reliance was not placed on mechanically operated control rods. Therefore a "liquid-control squad," composed of Harold Lichtenberger, W. Hyter, and A. C. Graves, stood on a platform above the pile. They were prepared to flood the pile with cadmium-salt solution in case of mechanical failure of the control rods.

Each group rehearsed its part of the experiment.

At 9:45 Fermi ordered the electrically operated control rods withdrawn. The man at the controls threw the switch to withdraw them. A small motor whined. All eyes watched the lights which indicated the rods' position.

But quickly the balcony group turned to watch the counters, whose clicking stepped up after the rods were out. The indicators of these counters resembled the face of a clock, with "hands" to indicate neutron count. Nearby was a recorder, whose quivering pen traced the neutron activity within the pile.

Shortly after ten o'clock, Fermi ordered the emergency rod, called "Zip," pulled out and tied.

"Zip out," said Fermi. Zinn withdrew "Zip" by hand and tied it to the balcony rail. Weil stood ready by the "vernier" control rod which was marked to show the number of feet and inches, which remained within the pile.

At 10:37 Fermi, without taking his eyes off the instruments, said quietly: "Pull it to 13 feet, George." The counters clicked faster. The graph pen moved up. All the instruments were studied, and computations were made.

"This is not it," said Fermi. "The trace will go to this point and level off." He indicated a spot on the graph. In a few minutes the pen came to the indicated point and did not go above that point. Seven minutes later Fermi ordered the rod out another foot.

Again the counters stepped up their clicking, the graph pen edged upwards. But the clicking was irregular. Soon it leveled off, as did the thin line of the pen. The pile was not self-sustaining—yet.

At 11 o'clock, the rod came out another six inches; the result was the same: an increase in rate, followed by the leveling off.

Fifteen minutes later, the rod was farther withdrawn and at 11:25 was moved again. Each time the counters speeded up, the pen climbed a few points. Fermi predicted correctly every movement of the indicators. He knew the time was near. He wanted to check everything again. The automatic control rod was reinserted without waiting for its automatic feature to operate. The graph line took a drop, the counters slowed abruptly.

At 11:35, the automatic safety rod was withdrawn and set. The control rod was adjusted and "Zip" was withdrawn. Up went the counters, clicking, clicking, faster and faster. It was the clickety-click of a fast train over the rails. The graph pen started to climb. Tensely, the little group watched and waited, entranced by the climbing needle.

Whrrrump! As if by a thunderclap, the spell was broken. Every man froze—then breathed a sigh of relief when he realized the automatic rod had slammed home. The safety point at which the rod operated automatically had been set too low.

"I'm hungry," said Fermi. "Let's go to lunch."

Perhaps, like a great coach, Fermi knew when his men needed a "break."

It was a strange "between halves" respite. They got no pep talk. They talked about everything else but the "game." The redoubtable Fermi, who never says much, had even less to say. But he appeared supremely confident. His "team" was back on the squash court at 2:00 P.M. Twenty minutes later, the automatic rod was reset and Weil stood ready at the control rod.

"All right, George," called Fermi, and Weil moved the rod to a predetermined point. The spectators resumed their watching and waiting, watching the counters spin, watching the graph, waiting for the settling down, and computing the rate of rise of reaction from the indicators.

At 2:50 the control rod came out another foot. The counters nearly jammed, the pen headed off the graph paper. But this was not it. Counting ratios and the graph scale had to be changed.

"Move it six inches," said Fermi at 3:20. Again the change—but again the leveling off. Five minutes later, Fermi called: "Pull it out another foot."

Weil withdrew the rod.

"This is going to do it," Fermi said to Compton, standing at his side. "Now it will become self-sustaining. The trace will climb and continue to climb. It will not level off."

Fermi computed the rate of rise of the neutron counts over a minute period. He silently, grim-faced, ran through some calculations on his slide rule.

In about a minute he again computed the rate of rise. If the rate was constant and remained so, he would know the reaction was self-sustaining. His fingers operated the slide rule with lightning speed. Characteristically, he turned the rule over and jotted down some figures on its ivory back.

Three minutes later he again computed the rate of rise in neutron count. The group on the balcony had by now crowded in to get an eye on the instruments, those behind craning their necks to be sure they would know the very instant history was made. In the background could be heard William Overbeck calling out the neutron count over an annunciator system. Leona Marshall (the only girl present), Anderson, and William Sturm were recording the readings from the instruments. By this time the click of the counters was too fast for the human ear. The clickety-click was now a steady brrr. Fermi, unmoved, unruffled, continued his computations.

"I couldn't see the instruments," said Weil. "I had to watch Fermi every second, waiting for orders. His face was motionless. His eyes darted from one dial to another. His expression was so calm it was hard. But suddenly, his whole face broke into a broad smile."

Fermi closed his slide rule—

"The reaction is self-sustaining," he announced quietly, happily. "The curve is exponential."

The group tensely watched for twenty-eight minutes while the world's first nuclear chain reactor operated.

The upward movement of the pen was leaving a straight line. There was no change to indicate a leveling off. This was it.

"O.K., 'Zip' in," called Fermi to Zinn, who controlled that rod. The time was 3:53 P.M. Abruptly, the counters slowed down, the pen slid down across the paper. It was all over.

Man had initiated a self-sustaining nuclear reaction—and then stopped it. He had released the energy of the atom's nucleus and controlled that energy.

Right after Fermi ordered the reaction stopped, the Hungarian-born theoretical physicist Eugene Wigner presented him with a bottle of Chianti wine. All through the experiment Wigner had kept this wine hidden behind his back.

Fermi uncorked the wine bottle and sent out for paper cups so all could drink. He poured a little wine in all the cups, and silently, solemnly, without toasts, the scientists raised the cups to their lips—the Canadian Zinn, the Hungarians Szilard and Wigner, the Italian Fermi, the Americans Compton, Anderson, Hilberry, and a score of others. They drank to success—and to the hope they were the first to succeed.

A small crew was left to straighten up, lock controls, and check all apparatus. As the group filed from the West Stands, one of the guards asked Zinn:

"What's going on, Doctor, something happen in there?"

The guard did not hear the message which Arthur Compton was giving James B. Conant at Harvard, by long distance telephone. Their code was not prearranged.

"The Italian navigator has landed in the New World," said Compton.

"How were the natives?" asked Conant.

"Very friendly."

A Poll of Scientists at Chicago, July, 1945

Four days before the first experimental test in New Mexico, A. H. Compton asked Farrington Daniels, as Director of the Metallurgical Laboratory, to take an opinion poll regarding the use of the bomb. The scientists working in their laboratories at Chicago on July 12, 1945, were asked, one at a time, to vote in this poll by secret ballot without previous discussion. The poll was entirely voluntary and informal. It read as follows: Which of the following five procedures comes closest to your choice as to the way in which any new weapons that we may develop should be used in the Japanese war:

1. Use them in the manner that is from the military point of view most effective in bringing about prompt Japanese surrender at minimum human cost to our armed forces.

2. Give a military demonstration in Japan to be followed by a renewed opportunity for surrender before full use of the weapon is employed.

3. Give an experimental demonstration in this country, with representatives of Japan present; followed by a new opportunity for surrender before full use of the weapon is employed.

4. Withhold military use of the weapons, but make public experimental demonstration of their effectiveness.

5. Maintain as secret as possible all developments of our new weapons and refrain from using them in this war.

After reading the questions, each of the scientists placed a number in an envelope expressing his opinion. The poll did not reach everyone, but all those who were approached voted and the number comprised more than half of the scientists.

The scientists were physicists, chemists, biologists, and metallurgists who had received an academic degree. The results were as follows:

* From Arthur H. Compton and Farrington Daniels, "A Poll of Scientists at Chicago, July, 1945," *Bulletin of the Atomic Scientists*, February 1948. Copyright © 1948 by *Bulletin of the Atomic Scientists*. Reprinted by permission.

Procedure indicated above	1	2	3	4	5
Number voting	23	69	39	16	3
Percent of votes	15	46	26	11	2

The Conscience of the Scientist

Science has, in recent years, brought so many new inventions of great power into our knowledge that the question is often asked whether a scientist should refrain from developing some instrument or other because he believes it is bad for humanity—in other words, whether the scientist has a conscience with regard to his invention.

One area in which this has been questioned most sharply is in connection with the first use of the atom bomb on Japan. An essentially new event in scientific history took place at that time, and it was an opportunity, very limited it is true, for debate on the use of a scientific development before it was actually employed. The historical facts are reasonably available,[1] although some of the great figures involved in it are no longer with us, for example, Arthur Compton, Niels Bohr, Enrico Fermi, Robert Oppenheimer, and Leo Szilard. There is considerable documentation of what went on at that time, and there is not much that one individual can add. However I would like to put in a few pages of my own thoughts as to what really was involved with the arousal of the scientific conscience at the time of the development of the atom bomb.

BACKGROUND OF WARTIME RESEARCH

The employment of scientists for research during World War II took place on an unprecedented scale. In World War I, small groups of scientists had been formed to employ their scientific skills for a few specific purposes, but for the most part they were not so employed, and actually either continued in their profession during the war or volunteered or were drafted into the army. The process by which scientists were slowly brought into the military effort of World War II is probably given as well as it can be in A. P. Rowe's very illuminating little book, *One Story of Radar*.[2] Rowe, who wound up as head of the Tele-Communications-Research Establishment, a very large scientific endeavor which did a great deal to strengthen the position of the British and the Allies during

---

[1] R. G. Hewlett, and Oscar E. Anderson, Jr., *The New World*, Penn State Press, 1962.

[2] A. P. Rowe, *One Story of Radar* (New York: Cambridge University Press, 1948).

World War II, describes how the utilization of radar as a means of defense against enemy attack was slowly brought into prominence and priority, and how this utilization gradually required the services of a wider group of scientists than are normally found in an engineering endeavor. By the time World War II was actively under way, a very high proportion of British scientists had left their positions in universities and were working in three or four rather large laboratories actively designing weapons or counterweapons which could be used by the armed services. They were linked tightly with the military, in a manner most unusual: sessions which in England were called "Sunday Soviets" were held between military and civilian scientists in which there were sharp discussions of problems and projects. This went on to an extent never before realized. The same process took place in the United States, except that they began approximately a year to two years later. In the United States, by 1940, it had become clear that some kind of concerted scientific endeavor would be a very wise and sensible thing in case the nation became involved in war. In addition, it was conceived that our interests were better served by the Allies and not by Germany, and therefore our friendships, scientifically speaking, were to be found in that direction. A loose organization of scientific effort began in June 1940. Phinney Baxter, in *Scientists Against Time,* described this development.

What is of interest here is what actually took place in the life of the working scientists. Between November 1940 and November 1941 a steady stream of scientists, averaging something like thirty to fifty per month, left their normal employment in universities and moved into laboratories working on a variety of things, such as radar, countermine measures, and proximity fuse construction. This intensive move was really mostly scientist-inspired. No real request, other than what might be called a gentle hope, came from the military, and it is interesting that in this period a voluntary scientific censorship of scientific publication began. I was personally involved in this, because I was writing a book on nuclear physics which was intended to be used by biologists and doctors as an exploitation of radioactive tracer work in medicine. To my surprise, I was asked by Dr. Gregory Breit if I would be willing to let my manuscript be looked over to see if anything should be withheld. This was not a procedure requested by any official, but one that was thought wise by the scientific group themselves. It was interesting that the first feeling that scientific knowledge should not be distributed too widely was not imposed on scientists by society, but was thought up and used by scientists, and this at least a year before restrictive procedures were set up for national security.

BACKGROUND OF THE DEVELOPMENT OF NUCLEAR ENERGY

This very intense story of scientific discovery has in it many elements which are almost mystical. For instance, the discovery of uranium fission was not made until 1939, although it had been latent in the world since 1936, when Fermi had been irradiating the heavier elements with neutrons; he had undoubtedly produced many fissions many times without knowing that he had done so. This rather strange and out-of-type behavior, on the part of one of the most intelligent scientists the world has ever seen, resulted in the delay by three years of the realization that vast amounts of power could be released from simple nuclear reaction. It is interesting that it is exactly this time which was occupied by the Nazis and the Fascists in developing their military machine. It is also interesting that Fermi made his discoveries in Italy and that certainly somehow the Italian government would have learned of Fermi's work had its significance been realized. I think that no one can doubt that the Axis powers would have made good use, indeed overwhelming use, of these discoveries had they had them first. The strange fact that a three-year delay took place is really something of profound significance. An equally odd circumstance is that Chadwick and Goldhaber [3] also were looking for energy release involving neutrons, and they looked at uranium in an apparatus in which they felt that the natural alpha particles emitted by uranium would confuse the result and so they carefully excluded these. By doing so they also excluded the really very obvious phenomenon that would have revealed the presence of uranium fission. Thus in two laboratories a discovery that would have changed world history actually did not take place. That there was this period of three years in which the technological change which would undoubtedly influence the whole world was delayed, is a strange and interesting phenomenon.

In the years 1939 and 1940 it became clear that high energy releases from nuclear reactions would be possible. And 1940 was also the time in which the exodus of scientific research men from their universities into laboratories associated with some sort of war effort was taking place. These scientists were willingly regimented, and they naturally worked on what they deemed would be the most useful type of effort for the war. Generally they wanted to work on something that would help the military *now*, rather than to take the long-term gamble on the development of an atomic weapon. Most felt that with enough effort an atomic weapon of some kind might be produced. That the effort and time might be too costly was an often-expressed opinion. All scientists felt that it would be huge and devastating in its potency. A great many felt that the effort

---

[3] Proc. Camb. Phil. Soc., *35*, 731, 1935.

to produce nuclear energy would be well worth while, but that it would not be of such character as would alter the war.

In the midst of this effort there began to be a rather large proportion of what might be called scientific emigrés in England and the United States. They were not so easily employed on the projects which were concerned directly with the military; they had no deep roots in the American or British culture; for one reason or another they were retained longer in the universities than a good many other scientists. They were nevertheless even more concerned over the outcome of the war than were the average American citizens and British subjects, because most were refugee Europeans; a good many of them began to work intensively on the problem of uranium fission and the development of power. Thus it is not surprising that from such a group were forthcoming the first indication that it would be worth while to pursue this new weapon. They were independently convinced of this in England and in the United States, and in the year 1942 their combined effort began. This, incidentally, meant that they pooled their hitherto secret information.

Now the essential interest of all these men, the most important, single-minded drive they had, was concerned with obtaining an atomic weapon, if such *could* be built, before the Nazis obtained it. They realized that in the hands of the Nazis the weapons would be decisive. (The Germans did have the upper hand until the last year of the war, and with this additional weapon that upper hand would have been decisive.) So all-out effort was put on the task. This task could be described, in scientific terms, as twofold: first to see if a weapon could be made (and to be sure that if it was believed that it could not be made that the decision was right), and, second, to make the weapon before the Germans could do so. With this type of incentive there was no difficulty to get scientists to work very devotedly and very effectively—as they did in the years 1941 through 1944.

Those involved had nothing on their consciences at all. They did look on themselves as fighting to save mankind from being conquered by what seemed to them a mentally unbalanced leader of society. They had no hesitation in working as hard as they could.

In the meantime, the course of the war slowly changed; the submarine threat was diminished and almost eliminated; the growing strength of the United States was being deployed usefully; the Germans began to retreat; and finally the war in both Russia and France took a victorious turn for the Allies, and the Germans were defeated. This defeat became certain by January 1945, and at about that time it began to be apparent that the primary purpose of the laboratory, to remove the threat of the Germans gaining the weapon first, need no longer be pursued.

It was at this stage that the high integrity, common purpose, and unity of the scientists in the Manhattan Project, who were working on the bomb, began to show a change. Working as they did, out of contact with the rest of the scientific community, and yet knowing that their scientific brethren were heavily involved in many areas of military effort, they had to justify their efforts both in terms of winning the war and in terms of using their skill constructively. It was clear by early 1945 that Germany could not win the war. It was also clear that the real pressure on the laboratory which had started them working was off. It was clear that the war with Japan would be won or at least settled in our favor, and so a phase came in which the laboratory, though effective, powerful, and still moving with great momentum, had really lost its underlying purpose. During this time the consciences of a good number of scientists began to be aroused. It became clear that a weapon was going to be made, and the scientific group that led the laboratory work began to ask themselves whether it should be used. If it *were* used, what would the purpose be in using it? Would the purpose be the same as for that of a normal weapon? If this were true, then why were they working so intensely? Their intensive work presupposed that the weapon would transcend all others, and therefore they had felt whipped, scourged, driven to get it. Then if this weapon would really transcend all others, should it be used, in the normal way, against Japan? One group thought so. However, the thought crossed many minds that perhaps a new weapon should be used in a new way, and another group favored the idea of planning a demonstration to show how such a thing could be done. Scientists have always been a little naïve about their science, perhaps overrating its impact, but this group really felt that they were dealing with explosive and destructive power so much larger than any previously achieved that a mere demonstration would be sufficient to convince everyone. Quite a group in the laboratory thought that this was the right thing to do. They acted in an unusual way and sent a representation, of which Szilard was the leader, to the Secretary of War, to suggest that the demonstration be put on. A vote was also taken in the laboratory on the subject.[4] It was clear that minds and thoughts were very much aroused. Nevertheless, the one clear fact did remain: the use of the weapon to shorten the war would undoubtedly be worth while. No one could deny that a conventional onslaught directly on Japan would be immensely costly to both sides—in men and in all the appurtenances of war. It is interesting that World War II in a certain sense really never did touch the American nation very closely, though it was more costly than any war that we had fought for a considerable time. Yet if we had had to involve ourselves in an

---

[4] A. H. Compton, *Atomic Quest* (New York: Oxford University Press, 1956).

onslaught on the Japanese mainland at a possible loss of half a million lives, we would have been greatly sobered by the whole effort. The use of the atom bomb very probably did make this invasion unnecessary; it did give us the sense of having won without costing greatly in manpower; and, on balance, it probably was worth while.

In all of these concerns that scientists were closely aware that their work had been requested of them by their nation or by their allied organization, and that they were loyal and effective servants of a cause. As the war ended, however, something new became apparent and here the consciences of the scientists did become aroused. It is often said that scientists have guilt feelings for having developed the weapon. This may be true, but I do not believe it. I do not know any scientist who shows such guilt feelings, nor does it seem to me that such guilt feelings would be natural in a group of scientists that worked in this way. The scientist is all too aware that he only reveals, he does not create. The latent ability to make a nuclear weapon was always there, and someone would have done it if they had not. So I do not think that the word "guilt" in terms of what they accomplished could conceivably be used to characterize the scientist. On the other hand, as the war ended and as humanity began to have to live with this new weapon, one could sense something quite different, something that really was bothering a fairly high proportion of the scientists who worked on the project. These men felt that the whole task had proved to be easy. Not that their own efforts were not extremely difficult, extremely well co-ordinated, and very effectively executed, but that what they had done in three years could be done at anytime by an equivalent group anywhere in the world in not much more than six. Thus they felt that atomic weapons were really *loose* in the world, and what was on their consciences was the high level of security in which the process of making the weapons was hidden. The overwhelming message they wished to give the world was this:

> *Atomic weapons are not just the property of ourselves but can be shared by the whole world.*

Because of security it was not in their power to give out this message. These scientists were also very concerned that this new weapon of giant magnitude should not be in the hands of just anybody. They devoutly wished that the whole development of atomic energy be controlled by civilians and actively worked on by international groups. One does not see in this any sense of guilt, but rather a sense of urgency—that the public should be given a scientific explanation of the truth of what had taken place.

This illustration of the way in which the scientific conscience can become aroused shows, I believe, that scientists will not hesitate to reveal the potentialities of their discoveries. They will not believe it is reasonable that they should hide them, or even that they *can*. Thus, if it is conceivable that we may be able to store memory chemically rather than by learning, or alter people genetically—and all these things are possible—then, even though their efforts may be inconvenient for society, scientists will not deem it necessary to withhold them. They will, however, want to explain what is happening. They will want to present the true relationship of their discovery to society. They will reject a fictional one imposed by some group which is essentially using the discovery for its own purposes. Scientists will resist this, and they will probably resist it in all nations, regardless of the ideology of the political organization under which they live. How effective their resistance will be under various kinds of government is another question.

ERNEST C. POLLARD, 1965

I I

The Electronic Part of the Atom

Our excursions in the nucleus, with all the fireworks of radioactivity and neutrons, has left in doubt the nature of the outer part of the atom, occupied by the electrons. At first it seems very easy to decide the fate of electrons; they must be like the planets about the sun. It turns out that this idea is a curious kind of half truth; it does not contain the whole story. In fact, this seemingly easy way to describe the motion of electrons was cast under suspicion fairly early on: J. J. Thomson rejected it because of the problem of radiation. What has proved to be true is that the electrons are held in something like planetary motion, but that the rules for the motion are different, and Newton's laws alone will not suffice.

First, consider planetary motion. A planet is attracted toward the sun: nothing attracts it very strongly the other way, therefore it must fall, or in other words, be accelerated. How can this be, when manifestly a planet does not seem to fall? The answer is that indeed a planet is falling into the sun all the time, but that it is also sweeping around the sun so fast that, while it falls, it gets no nearer.

This seeming paradox is not really so bad, but to resolve it does cost a little thought. The essence of the resolution is that it is possible to fall while going around, and that at just the right speed you can fall the desired amount by going around and still not get any nearer. Figure 11.1 is designed to illustrate this.

On the left is a diagram of a planet moving around the sun. Let us suppose its velocity around in its orbit is v. Also, suppose that, as is the case for a real planet, the *magnitude* of v does not change. While this is true, its direction *does* change, and, in fact, is changing all the time. Since a vector which changes direction is, indeed, changing, we can see if we can estimate that change. Hopefully we can do more—we can measure the rate of change with time and then have the acceleration.

274

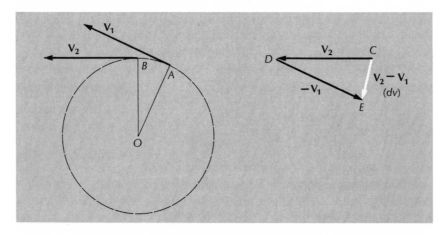

Fig. 11.1. The change in velocity for a point moving in a circle is a vector
directed toward the center.

On the right we have drawn the triangle which enables us to find what
results when we subtract the first vector from the second and so find the
change in velocity. To do this, as you recall, we reverse the direction of
the vector to be subtracted and then add it, so we add $(-\mathbf{v}_1)$ to $\mathbf{v}_2$. Our
rule for addition produces the triangle at the right and the short side
gives us $\mathbf{v}_2 + -\mathbf{v}_1$, and also its direction. It is aimed *toward the center*.
This is exactly what we want: it means that, in response to a force toward
the center, there is an acceleration toward the center. In the figure the
line CD represents $\mathbf{v}_2$ and DE represents $-\mathbf{v}_1$. Then, *on the same scale,*
CE represents $(\mathbf{v}_2 - \mathbf{v}_1)$ We propose to call this length dv. We intend to
remind ourselves that the direction is toward the center.

Now we really also want to know dt, the time in which this change
took place. We can rather easily find this by looking at the circle itself.
We see that, if we say that the time is the time to go from A to B at a
speed v, then if dt is the time,

$$\frac{AB}{dt} = v; \quad \text{or} \quad AB = v\,dt.$$

Now we can use some old rusty geometry. We can easily show that the
two triangles O A B and D C E are *similar*. This means the ratio of any
two sides in one is the same as the ratio of the corresponding sides in the
other.

So
$$\frac{AB}{OA} = \frac{CE}{CD}.$$

Now we note that OA is the radius and CD is the magnitude of the velocity, or v. So we can put:

$$\frac{v dt}{r} = \frac{dv}{v}$$

where we use r, to represent OA, the radius. Then we get, with a little juggling, for $\frac{dv}{dt}$, the acceleration:

$$\frac{dv}{dt} = \frac{v^2}{r}$$

Long experience has taught us that this is one of the most distasteful derivations of a formula in physical science. It is too glib, say critics, and besides, it seems to put something over on us. The body is going around: how can it be falling? How can it be accelerating if it has a uniform speed? This very often proves to be a kind of division point between the physicist and the student. The physicist is aware that his intuition is sharpened by the mathematics, and by the use of vectors and the rules for their algebra: he is delighted by what he finds and he does not need to see it somehow else. Not so the student. He is not ready to let go his purely intuitive thinking and put his trust in mathematics and a formula. So maybe there is a need for some more discussion of this finding.

The only honest thing to say first is that the best way to increase our understanding is to think about what was said and to think resolutely about vectors and the meaning of acceleration. Having said this, we can try to find some other way of thinking which will convey some feeling of reality with it. The most troublesome problem to nearly everyone is the *double* event of "falling while going around." Everyone seems to want to think of either one or the other and not both at once. Yet it is precisely because both take place at once that the events are as we have described. Let us think of one of our space flights. It takes an astronaut about 2 hours to orbit the earth, which is about $3\frac{1}{2}$ miles per second. Now in one second a falling body falls 16 feet. If we draw a straight line outward, representing the astronaut's motion for $3\frac{1}{2}$ miles, we must correct it at the end by allowing for the 16 feet fallen. In the next second the astronaut goes another $3\frac{1}{2}$ miles, but again we must correct it by allowing the astronaut to drop 16 feet. This rather arbitrary way of describing what is happening, obviously approximate, nevertheless will give us a curved path—though admittedly one with steps of 16 feet every second. The reader will not mind when we say that the 16 feet is not stored up for one second and *then* forced on the spacecraft: he will concede that the curving is such that the astronaut describes a circle, and so never gets any nearer to the earth. It would be special, of course, but it could happen. When it does, we have an orbit.

We can say one more thing. The formula for acceleration contains v^2 and $1/r$. We can see why this should be so. The velocity enters twice because the bigger it is the more there is to change, and also the more distance around the circle is traveled, meaning that there is more change of direction. So v^2 is reasonable. The bigger the radius the more gentle the change in angle, so it takes a small radius to give sharp angular change. So we see the radius on the bottom.

Planetary System

We are now in a position to understand how a planet stays in the same orbit around the sun. The planet is attracted by gravitation and the force of such attraction equals the mass times the acceleration of the planet as it sweeps in its curved path. In terms of an equation we have

$$\text{Force due to gravity} = G\frac{Mm}{r^2}$$

where G is the gravitation constant, M is the mass of the sun, m is the mass of the planet, and r is the radius of the orbit.

$$\text{Acceleration} = \frac{v^2}{r} \text{ where } v \text{ is the velocity in the orbit.}$$

So Force $=$ mass $\times$ acceleration, or

$$\frac{GMm}{r^2} = \frac{mv^2}{r}$$

and manipulation gives us $r = GM/v^2$ so that, for a certain value of v, there is a certain value of r. Unless v changes, r does not change. Thus the moon, moving changelessly in the vacuum of space, stays at the same distance from the earth.*

Exactly the same kind of thing can happen in an atom, where an electron rotates about a charged nucleus. If the number of charges on the nucleus is Z, the charge of each (the same as that of the electron, only positive) is e, and the radius is r, then the the attractive force is

$$\frac{(Ze)e}{r^2}$$

---

* The radius of a circle is $2\pi r$ and the time to go around at a velocity v is T, where $T = \frac{2\pi r}{v}$. So we can put $v^2 = \frac{4\pi^2 r^2}{T^2}$, and we get $r = \frac{GMT^2}{4\pi^2 r^2}$, or $r^3 = \left(\frac{GM}{4\pi^2}\right)T^2$. This is *Kepler's Third Law* of planetary motion and it can thus be derived from Newton's Law of Universal Gravitation and Newton's Second Law of Motion.

and, again, force = mass × acceleration, so

$$\frac{(Ze)e}{r^2} = \frac{mv^2}{r}$$

where v is the velocity of the electron in its orbit and m is the mass of the electron.

Again, we get

$$r = \frac{Ze^2}{mv^2}$$

and so long as v does not change, r does not change.

Once more there is an orbit.

EFFECT OF ACCELERATING ELECTRIC CHARGE: RADIATION

The above is very good, and reassuring, but now the question arises: Does the fact that the electron is charged make any difference? It does. It makes a lot of difference.

The extension made by Maxwell, that a changing electric field caused a magnetic field, led him to construct a whole electromagnetic theory. In the process he discovered that an accelerated charge should send out a combined electric and magnetic field, each supplementing the other, and he used this to suggest that light is made up of electromagnetic waves, of a very high rate of alternation. We thus have the important fact that an *accelerated charge radiates.*

This was proved by Hertz, reasonably directly, in 1880, ten years after Maxwell formulated his theory. Hertz used the first antenna, and created in it a back-and-forth surge of electric charge by means of a spark gap. He found that another antenna placed near by gave a spark in "sympathy." This was the first discovery of electromagnetic radiation. The back-and-forth surge of charge must mean that the charge is accelerated, for it travels fast in the middle and slow at the end. This experiment confirmed Maxwell's theory.

Shortly after J. J. Thomson discovered the electron, he too gave thought to an atom based on the planetary system. But he rejected it because he calculated the amount of radiation that should be given off by the accelerating electron in such a case. The amount was so huge that the kinetic energy of the electron, $\frac{1}{2} mv^2$, would become less. So would the potential energy. The loss of two together would cause the electron to spiral into the nucleus, and so the atom would quickly cease to exist.

So great was this problem that, until Rutherford's experiment demanded the presence of a nucleus, no one wanted to use the nuclear atom.

In 1911 Niels Bohr went to Manchester to work in Rutherford's laboratory. He was interested in the theory of the atom, and had begun to concern himself with the way in which the atom emitted light. This subject of the production of radiation, which includes light, was very much to the fore in the first ten years of the twentieth century. A start had been made by Max Planck, who had approached the subject of the radiation given out by a very hot glowing body and had found that he could explain the findings of experiment only by a radical supposition about the way the energy inside a solid body and the energy in the form of radiation were related. His supposition amounted to the idea that radiant energy is in separate and distinct "packets," and that their size is determined by the frequency (the number of vibrations of the radiant waves per second) times a "constant." This constant, universally denoted by h, is called Planck's constant in honor of him. Planck's ideas were startling and rather unwelcome, even to Planck, but they were given impetus by Einstein, who suggested that the same idea could be used to explain how electrons were ejected from metals by light. Einstein's relation worked just as well as Planck's. Into this confusion about radiation, and with these sharp, successful clarifications of certain features of radiation, came Bohr, then aged twenty-six.

Bohr was interested in the simplest atom: hydrogen. He knew that hydrogen gas, when heated or put in an electric discharge, gave out light in certain sharply limited ways. These ways took the form of special lines, of which we say more in Chapter 13. For now we can say that these lines formed several distinct series, the first of which was discovered by Balmer in 1888, and the others later by Lyman, Paschen, and Brackett. Bohr accepted the challenge of finding a way to predict the frequencies of these lines of light by means of a theory of the atom. To do this he decided to use the ideas of Planck and Einstein. In addition, he knew he had to invent a restriction to prevent electrons from radiating in the ordinary way, and that he had to invent a reason for the radiation when it did happen. He developed what are known as Bohr's postulates. Using Rutherford's nuclear atom, Bohr designed the first of these postulates to limit the kinds of orbits which are possible. In addition to the requirement set on the orbit by the attraction of the nucleus, which permits an agreement between speed and radius for any radius, Bohr said that only certain orbits of certain radii, fixed by the relation

$$mvr = \frac{nh}{2\pi}$$

in which m is the mass of the electron, v its velocity in its orbit, r the radius of that permitted orbit, h Planck's constant, *and n is one of a set of integers, 1, 2, 3, 4, 5, 6, etc.,* could exist.

Bohr's second postulate was that radiation only takes place when the electron makes a transition between these orbits. When it does so it obeys a relation very much like that of Planck and Einstein, as follows. The number of vibrations per second, the *frequency*, v, is given by

$$h v = E_2 - E_1.$$

Here we have used E_2 and E_1 to denote the energy possessed by the electron in the orbits corresponding to the integers 1 and 2 in the first postulate. Transitions for 3, 4, etc., are also to be expected. Bohr said that these separate transitions each made one of Balmer's or Lyman's or Paschen's lines.

Using these postulates (and some mathematics which are well within the scope of our readers, which, however, we will omit), he predicted that the frequency (v) of the lines emitted by atomic hydrogen should be

$$v = \frac{2\pi^2 m e^4}{c h^3 \left\{ 1 + \dfrac{m}{M} \right\}} \left[\frac{1}{1^2} - \frac{1}{2^2} \right], \quad \text{or} \quad \left[\frac{1}{1^2} - \frac{1}{3^2} \right], \quad \text{or} \quad \left[\frac{1}{1^2} - \frac{1}{4^2} \right], \text{ etc.}$$

In this formula m is the mass of the electron, e its charge, c the velocity of light, h Planck's constant and M the mass of the nucleus of hydrogen.

Did Bohr's formula work? It can be tested in three ways. First, the term in the square bracket must represent one spectral line. So the various lines must have frequencies related to one another by these very simple numerical quantities. No deviation may be allowed at all: one cannot have "almost" an integer. It is 1 or 2, etc., or it is meaningless. Bohr's theory met this stringent test. Second, there will be series in which the first term in the square bracket can be different. These must be the series found by Lyman, Balmer, and others. They were—exactly. Finally, the big assembly of "constants" in the formula contains not one single thing which can be "adjusted to fit." It must be exactly right: there can be no weaseling at all. This number can be measured with great accuracy by the spectral line measurements. Bohr's theory gave 109,677.50; the experiments gave 109,677.59. The agreement is spectacular.

Just how spectacular is hard to convey. To a physical scientist it is overwhelming. Perhaps we can put it like this. Suppose at the start of the football season someone handed over a sealed envelope with a list of the exact scores of all the games to be played by, say the "Big Ten." Suppose the envelope was opened at the end of the season, and every score in every game was found to be exactly right. To put it mildly it would excite interest. Suppose now, the same "expert" turned to the Pacific Conference the next year, and repeated the same performance. One can easily see that by the third year, when he started on the Ivy League, something would have happened. The most likely thing is that he would have been kidnapped, probably by the professional gamblers, for he would have been able to win a sum about equal to our National Debt.

This is the kind of emotional thought which will convey the impact of this tremendous success at prediction. While the nuclear atom had been successfully proposed by Rutherford in terms of his alpha particle experiments, and adopted by many, the success of the Bohr theory left no doubt at all that the nuclear atom was *it*.

DIFFICULTIES OF THE BOHR THEORY

With this success, attention at once began to be paid to the theory and attempts to extend its scope were made. In place of circular orbits, as described, elliptical orbits, in which the electron can speed up and slow down as it goes on its path, were considered. Great attention was paid to the experimental science of spectroscopy, the measurement of the frequencies of the light emitted by atoms and molecules when they are disturbed by heating or by being part of an electrical discharge. The result was a mixture of great success and dismal failure. A doctrine for explaining spectral lines in terms of several kinds of integers was worked out, and when it worked it was perfect. But when it did not it was hopeless. Gradually it became apparent that there was only success when there was a single electron to consider. An atom like helium with two electrons could be accurately understood if one electron were removed, (ionized helium), but if both were there, it was far wrong. More study and more theory piled up the mixture of success and failure. Patching up processes grew very elaborate and distasteful.

In 1924, de Broglie, striving to make reason out of this dualism, made a suggestion that the error rose out of thinking always of the electron as a particle, a grain of sand, and he suggested that under some circumstances it might be thought of as a *wave*.

WAVE MOTION

To understand this we have to spend a little time thinking about wave motion. It is very familiar. The bathtub is the place to study it. A wave is a succession of crests and troughs, and generally waves move progressively. In the case of water waves the reason for waves is an alternation of energy between kinetic and potential in such a way that the alternation can advance and move the wave forward. Waves can, also, very easily be generated on a string or clothes line. In such a string, the same is true, the potential energy being due to the temporary stretching of the string in the wave. Electromagnetic waves are due to an alternation between electric and magnetic fields. The next chapter is devoted to an elaboration of this discussion of waves.

PROPERTIES OF WAVES

There are two important properties of waves. The first is their frequency. If you watch the ripples hitting your toe in the bathtub and count the number of ripples per second, this is the frequency. It is the number of alternations per second.

The second is the wavelength. This is the distance from crest to crest or trough to trough.

Usually frequency is denoted by ν and wavelength by λ.

THE TESTS FOR THE PRESENCE OF WAVES: THE RAINBOW

From almost the very beginning of physical science there has been a strong influence of geometrical study on the subject. One sees so many of the deductions in Newton's *Principia* in geometrical terms. Nowhere has this use of geometry been more important than in the study of the nature and properties of waves. We will really devote the whole next two chapters to this topic, for the subject of astronomy is so deeply involved with light that it, too, relies largely on the properties of waves. We do not want to confuse the study of waves with the study of the structure of the atom, though they will shortly be seen to be very hard to separate. For now, we want to give the reader some idea of the way experiments were done to show that the electron, one of the new *particles* of modern physics, must *also* be thought of as being a *wave,* a statement which means, to the physicist, that we have to look at the electron in a dual way.

To put it very briefly, and to fix our ideas, we say that the test for wave motion involves the use of a regular array of some kind, through which the waves are made to go, and the study of angular relationships which appear as a result of the process.

The simplest illustration of the way these angular relationships develop is the rainbow. The relationship in the case of the rainbow is between the light from the distant sun, the refraction and reflection of light inside a spherical drop of water, and the eye of the delighted traveler. The geometry of reflection and refraction, one example of which is shown in the insert in Figure 11.2, requires that the brightest concentration of light be at $42\frac{1}{2}°$ from the entering light. The observer must therefore stand with his back to the sun and look up in the sky so as to see light at $42\frac{1}{2}°$. He doesn't have to go to all that trouble, for in a rainstorm there are billions of drops, and the only drops which will send him any of the light from the sun are just those which are at an angle of $42\frac{1}{2}°$. These

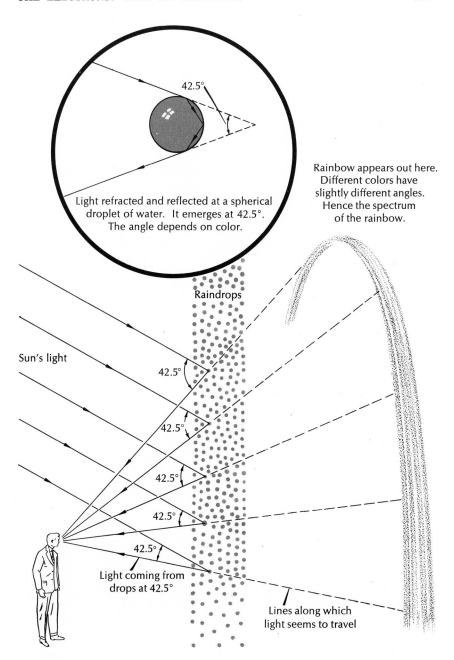

Light refracted and reflected at a spherical droplet of water. It emerges at 42.5°. The angle depends on color.

Rainbow appears out here. Different colors have slightly different angles. Hence the spectrum of the rainbow.

Raindrops

Sun's light

Light coming from drops at 42.5°

Lines along which light seems to travel

Fig. 11.2. The arc of a rainbow due to a fixed angular relationship. In this case the relationship is imposed by refraction and reflection in a spherical raindrop.

form a circle, which is cut off by the horizon, and so we have the arc of the rainbow. Another angle which is bright involves *two* reflections inside and is 52°, so often we see two rainbows. We don't see more because the third and fourth are at angles which make us look in toward the sun, and the light in that direction is too bright for the faint rainbow to be seen. We can do all this splendidly with the garden hose and our thumb, causing a fine spray, and full circular rainbows can be seen. The actual angle depends on the wavelength of light and hence on the color. So the rainbow is colored.

Now if a narrow beam of X-rays, carefully selected to be generated in one way only, is sent through a crystalline powder, a whole set of circular rings appear, as shown on the left in Figure 11.3. Unlike the rainbow, there are many more than two rings, and we have so many rings that we can thoroughly examine what is happening, and why the experiment shows this behavior. The conclusion we reach is that X-rays are *waves;* that they are able to influence the electrons in atoms, and this influence causes each atom to be a new origin of X-rays; and that the regular array of atoms in the crystalline powder gives geometrical relationships like the rainbow, and the geometrical relationships can be exactly figured from the wavelength of the X-rays and the distances in the regular array of the crystal. This is a great deal to claim, but, in truth this discovery of the relationship between X-rays and crystals has been one of the most potent discoveries in the whole of physics. We have to ask the reader to accept much of what we say here on faith. Chapter 12 has more.

The startling, almost shocking, further discovery, can be seen on the

Fig. 11.3. X-ray and electron diffraction. On the left are the rings due to exact angular relationships for X-rays passing through many tiny crystals. On the right we see the same kind of rings, but these are produced by electrons. Thus electrons also share the property of waves.

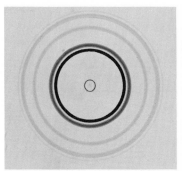

right of Figure 11.3. Here *electrons,* not X-rays, are sent through a gold foil, and we can see at a glance the most beautiful rings, which are obviously in some way related to the rings seen in the X-ray photograph. This experiment, done by G. P. Thomson, the son of J. J. Thomson, is one of the spectacular demonstrations of something new. We need to pause for a moment and take in some background material.

DE BROGLIE FORMULA

We have already mentioned that the inconsistencies of the expanded Bohr theory had developed some sharp frustrations, and that de Broglie had made the suggestion, born of these, that there needs to be a dualism in our thinking about matter: it is to be thought of, not singly, as *particle* or *wave,* but doubly, as particle *and* wave. In the process he proposed that for matter—by which we mean electrons, protons, and so on—there be a wavelength, λ, associated with each item, given by the relation

$$\lambda = \frac{h}{mv}$$

where h is Planck's constant, already encountered several times, m is the mass of the particle we are talking about—the electron in this case— and v is its velocity. This is known as the *de Broglie formula.*

DAVISSON AND GERMER'S EXPERIMENT

In 1926, Davisson and Germer, working at the Bell Telephone Laboratories, were studying the way in which electrons are scattered off nickel. During the experiments the nickel became heated, and it cooled very slowly in the vacuum of their apparatus. This slow cooling proved to be the method by which the jumbled mass of many tiny crystals which had previously formed the piece of metallic nickel formed into one single crystal, regular in all ways. When they looked at the way in which electrons were scattered by the single crystal they found it to be changed, and to show special directions in which the electrons preferred to travel. Once again, the geometric relationship was apparent. They were able to analyze their experimental data in terms of the idea that the electrons had the same properties as waves and they were able to show that the de Broglie formula is able to describe the wavelength of the electrons. They did this one year before G. P. Thomson's very beautiful experiment, and to them goes the credit for the first direct demonstration of the truth of the de Broglie formula.

We must add that the de Broglie formula does not only apply to electrons. It is true for *any* matter: in principle, it applies to ourselves as we walk down the street or fly in an airplane. Only for very small masses does it have any useful meaning. That it works for other particles has been shown for neutrons, protons, and whole atoms and molecules.

SCHRÖDINGER'S USE OF THE WAVE NATURE OF THE ELECTRON

In 1926, Schrödinger, an Austrian physicist, adopted the de Broglie formula into a whole scheme called *wave mechanics*. Schrödinger's achievement is discussed a little more in the next chapter, but we can see the main features of his theory by considering something much simpler than his whole analysis: the phenomenon of *standing waves*. These are very familiar, as almost all musical notes are produced by standing waves, either in a pipe or on a string. Wave motion which is confined in any way results in what are called standing waves, and these produce a selection of wavelengths.

The reasoning goes as follows. If the electron is confined to be around a nucleus (and it certainly is) then it must be present as a standing wave. If r is the radius of an orbit then the length of the whole circumference must be either a whole wavelength, or *two* shorter wavelengths, or *three* still shorter wavelengths, and so on. Figure 11.4 indicates the kind of selection, and really it is much easier to see the process from the figure than it is from a description. For the first allowable orbit, using the word orbit in this special way, we have $2\pi r = h/mv_1$, where r is the radius and v_1 is the velocity. For the second we have $2\pi r = 2h/mv_2$, where now v_2 is the velocity. For the third the relation is $2\pi r = 3h/mv_3$. It takes very little manipulation to see that

$$mv_1r = h/2\pi, \quad mv_2r = 2h/2\pi, \quad mv_3r = 3h/2\pi$$

Fig. 11.4. Fitting de Broglie waves into the circumference of a circle. The pattern of a standing wave must exactly fit and exactly repeat. To do so, one whole wave must fit into a circumferential distance, so $\lambda = 2\pi r$, and so on.

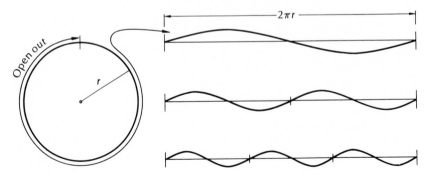

and so on. These are exactly the restricting conditions Bohr made in his first postulate.

Now such a "trick" derivation of Bohr's postulate would not really mean so very much. But the elaboration of the idea into a whole science of wave mechanics goes far beyond this trickery. It provides a solution of the embarrassing problem of two or more electrons, and explains alpha particle decay, field emission of electrons, and many other previously unexplainable phenomena. For this reason, although it introduced some very unpleasant reversals of previous thinking, wave mechanics grew rapidly to be accepted. In gaining acceptance, the ideas of wave mechanics or, more correctly, "quantum mechanics," brought with them some inherent difficulties, some so profound that even forty years later the adjustment which has had to be made seems very hard. But in spite of these difficulties, we have accepted wave mechanics—*because it works*.

We have come to realize that these discoveries in atomic physics have led us to a tremendous intellectual revolution, and some comment on the nature of this revolution is in order.

If we are prepared to say that an atomic particle can have a dualism, that it has wave properties and also particle properties, then we have automatically abandoned exact description of very small things. This was pointed out by Heisenberg, who formulated the *uncertainty principle*. The underlying idea is not hard to grasp. Let us first concentrate on the wave nature of a particle. If we want to know how fast it is going, we need to know the wavelength, λ, so as to apply the de Broglie formula $\lambda = h/mv$. To make any sort of accurate measurement of a wavelength we should have a fairly long train of waves. This long train of waves is just what we do not want if we want to know where the *particle* is, for a long train of waves is automatically spread out and so we cannot say accurately where the particle is. In the same kind of way we may want to measure energy by the relation $E = h\nu$. To do this accurately we must measure the frequency, ν, and so we need many vibrations in order to know how many there are per second. But if we have many vibrations they will take time, and so we cannot accurately measure the energy *as well as* the time.

Heisenberg summed up this kind of thinking with three relationships between "uncertainties," and these relationships took this form:

Uncertainty in momentum $\times$ uncertainty in position　　　$= h/2\pi$.
Uncertainty in energy $\times$ uncertainty in time　　　　　　$= h/2\pi$.
Uncertainty in angular momentum $\times$ uncertainty in angle $= h/2\pi$.

These three relations of the uncertainty principle act to limit our permitted knowledge. The second and third are perhaps easiest to think about. The second relationship says that we can have accurate knowledge of an energy value in any system, if we do not especially care about the time involved in measuring it. Very often, in making spectroscopic observations, we are concerned with the average energy value of a huge swarm of atoms, and we do not concern ourselves with the time events in any one atom. Such energy measurements are capable of great precision. But as soon as we try to measure energy values under special circumstances—let us say for atoms which have been bombarded at an exact time, which we know—the measurement of energy develops the spread predicted by the relation above. Again, if we do not know anything about the angle of direction from the nucleus to the electron in an atom, so that there is great uncertainty about it, the value of the angular momentum can be found accurately.

These ideas were formed by Bohr into a philosophical principle of complementarity, which suggests that there are often two aspects of accurate knowledge, one of which operates to prevent accurate knowledge of the other. Whether or not this principle has any validity outside physical science is hard to say.

In any event, the reader can sense the strong distaste the scientist has for this type of limitation on his thinking. It is only because he gets something in return for it that he is willing to accept it at all. We can briefly consider the gain involved, to make it apparent why this system of thinking is adopted.

In using this idea of the duality of a particle, it soon became apparent that a region which would confine a particle would not confine a wave. So it had to be agreed that this duality would allow the escape of particles from the influence of fields of force into regions where the force did not operate. This thinking was found to give a good explanation for the escape of alpha particles from nuclei, and of electrons from metals under high electric fields. It was noticed by Heitler and London that if two hydrogen atoms were very close together, then an electron could leave one atom and go to the other and vice versa. The same kind of thinking which works for alpha particle emission suggests that this *exchange* of electrons is very rapid. Heitler and London inquired as to the consequence of this exchange according to quantum mechanics and found that this process would modify the force between the two atoms of hydrogen, making it sometimes much more attractive, and sometimes repulsive. Using a principle enunciated by Pauli, to the effect that no more than two electrons can be found in any single energy level, they were able to relate the attractive and repulsive conditions to this requirement. Their work resolved a major difficulty which had essentially separated physicists and chemists, in that they could show the way in which quantum mechanics explained the covalent bond, the bond which ties together two hydrogen or two oxygen atoms, and which operates in the tremendous realm of organic chemistry, among the compounds of carbon. This idea also made it possible to understand the periodic table of the elements in terms of the ways in which electrons can group themselves around atoms of different nuclear charge.

This interpretation of the periodic table of the elements is worth some consideration. It rests upon four ideas. The first is that the nuclei of the elements are made up of protons with positive charge and neutrons with no charge. Only the protons can influence electrons. The second is that the electrons move around these nuclei according to the laws of quantum mechanics and that the most stable condition is that which has the lowest permissible energy. The third is the *Pauli exclusion principle,* which we have already mentioned: no more than two electrons can occupy one fully described energy level. The fourth is that electrons can exchange between atoms if the levels allow it and that forces will develop to bind the atoms together as a result. It is apparent at once that figuring out the way in which the electrons move is the key to describing how any one atom, having a certain number of protons in its nucleus, will combine with others, and so where it should be grouped by chemists. The job is hard: in fact, it has not yet been done, though the computer experts are closing in on it. What can be done is this: we can examine the kind of behavior of electrons in a *central field,* the attractive field of a heavy nucleus, which is like the attractive field of the sun. Then although the whole motions cannot be worked out, it is possible to work out the way the outer electrons behave, at least approximately. These are the electrons which can exchange, and they are responsible for the chemical combination. Doing this, we find that the energy levels are described in terms of whole numbers, each of which is related to other whole numbers by very simple rules. The universal convention is to call these numbers n, l, and m. Then n must be greater than l, and m must lie between $-l$ and $+l$. One would not think these rules would do much for us, but they do. To see how this could be, let us look at the "first" three elements, hydrogen, helium, and lithium. (Because we like to list numbers starting with one, we call them the first three. In reality, they may have been created quite late: we do not know.) Now with one proton in the nucleus, the very first energy level of all, with $n = 1$, is the lowest in energy. We can assume that hydrogen uses it. If another hydrogen comes near, then the two electrons could exchange, because we can put two into one level. So two hydrogens will attract. A third will *not,* because that would involve three electrons in one level, and we cannot do that. When hydrogen combines with one other hydrogen it has a *valence* of one.

The next element, has two protons, hence it will have two electrons to be electrically neutral. If both these occupy the level for $n = 1$, then all rules are obeyed, but no extra electron from anywhere is allowed. So by our reasoning helium should not combine at all. This is what is found. The third element has three protons, hence three electrons. Only two can go in the level for which $n = 1$, so the third must go in the level for $n = 2$. Now for $n = 2$, we find something new about our relationship between numbers. For $n = 1$, we can only have $l = 0$, for n must be greater than l. But for $n = 2$, we can have $l = 0$ or 1, and if $l = 1$ m can be -1, 0, or $+1$. So a richness in energy levels starts. The lowest energy proves to be $n = 2$ and $l = 0$, so that lithium is like hydrogen. It, too, has a valence of unity. Now for other elements the pattern elaborates. It is not our intent to look at this elaboration: all we want to do is to show the reader that very great dividends are to be had from adopting quantum theory. Not only does it unify the fundamental premises of physics and chemistry, it also gives the chemist a firm basis for his periodic classification of the elements, a classification which was at first scoffed at, and which had to win acceptance with difficulty.

Our present position is, then, that quantum mechanics, with its paradoxes of uncertainty, is our adopted basic mechanics. Its character is such that it appears just like Newton's laws if the system is large and of the scale we are used to. As the system approaches that of atomic particles, the new way of looking at the subject takes over. It is a little complicated in one sense, but not so bad in another. Over a very wide realm of Nature it works remarkably well.

HIGH ENERGY PARTICLES

We have repeatedly stressed the idea that the atomic nucleus is the seat of the energy in the atom. The force between a neutron and a proton is suspiciously like that between two hydrogen atoms, in that it, too, shows the property of saturation: protons and neutrons do not attract one another indiscriminately—they like pairs, and if one allows for the presence of two particles in nuclei, one can construct a periodic table much like that of chemistry. This is known as the "nuclear shell" model. The only trouble is that the exchange process cannot be one involving electrons, for if it were, the force would be rather like that between two hydrogen atoms and not of the huge strength we know it to be. With this in mind Yukawa suggested in 1936 that the particle exchanged should be a new particle, of mass between that of the electron and the proton, and now called a *meson*. He was right. To produce these mesons great energies have to be used to perturb nuclei, or one has to look closely at what particles Nature herself sends into interstellar space. Both methods have been used; machines for very high energy now dominate the study. The result has been the discovery, not only of Yukawa's mesons, called pi-mesons, or *pions,* but a rich supply of other particles, which are perhaps being correctly classified and codified today, perhaps not. Somehow these particles fit into a scheme of a world of huge energies, and minute size, the nucleus of the atom, and the realm from which it springs. The study of this subject is philosophically engrossing, as it underlies cosmology and creation. It is also enormously expensive.

THE "MACROMOLECULES" OF LIFE: DNA, RNA, AND PROTEIN

The elements carbon, nitrogen, oxygen, phosphorus, and sulfur each have the kind of electronic structure which we characterized above as "rich." By this we mean that they have various ways of sharing electrons with one another, each representing a firm combination, and yet each different. The element hydrogen can also be introduced in many ways, always firmly and yet always with variety.

Somehow, in a manner only partly understood, a very limited set of these combinations have conspired with one another to develop an enormous regulated complexity which we know as life. Life has great variety, which is perhaps its most striking aspect, and almost incredible unity, which has today become apparent. The unity results from the evolution of three vast molecules, each of which has its own firmness and integrity, and which act in three ways to regulate the formation and behavior of the limited set of smaller molecules we have mentioned above. To describe all this requires an extensive excursion into biochemistry, where we would be very long occupied, but the principles which are at work are more general and worth a moment here.

The variety of living things is not possessed by one species. Flies look much alike (though they differ in detail) and so do people from one point of view. One necessity of life is therefore the accurate regulation of a large set of cells to become a fly or a human being. The accuracy has to be achieved on a small scale, for we are made of many small cells, each quite carefully organized. On this small scale, molecular motions show a randomness which would prohibit the uniform reproduction of the same cell. So somehow it must be controlled. The need for this was seen by Schrödinger, in 1945, and he suggested that life must be regulated by "aperiodic crystals." Today we don't use these words, but we recognize that the gigantic molecules of DNA, made of millions of separate units, whose order is all-important, are the permanent molecular record of the nature of the cell, and of the whole being.

Accurate relationships between these tremendous molecules and a smaller but still large kind of molecule, RNA, are established in such a way that many copies of the RNA can be generated from the DNA. In turn these many copies act to compel the exact formation of large molecules of protein, and these act to direct and drive the chemical processes of synthesis, energy development, breakdown, and change which go to form the biochemistry of the individual. Thus at its very essence, life utilizes the interatomic relationships made possible by the nature of atoms and the laws of quantum mechanics.

Like that of high energy particle studies, this field is elaborate, and it is becoming expensive. It is also concerned with the very basis of philosophy, not so much in terms of cosmology and the creation of the universe, as with the nature of life and the creation of living beings, with the nature of memory, thought, and consciousness. Again, it is not a subject that the research worker is tempted to neglect: rather it is of absorbing interest and excitement. Most of the discoveries described in the last few paragraphs were made in the last ten years. Where we will be in ten years' time is a sharp question. Perhaps we shall have mastered the process of the creation of life. If so, the reader will agree that for every human gain which results from an achievement, human problems will also be posed to society. Thus science has lost none of its restlessness as it has advanced, and the relation of science to society still remains one of difficulty, and one needing understanding.

Suggestions for Further Thought.

1. Suggest a rational place for scientists in society, including a discussion of (a) whether they should be cabinet members and (b) methods of explaining science to non-scientists.

2. Given that the energy radiation by a charged particle is

$$\frac{2}{3}\frac{e^2 a^2}{c^3}$$

where e is the charge, a the acceleration, and c the speed of light, discuss the problem of designing an atom that is like a solar system.

3. Show how the mass of the sun may be computed from the Law of Universal Gravitation, the definition of acceleration of circular motion, and the fact that it takes the earth one year to complete one orbit around the sun.

4. Discuss the Bohr theory of the atom. What were its successes and failures?

5. Describe the reasons why electrons were thought to behave like waves and the experiments which showed wave-like properties of electrons. How is the wavelength related to the property of a particle? What is the wavelength of a man (mass of 70 kgm.) running at a speed of 6.8 m./sec.?

6. Discuss the modern idea of quantum mechanics in relation to the atom and to the uncertainty principle.

Molecular Biology

The content of the last chapter has an important message in relationship to recent studies about living organisms. Because this is so, a short essay on the present-day attitude toward biology is in order. It is an interesting essay to write because, once again, it emphasizes the remarks we have often made about the way science inverts our cherished ideas. Very early in the book we made the claim that no aspect of Nature could be explained by science as it is seen by common sense. In many respects one feels this applies only to the physical world, but now we see the same kind of thinking appearing in the biological world.

One of the first things about the living world that strikes us is its diversity. One has only to look at grass, trees, flowers, insects, lichens, birds, dogs, snakes, bacteria, to see what looks like an enormous variety. This variety is so great that usually one of the first things that the biology student is required to know is a very elaborate and carefully worked-out method of classification. That classification introduces the idea that there is a huge area of diversity. One of the first to dissent from this idea of diversity was Darwin, who suggested, in his *Origin of Species,* that all of the living things we see could have had a common origin and that the diversity could have developed as a result of their modification to meet their environment. As everyone knows, this began a considerable storm because it moved in on the cherished area of religion, where the creation of man was something special and where regarding man as an evolved animal was an overthrow of our thinking.

The storm of the mid nineteenth century has since died down, and in this century, a scientific realization that the concept of a common origin is extremely potent and highly challenging has come forward. To make the point a little more strongly we can consider, in a single human being, the eyelids, tongue, liver, and bone marrow—all of which seem to be very different parts of the body. But we must realize that, with all their differences, in their structure and content the cells which constitute these parts of the body are in reality based on a common essential. They all have the same codescript, better called genetic information, and it is the manipulation of this which achieves the difference between the organs. The cells which make up all the organs are themselves closely related.

The common basis for these forms of life, whether it be between whales and insects and grass, or between eyelids and bone marrow, has been discovered in the past fifteen years. It is today called molecular biology.

The first origin of the concepts of molecular biology that impinged on the author were written by Schrödinger in a very beautiful little book entitled *What is Life?*, which was the substance of some lectures given by Schrödinger at Dublin. He pointed out that if the exact characteristics of a living system had to come from small molecular parts, then they could not come in a statistical way (for there would be too many fluctuations) but had to come in a firm way, and the only firm way would have to be in the atomic patterns which we have already described in the previous chapter. These atomic patterns would necessarily have to be arranged in a manner that was anything but simple, and Schrödinger coined the word "aperiodic crystals" to designate the character of the structures from which living systems would have to develop.

Recently much work has been done in this area of the molecular basis of life by biochemists, geneticists, physicists, and molecular biologists. A year or two ago I characterized these workers in some lectures: "These individuals are not a homogeneous group; they are bound by little more than an intense intellectual fervor; they can disagree sharply with one another, and they accord respect to anyone with the greatest personal reluctance. These are all symptoms of men of science who have suddenly developed sharp insight and who are building a doctrine which will be used to interpret living things for the future, and probably the long future."

As a preliminary to describing the work of the molecular biologists, a very short statement about enzymes has to be made. Almost everyone knows what an enzyme is. It is a protein molecule ordered in a special way and it has a relationship to the contents of a living cell which is highly functional. Any one enzyme will produce a rearrangement of atoms, that is to say, a chemical reaction, which is just a particular rearrangement and almost no other. The chemical reactions are achieved very rapidly and very efficiently and the existence in a cell of something like 500 different kinds of enzymes guarantees that 500 production lines needed for the functioning of the cell will automatically work rapidly and efficiently. Therefore, we can look on the enzymes in the cell as the doers in the cell; they are the ones that achieve the actual formation of the structure, and the growth of the cell will be in direct response to the enzymes that are produced in it.

Let us look at some kind of cell. In our Figure we have chosen the best-studied of all cells, a bacterial cell which, as seen from the outside, has a strange sausage-like appearance with little excrescences on the surface. If we cut it away, as shown in the second part of

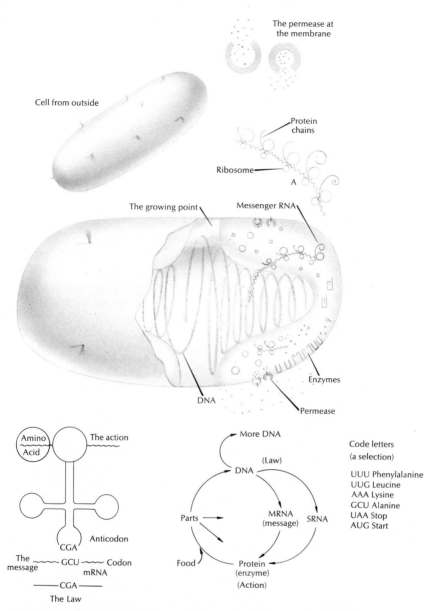

The permease at
the membrane

Cell from outside

Protein
chains

Ribosome

A

The growing point

Messenger RNA

DNA

Enzymes

Permease

Amino
Acid   The action

More DNA

(Law)

DNA

Parts

MRNA
(message)   SRNA

Food

Protein
(enzyme)
(Action)

Anticodon

CGA

The
message   GCU   Codon
mRNA

CGA

The Law

Code letters
(a selection)

UUU Phenylalanine
UUG Leucine
AAA Lysine
GCU Alanine
UAA Stop
AUG Start

The molecular patterns that govern the exact form of cells. This is a bacterial
cell. The center figure shows schematically (that is, not exactly, but to guide
thought) the arrangement of the DNA, the long double molecule that is coiled
inside the cell. This DNA has an exact pattern, and partial copies called
messenger RNA, are made, from which proteins are built. Underlying the
whole process are the exact relationships between atoms, relationships which
determine the chemical combinations and the physical arrangements. Thus
physics and chemistry are at the basis of life.

the figure, we can see the DNA, the long molecule. This is a true molecule, a genuine structure in which the removal of a single atom will produce a discernible change in its properties; it has a length 1,000 times that of the cell, is very thin, is double, in that it has two molecules twined together with a special relationship between them and it has the gigantic molecular weight of two billion. This means it comprises two hundred million atoms. It is moving steadily in the living cell; it moves through a point which is on the surface of the cell, which is called the growing point, and there it is made into the beginning of two daughter cells.

At one side of the cutaway is indicated what is called the process of transcription. Here we see the operation by which the special protein molecules of the cell are made: the doers of the cell. These proteins are chains made of small molecules, called amino acids; they cannot be *any* chains because then we would not have a true cell; we must have our special cell, and our special cell is primarily made by our special proteins. These proteins, therefore, must be made in response to a law, and this law must be executed by, first, the giving of a message, and then, the translation into action. The law is contained in the order of the parts of the DNA, the so-called bases. The message is a transcription of this law into a different but very similar form and the action is produced by the translation of the message into enzymes. What we see is a formation on the DNA molecule of a molecule of "messenger RNA." On this are sets of two little objects known as ribosomes and at each ribosome the new chain of protein is seen as developing. (Insert A in the Figure shows more of this process.) Where the protein chain is most complete it is starting to fold into a very special shape; the folded protein is indicated in the cell. Probably the inner membrane of the cell is the region of most activity and must have much of this protein on its surface. Some of it is shown. The whole cycle of the cell can be seen in tabloid form in the middle bottom insert. The center piece is the DNA, which generates RNA to form the message, and this causes the formation of protein—then enzymes. The cell takes in food, the small molecules from the outside world, and these are made, by the enzymes, into the parts which go into the structure of the cell, into more DNA, more RNA, and more protein and membrane. We have shown the DNA as the *law,* the RNA as the *message,* and the protein as the *action.* Molecular biology has had its startling successes in describing the details of the processes shown in this insert.

The code operates in terms of triplets of three bases in the DNA; these are then transcribed by a firm and rather interesting relationship. The code is made of four "letters"—adenine, thymine, guanine, and cytosine, four bases usually represented by the letters A, T, G, C. Wherever an adenine appears in the DNA there will appear either thymine, in which case more DNA is being made, or uracil, a very similar base which is found in RNA if we are producing message. Wherever there is a guanine we will find a cytosine, always. Wherever there is a uracil there will be an adenine, and wherever there is a cytosine there will be found either a thymine (in DNA) or a uracil (in RNA). With this strange chemical relationship we can build up a system of the law giving DNA; the message, messenger RNA, which contains triplets called *codons;* and then the action, which is by means of what is called "soluble RNA" in which we have the *anticodon.* Our little insert shows a soluble RNA molecule, which is thought of as being in the form of a cloverleaf. The anticodon is on one side and a particular amino acid, a component of protein, is on the opposite side of the cloverleaf. This message is therefore first *transcribed* and then *translated,* and the result is a special, exactly formed set of proteins. These are not all the same, because from the different parts of the DNA, which are different in sequence, different kinds of protein can be developed. In this way precise molecular structures determine precise enzymes and the precise enzymes then determine the precise character of the living cell.

If we examine a section of the membrane of the cell this again shows a remarkable structure. It is remarkable in two ways. The first is that the membrane represents a barrier to materials from the outside of the cell and forms a selective mechanism for what goes in. A schematic suggestion of how this happens is shown in the two protein molecules in the upper insert of the Figure. These are thought of as going back and forth between the two positions drawn, in the first case catching some molecule from the outside, and in the second case releasing it to the inside. This process requires energy, and the cell must be living, growing, and developing in order for this action to occur. In addition to this interesting aspect of the "permease" (the penetration enzyme) we have just described, there is also the aspect of the steady growth of the cell. While the reader reads these paragraphs he has to think of the membrane and the cell wall as actually having grown before his eyes. They grow by the insertion of new protein molecules. New elements of the membrane are being put in almost as he watches. It is anything but a static, inert, simply "physical" system.

The reader who has thought about Chapter 11 may wonder about the operation of the uncertainty principle. After all, there really are only exact molecular configurations if the price of enough time to observe is paid for them. We cannot have an exact energy unless there is a long time for that energy to be observed. Therefore, if the cell is to use exact molecular configurations, it must so function that these are not caught in a fluctuation, so to speak. If they *are,* then an "exact" configuration is not exact. For this reason, the mechanism of functioning of the cell must be relatively slow, in terms of atomic changes, and thus many of the individual processes in the cell must take thousandths of a second and not hundred billionths of a second. This is interesting, because once in a while one see in a strange way the presence of what might be called errors in cells. These errors can be the reason for mutations; their occurrence is very, very seldom but their occurrence is there. It is possible that in the presence of mutations we are seeing in molecular biology the operation of the statistical nature of atomic physics.

It is absolutely essential to living systems that there be the precise conformational relationships of molecular structures. These relationships are definitely and firmly the very basis of life itself. Therefore, if anyone has any question as to whether there is a relationship between living systems and the world of physics and physical chemistry he should immediately forget it; there *is* such a relationship; it is firm, absolute, and completely basic to the nature of living systems.

This leads us to the subject of biophysics—the physics of living things. It is a subject which is just beginning although many people have been working on it for many years, and its essential region of operation lies in the study of the precise structure of living cells and the precise process by which they carry out their functions. Thus if we look at the little insert in the Figure that shows the law, the message, and the action—the DNA, the codon, and the anticodon—we can see immediately that many unanswered questions arise. What is the character of the forces which hold the codon and the anticodon together? This is a problem in physics and it has not yet been solved. What is the actual way by which the soluble RNA approaches and attaches itself to the message? This has not been solved. What is the way in which it leaves the message when it has ceased its function? This has not been solved. All of these causal problems represent the problems of the detailed consideration of physical action in living systems and they are one aspect of modern biophysics.

One can finally ask the question, is the whole content of living systems to be found in what we already know about physics? Does the material contained in this book cover all we need to know to understand living systems? Or are there other principles? We do know there is one other principle, discovered by Darwin, the principle of evolution, by which a living system will change and alter so as to match its environment. Is there more than this? Is there some directed way in which the complicated system will generate form in a surprising way in response to a living principle? This we as yet do not know. One day, with detailed, careful study of the way physical principles are to be found operating in living systems, we may perhaps get the answer.

ERNEST C. POLLARD, 1967

1 2

Wave Motion

"Ever Climbing up the Climbing Wave"
Tennyson, "The Song of the Lotos Eaters."

If we were to look at physical science more like socially conscious
people to wonder what is "in" and what type of group has become
prominent, the advance of the idea of wave motion and its growth
as a dominant idea in physical science would attract our attention.
Waves have, of course, been familiar whenever there is water, and
there is much poetry about them, certainly going back as far as we
can go. Waves are intriguing; they have a kind of life of their own
even though they are not living. They have a kind of durability and
unpredictability which make them interesting, and waves on water
have certainly whiled away many an idle hour for many a person.
For centuries this was all. No attempt was made, in any accurate way,
to represent anything which was not obviously a wave as being a wave
until it became clear that sound must be thought of in this way.
That sound was associated with vibration was easy to establish. Anyone
playing a musical instrument can feel the vibrations, especially in the
low notes, and it is not hard to go from that realization to the idea
that the vibrations are picked up by the air, or water, and carried along
in the form of waves.

How to consider light was for many years a strongly controversial
matter. Huygens suggested that wave motion was reasonable, and Newton,
who perhaps made one of the basic discoveries regarding what we
consider to be wave motion, the discovery of the spectrum of light,
nevertheless considered light to be an emission of particles. Since the
demonstration by Young and, much more elegantly, by Fresnel, that light

300

has the property of interference, which is accurately explained by the inherent nature of wave motion, light has been considered to be a kind of wave motion. From the time of Maxwell and Hertz, light has been interpreted as electromagnetic waves.

Now all these kinds of wave motion are in a sense rational and easy. Wave motion itself is a little subtle, but once one accepts the basic process of energy transfer, and the basic equations, then it is not any problem to see how all the kinds of waves we have described can arise. Modern physics has something new for us, something we have already discussed, and that is the idea that the particles which make up atoms, and indeed any particles, move in a way determined by the idea that they too are composed in some manner of wave motion. This type of wave motion does not arise easily and simply from a previous description of these particles. It is an idea which is just about forced on us by the necessity to find a rationale for knowledge about atomic behavior, and although it may seem to be forcing the idea, yet the power of prediction which results when one accepts this concern of wave motion with particulate matter is so great that one dare not ignore it. So we live with a great new subject of wave mechanics, perhaps better called quantum mechanics, a subject of strange postulates, but great power and beauty.

Because of this preoccupation of modern science with wave motion, we feel we need to give the reader some ideas about it. It is a difficult task, because the subject is traditionally considered with mathematics that become a bit intricate, and it is very hard to do justice without the mathematics. Nevertheless we can try to make some sense out of it.

Perhaps the simplest way to introduce wave motion is to think about a very special case—for example, a long, stretched, piece of rubber tubing. If we take hold of this at one end and pull it to one side, it will stretch as we demand it, but when we let it go it will not just subside back, but instead a little bowed out region will travel along the rubber tube, reaching parts which we did not seem to touch at all. It works even better if we make the pulling aside rather rapid.

This bowed out region is a very simple example of a *traveling wave*. Had we pulled one end of the rubber tubing up and down instead of just to one side once, a more complicated pattern would move down the tubing. We can see these patterns best by dropping a stone in a pond and watching the waves radiate outward from where the stone fell.

Now the origin of this wave motion requires two factors to be present. The first is that a displacement in the tubing produces a force along the tubing. The second is that the tubing itself has inertia, so that it does not stop going when it gets to the original position, but *overshoots* and carries back to the other side.

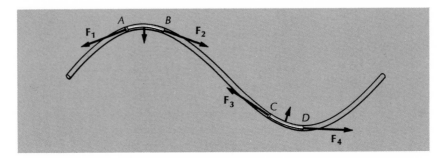

Fig. 12.1. Schematic picture showing how the forces due to the tension in the
stretched rubber tube act to accelerate each part of the tube.

These two factors produce effects which we can think about separately
for a moment. The inertia property is interesting because it guarantees
a back and forth motion of any one part of the rubber tubing, a motion
which will only die out if some kind of way to take energy away from
it is found. The force along the tubing means that exactly such a way
of taking energy away is available: any one part of the tubing stretches
the nearby tubing and makes it move up and down and this creates a
demand for energy which is lost from the first part.

So if we look at Figure 12.1 we see that the little segment of the
rubber tubing, AB, has two forces on it, both along the tube and both
nearly, but *not quite,* opposite to one another. Because they are *not*
quite opposite there is a net downward force, indicated by the arrow
and made clear by the vector diagram in Figure 12.2. The sum of the
two forces F_1 and F_2 formed by the rule for vector addition is **F** and it is
downward. It is also bigger, the more curved the rubber tube gets.

Now Newton's Second Law will work on the little piece of stretched

Fig. 12.2 (left). The vector addition of forces F_1 and F_2 to give a sum **F** which
is *downward.* This force imparts an acceleration to the segment of tubing.

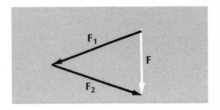
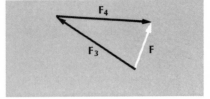

Fig. 12.3 (right). Another vector diagram for section CD. Now the sum of
forces is *up.*

rubber, AB. The downward force will create an acceleration a such that, if we call the mass of AB m,

$$F = ma.$$

Thus the stretched rubber accelerates toward the normal position in a way dependent on F (how strong the rubber tube is) and on m (how thick and dense it is). This will make a back and forth motion, like that of a pendulum, because of the overshooting phenomenon.

However, the rubber tube gets stretched farther along. This means that a section DC is also subject to forces F_3 and F_4. The vector addition of these is as shown in Figure 12.3 and is a force F driving *that section* up. So it is clear that what we start at one place *spreads,* and the spreading process, associated with back and forth motion, is called a *wave.*

We can see one other aspect of this motion which we mentioned in the early part of the chapter but have not made anything of as yet, and that is the property of inertia. The rubber tubing will respond to Newton's Second Law when we let it go, and it will accelerate toward the normal position of the tubing. But in the process it will also gain speed, and by the time it reaches the unstretched position it is going pretty fast, as any slingshot artist knows. What stops it when it gets there? The answer is that nothing stops it: it must stop itself. To do this it must somehow get a negative acceleration, to reverse the first motion, and it does this by continuing along past the center point—overshooting—until the stretch in the tubing on the other side produces the same kind of acceleration, only now reversed in direction, so that the tendency is to return. All the while this is happening a related set of events are taking place at CD and points along the tubing on each side of AB. These events cannot be without influence on AB itself, and they do influence the motion of the initiating point, so that the disturbance we start gets less at the place where it began and, instead, a back and forth disturbance is *propagated* down the tubing.

The authors know only two ways to begin to feel familiar with waves: the first is mathematical; the second is to generate them, for example in the bathtub, or on a clothesline, and watch them. To talk about them with words, which is what we have to do here, though it is the best we can do, is not enough to give a real feeling. The reader should find some way to make them and study them. All the same, without too great familiarity with wave motion we can use some terms and say what they mean. The first is the number of waves which occur at one point per second, which we call the frequency and denote by the Greek letter nu, ν. If we were to take a wave on water as an example, then by watching a cork riding on the waves, with our watch in our hand, and counting the number of times it bobbed up and down per second we would have measured the frequency. Frequencies can be large numbers per second, or very small. The frequencies of sound go from fifty or so to 20,000 per second, where the ear stops hearing them. Dogs and children can hear higher frequencies. Bats use pulses of high frequency sound and guide themselves by the echoes they get back. Good visible light has a frequency of 6×10^{14} vibrations per second. Gamma rays are in the vicinity of 3×10^{20} per second.

Another term of importance, which we have already mentioned in earlier chapters is wavelength. It means just what it says. If one can take a very short exposure picture of a train of waves so that they appear to be still, then the distance from one crest to another, or from one trough to another, is the wavelength. It is usually designated by the Greek letter lambda, λ.

If we watch a train of waves we are at liberty to focus our eyes on one crest and watch it sweep forward. The speed with which it does so is the velocity, and it is not hard to see that wavelength, frequency, and velocity are related. If we watch our cork, then we are soon conscious of the fact that the up and down motion means the completion of one wave, which is then one wavelength further along. So in one second there will be a number of completed waves equal to the frequency, each of which has pressed on by a distance of one wavelength. So the velocity is the number of waves, the frequency, times the wavelength, giving a famous formula:

$$v = \nu\lambda$$

Ordinarily we think of waves as traveling in or on something, which we call the medium. The medium has become less and less important as time and the study of wave motion has advanced. In the case of light, or electromagnetic waves, we think of the medium as space itself, and imbue space with the property of supporting electric and magnetic fields as part of its inherent character. When we come to matter waves, the waves of which electrons and protons seem to be formed, the medium is still less clear and the topic is just not introduced.

Whether or not we think of a medium, there are regions in which the wavelength of a wave can alter, while the frequency need not. This is the case for light moving in any transparent substance: it has a different velocity than it does in a vacuum. The ratio of the velocity in a vacuum to the velocity in the medium is called the refractive index. It is an important feature of wave motion, and is discussed in many different connections, none of which, however, are very important to us. This property of different wavelengths and different speeds underlies the use of the prism spectroscope, essentially first discovered by Newton.

Standing Waves

A property of wave motion which is of the greatest importance to us is the property of forming standing waves. In reality these are by far the commonest which we observe, and are present in quantity at any concert, on the strings of every violin, and in the convolutions of the horns. The sound waves which travel to our ear are generated first by the standing waves on the string or in the horn, and represent a small percentage of the energy being spilled over for our enjoyment. Standing waves are produced in a great variety of ways, of which the simplest is the reflection of a wave exactly back on its path. As the return wave goes back, there is clearly a mixed process, in which the original wave and the return wave are both operating, and one might well expect a considerable confusion. But it need not be so at all. If the two waves, the oncoming and the reflected, are generated very exactly, so that there is always a very accurate relationship between them, the two conspire to produce a pattern which has both a fixed character and a moving character.

We must try to explain what happens, for it is a very important process, perhaps the most important in physical science. We give a diagram, Figure 12.4. It is a hard one to draw and we do not expect the reader to gain more than one point out of it. This one point, all the same, is crucial. What we have done is to draw two waves, and move one one way and the other the other way. Then we have added up the disturbance at the various places at the instant appropriate to the picture. In doing so we invoke a most important principle of wave motion, the principle of superposition, which says that the disturbance due to two waves, or indeed to any number of waves, at any place is the total of the separate disturbances, added algebraically, that is to say, subtracting away negative.

In the first figure it is very easy to see what must happen. If we suppose the waves to be on a string, then the two waves cancel everywhere and the string is without motion everywhere. Now as one moves one way and the other the other way, the string starts to bow, something like the way we have drawn it here. Two points on the string are stationary, because the string is partly up and partly down. Now as the two waves separate still more the string bows still more, and, in fact, at the maximum, it reaches twice the extent of each wave separately. But the stationary points are still without motion, and the interesting result is reached that these points never move. At the same time it is apparent that the place where maximum motion took place is the same, and it will always be going up and down with great vigor. It is the static character of the pattern of motion, which contains some

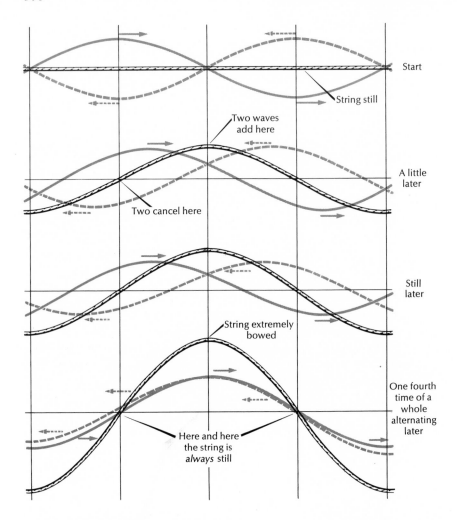

Start

String still

Two waves
add here

A little
later

Two cancel here

Still
later

String extremely
bowed

One fourth
time of a
whole
alternating
later

Here and here
the string is
always still

Fig. 12.4. Two exactly equal waves traveling in opposite directions on a
string. At some places the waves always cancel each other and at others they
produce vigorous up and down motion. The cancellation points are called
nodes and the whole behavior a *standing wave*.

quite stationary points, which has given rise to the name "standing
wave."

The reader will have no trouble at all convincing himself, that such
a definite pattern cannot be obtained unless the relationship between
the two waves is maintained perfectly. The natural question arises: how

can we maintain this perfect relationship in practice? It proves to be relatively easy, on one condition: we must confine the waves in some way. For instance, if we fasten one end of a clothesline and try to generate waves on it we soon find that the fastened end won't budge, and that any waves we want to produce must take that requirement into account. This very simple thing has a very impressive name given to it by theorists, it is a "boundary condition." However, the boundary of the fastened end has the desirable effect of making one guaranteed stationary point on the line, and so forces our operation of wave manu-facture to conform to it. We shall soon find that by managing the way in which we shake the end of the string in our hand, we can develop a pattern in the string, and that this pattern is a standing wave. In the same way, the violin string, which is confined at both ends, can be bowed with reasonable skill to yield a firm pattern on the string, and as this vibration is connected to the resonant wooden box of the violin, which is made from expensive materials and with great care, there results a musical note, which is often pleasing.

In both these illustrations we have chosen a rather adaptable way of producing the waves: in one case our own swinging up and down of a line, and in the other case a bow which can be applied with chosen pressure and skillfully drawn across the string. Both these methods represent ways of producing energy which is in the form of an oscilla-tion, and managing the energy form until it agrees with the proper pattern in the clothesline or violin string. In each case it is possible to tell when the process of feeding in the energy has been properly done: by watching the line in the first case and by the ear of the musi-cian in the second. In the general case in Nature, and there are many of them in which standing waves can be brought into being, the process of feeding in the energy in a flexible way is not so simple, and this has some very important consequences. We shall return to these before long. In the meantime it is important to develop the theme we have just started. A fastened system, like a violin string, stretched across the bridge and clamped at the other end, is an example of a region in which certain standing waves can fit the pattern of fixedness and a vast number cannot. It will pay us to look at the violin string somewhat more closely, for it is a model for all such systems.

In Figure 12.5 a simple version of a violin string is shown. In place of the bridge and the upper end, two fastenings are shown. These remind us that the string cannot move at either end, and so must man-age its standing waves to permit this condition to hold. One very simple way to make this true is shown in the first figure. The string does not move at the two ends but is vigorously moving in the middle.

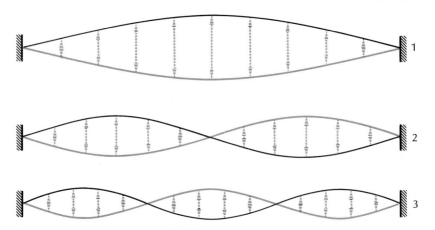

Fig. 12.5. Vibration of a violin string, showing the fundamental and two harmonics. In each case the string must not be moving at the two ends.

This very simple vibrational pattern has a special name: it is called the *fundamental*. If we go back and look at Figure 12.4 we notice that the distance between two completely stationary points on the string is just half a wavelength. So for the simplest kind of vibration of a violin string the wavelength of the wave on the string is double the distance from the bridge to the top. The reader may well think that this is another glimpse of the obvious, and may want to know how this kind of vibration somehow gets related to the sound the violin gives out. It is not very hard to make the relationship apparent, but first we have to know something about how fast waves travel on strings. The speed depends on the tension in the string, tension applied in the violin by the process of tightening the pegs, and on the density along the length of the string, or the mass of a unit length of the string. The actual relationship for the velocity, v, is

$$v^2 = T/\rho$$

where we use T for the tension, or the force in the string, and ρ for the density per unit length of the string. Thus for a given tightening of the peg and a given kind of violin string there is a definite velocity of the waves in the string. Now we have just drastically confined these waves to vibrate only in the pattern of the first figure of 12.5. This means that we have set both their wavelength and their velocity, and this means that the relation

$$v = \nu\lambda$$

will require that these be of only one frequency, ν. This frequency we recognize in music as the pitch, and what we have done by choosing a string, a violin, a tightening of the peg, and proper bowing, is to choose a pitch or a musical note.

In the case of the violin we do not hear the string, or only slightly so; what we hear is the effect the vibration of the string has on the whole structure of the violin, mainly the odd-shaped wooden box, with holes in it, which vibrates in answer to the string, and starts the air vibrating also, which vibrating air is finally the sound which we hear. It is not surprising that a good deal of art goes into the process of making the body of the violin of the right shape, right wood, and right varnish, and with the holes of the right shape for the escape of the sound. Add to this the uncomfortable truth that musicians' ears are very sensitive and demanding, and we add up to an expensive instrument, a long development away from the simply confined string.

Now the fundamental, the simplest way of vibration, is not the only way. In Figure 12.5 we show two more of what is an infinite number of ways of vibration. The second figure is easy to follow once the first has been accepted. Because the only firm condition we must obey is that the string have a static character at each end, we can have completely still points (called "nodes") in the middle as well. In the second diagram we have one such extra node. This means that the wavelength, which is twice the distance from node to node, is now half what it was for the fundamental. But the velocity of the waves is not changed, at least it is not unless we have tightened or loosened the peg. So we have the same velocity, half the wavelength; accordingly, by the relation $v = \nu\lambda$, the frequency is double: we are playing the octave. We can keep on going: the next will be one-third the wavelength, and the frequency will be three times. It will not take much of a struggle to see that the possible kinds of vibration will produce frequencies of 1, 2, 3, 4, 5, etc., times the bottom one, or fundamental. This is an inherent property of this kind of standing wave. The multiples of the fundamental are called *harmonics,* and it is the existence of these which has formed the basis of the whole of music. The musical scale is a modification of the harmonics of a single note, the keynote or tonic, by taking simple fractions of the frequencies of the harmonics, thus the dominant, instead of being $3 \times$ the tonic, is $3/2$ times.

While we are about it, it is hard to resist one more comment about a musical note, which relates to its "quality." In any practical situation it is very hard to evoke the fundamental alone, one always has a number of the harmonics at the same time. If the reader were prepared to draw the pattern resulting from all three of the vibrations of Figure 12.5, there would result a very odd shape, something like that in Figure 12.6. This will interact with the wood of the violin in an even more strange

Fig. 12.6. A violin string with fundamental and two harmonics going at once. The resulting shape is different, giving rise to a different *quality* to the note.

way, and the resulting sound will be different. Sometimes we call it "richer." In any event, the number and relative amount of the harmonics present in a musical note, govern what we call its *quality*. It is interesting that the ear is so interested in the fundamental, that even if presented with a set of harmonics related to a fundamental, but not *the* fundamental, it goes ahead and "hears" the fundamental. Cheap recordings have taken advantage of this many times. This strange power of synthesis is only one example of the way the brain handles sensation. It usually does so in very subtle and often remarkably economical and efficient ways, as modern studies in vision are beginning to show.

MORE COMPLICATED STANDING WAVES

Almost any fixed material thing whose shape is definite in any way can develop standing waves. To predict the nature of these wave patterns is not at all easy, but to show that they are there is often not so difficult. A very beautiful way to show more complicated standing waves is by a device shown as Chladni's plate, which demonstrates the kinds of standing waves that can arise in metal plates. Chladni was a German physicist who lived through the times of Napoleon. He devised the "plate" in 1809. It is very simple, and consists of a firm stand, with a screw sticking up at the center. A square, or round, or oval brass plate is fastened on by putting a hole in the center of the plate and fastening it to the stand. By moving a violin bow across the plate, it rapidly becomes obvious that the plate is "trying" to emit sound, and the pattern of vibration of the plate can be shown by shaking light sand on to the plate. The nodes do not move, while the rest of the plate does, and the result is that the sand rapidly travels to the nodes and reveals the pattern which they form. By bowing skillfully, various fundamental modes of vibration can be produced and it is not hard to show the existence of the harmonics. This very beautiful device should be seen, and indeed heard, but in default of that, a few patterns are shown in Figure 12.7.

Mathematical Ways to Look at Wave Motion

A little earlier we said that one way to become familiar with waves was mathematical. We do not intend to inflict the mathematics on the the reader, but it is worth a moment to see why mathematics might be worth some effort in understanding waves. Take waves on a string—for example, the type we discussed on the rubber hose. There is a relationship between the distortion of the hose and the acceleration of the hose. The distortion is concerned with the behavior of neighboring parts of the hose, and the result is a regular geometrical sweep along the hose, which we call a wave. So we ask ourselves whether we can devise mathematical ways to represent the acceleration and the distortion, and we soon find that we can. Next we ask whether we can find the consequence of Newton's laws operating between the two, and we can. When we do, we find that we can develop a relatively simple equation that portrays an endless alternation in terms of time and distance. With it we can predict the velocity of the waves, and we can produce mathematical expressions for the standing waves we have dis-

Fig. 12.7. Vibrational patterns of metal plates as seen using Chladni's device. The sand comes to rest along the lines of *no* vibration.

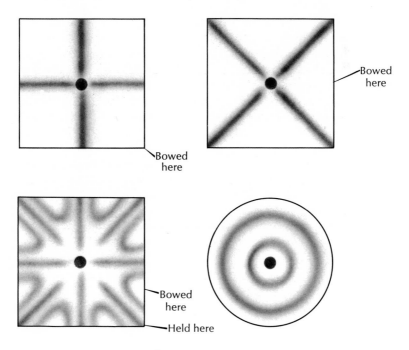

cussed. All these ideas are found to be summarized in a *wave equation,* simple to a mathematician, but not appropriate here.

Among the kinds of waves treated in mathematical theory are sound waves, waves on water, a myriad kind of waves in solids, all worked out beautifully by Rayleigh. All the forms seen in Chladni's plate can be explained by elaborate mathematics, using special forms of "functions," which one might have thought would be buried in highly specialized mathematics texts. By assuming light to obey this relation, one can make remarkable predictions of what should—and does—happen when light encounters various obstacles, some of them most surprising—for example, that the very center of the shadow cast by a penny, using a bright point source light, is as bright as if the penny were not there. This surprising prediction was made by Fresnel and Poisson and it seemed so obviously wrong that no one wanted to try it. It turns out to be true.

Maxwell, when he made the suggestion regarding the need for a changing electric field to produce a magnetic field, was able to show that the two fields of electricity and magnetism conspired to produce this kind of wave equation, and suggested that light is the wave motion made by that kind of mutual dependency, or as we now put it, light is electromagnetic radiation. His equation came out in terms of the units of measurement of electricity and magnetism, as one might suspect it must, and for the theory to work, a ratio of these units was required to be the velocity of light. It was found to be so, and this was one of the spectacular successes of theory of all time.

The greatest surprise of all in connection with the wave equation must be credited to Schrödinger. We have already discussed this in Chapter 11. Using the two ideas of modern physics developed by Planck and de Broglie, that there is a relationship between energy and frequency, of the form energy $= h \times$ frequency, and between velocity and wavelength of the form wavelength $= h/mv$, Schrödinger set out to include them into an equation of the form of the wave equation. It proved not to be hard, for it is not very complicated to assemble trial forms of the wave equation which will do what is wanted: that is, automatically give Planck's and de Broglie's relationships. Schrödinger worked one of these out, and then began one of the most astonishingly successful exploitations of a trial idea in the history of science. He did not really know what the waves were of: he designated this unknown quantity ψ, and proceeded to follow the well-tried path of Rayleigh, using many of the same results, the same mathematical functions, and indeed, the same mathematical techniques. And, in rapid succession, the hitherto unexplainable difficulties of the Bohr theory, were overcome. A basis for the unknown, ψ, even more obscure than lack of knowledge, was given by Max Born, who suggested that ψ^2 be considered as a way to measure the probability of finding an atomic particle where it was sought. This idea proved to be a powerful means of suggesting the way to make the theory complete and mathematically unassailable: the subject of "Qantum Mechanics" was founded.

This extension of the idea of wave properties into the realm of matter itself provoked one of the greatest intellectual explosions of all time. Talented and young theoretical physicists, among them Heitler, Dirac, Fermi, Pauli, and Heisenberg, took on the job of developing and extending the theory, always with startling and gratifying success. Here is a partial list of their achievements:

The explanation of the curious energy values of an atom with two electrons, which had not been intelligible by the Bohr theory.

The explanation of the covalent bond, the bond between two atoms of hydrogen, for example. This ended a long-standing "feud" between theoretical physics and theoretical chemistry, and really has begun a strong unifying trend in physical science.

The explanation of alpha particle emission.

The melding of the theory above with Einstein's special theory of relativity, which led to the subject of "quantum electrodynamics," and to the discovery of "antimatter," first seen as the positron, and also followed by a whole range of new particles, starting with the mesons.

The development of an adequate theory of the solid state, in which paradoxes regarding heat and electrical behavior were understood.

A good start toward understanding the structure and energy relationships of the atomic nucleus.

A good understanding of the way in which all kinds of radiation interact with matter, including a very wide range of energies.

These successes have been so sensational to those working in each of these areas of speciality, that the phrase "almost mystical," used previously, is not badly used. One has to imagine the feeling of a hardworking, competent, imaginative individual like Sommerfeld, who developed many of the more elaborate forms of the Bohr theory, or indeed, of Bohr himself, when the strange "stretchings" of theory, the approximations which worked only a little better, were found to be unnecessary, and instead, with clear beginnings, easily applied postulates, and already developed mathematics, exact solutions were found which fitted experiment precisely. Nearly all the advances mentioned in the previous paragraph were made in five years, many of them by theorists who had not yet reached the age of thirty. Nearly all of them are still living. The words "intellectual explosion" are justified.

To wind up this short account of what is obviously a very considerable topic, we would like to say, as sharply as possible, what impresses us about this subject of wave motion and its strangely basic relationship to the description of matter and radiation. The first impression is the tremendous illustration of what we have called "the growth of complexity." While these ideas are really not elaborate, and the theory which emerges from them not hard in terms of its mastery by competent scientists, yet it contains in its simple premises the power of yielding vast complexity. An ordinary pine tree issues a kind of challenge to us. How do Dirac, Schrödinger, and company tell us what that tree is all about? The answer is that, so far, they cannot: we still have something to find out about that tree. But that answer is too glib. Modern atomic and molecular theory does make a start on telling us about the tree. First, if we talk to the biologist, he will admit that the tree is not only made of many separate cells, but the tree *began* from one cell. And he will also say that the one starting cell had a majority of what really matters about the tree in it. So we can strip some of the complexity out of a tree and ask about something simpler. And if we talk to the cytologist, he will say that a cell, in turn, has a "molecular biology," which governs its development: a relatively small number of molecules have the ability to determine the way the cell will develop. So we are down one level less in complexity. Are we down to a level such that the ideas of modern physical science, of Dirac and Schrödinger, can explain and predict what the molecular biology of a cell will do? Some say "yes," some say "maybe." Whatever one says, the startling thought appears, that it is not *ridiculous* to think of tracing the regular behavior of the confined system of atoms, through the still regular but more complex behavior of molecules, to the formation of cells and the development of a tree.

The second impression we cannot ignore is that the patterns of atomic form, like the patterns of Chladni's plate, have an interest and an appeal to them: they are certainly good starting motifs for a design. So far, the only patterns we can attempt to draw are the very simplest, the most repetitious. The patterns of even a simple molecule are much more subtle. If they represent the underlying formative patterns of all things, then surely it is not absurd to believe that, to some truly perceptive individuals, they have great beauty.

The third thought is that none of this theory, in the honest sense of the word, is contrived. To many it must seem so, and to many men of science it did seem so. But no one sought to contrive it for its own sake. Actually, the notion that such equations could describe the behavior of matter was met with a storm of protest. Only as the theory began to explain, suggest, and predict, was it accepted. Because it is not contrived, and because it has a sharpness of concept and a definitely mathematical origin, one is led to the idea that it is truly suggestive of the real character of Nature. It is not what we would have expected, but all through all the other chapters our burden has been that the physical scientist has had to explain reality in contradiction to observation and common sense. Perhaps, then, the sharpest thing we have to say is that nowhere near enough of us humans are thinking in the terms of the ideas in this chapter. Far from rebelling at the use of abstraction and symbolic representation, we should be cultivating it, developing it, sensing the beauty in it, and trying to see where else in understanding Nature we can use it. Perhaps the successes have only just begun.

Suggestions for Further Thought.

1. Briefly describe the nature of wave motion, with particular reference to standing waves.
2. Find the frequency of (a) a radio wave of 20 cm. wavelength and (b) blue light with 4000 Å wavelength.
3. It is claimed that abstract thinking is necessary to penetrate the nature of the "unseen real world." Discuss and illustrate this point.

Reference

Louis de Broglie, *Matter and Light: The New Physics* (New York: Dover Publications, 1955).

13
Spectroscopy, Atoms And Stars

Very early in the text we gave a quotation from Lord Kelvin, about the power of expressing knowledge in numbers. One branch of physical science has succeeded in doing this with a very high degree of accuracy. The authors can recall eloquent presentations by Professors Rabi and Kusch, two Nobel prize winners, in which measurements, precise to many decimal figures, were described. Both showed their keen sense of satisfaction with the whole process, indeed, their sense of the power of decision such numbers gave them, and also the scientific beauty of the whole story. This branch of physical science, which has achieved this great power, can be described broadly as *spectroscopy*.

Measuring Wavelength, or Frequency

In Chapter 12 we introduced the subject of waves, and we pointed out that a wave is described by a frequency of oscillations per second and a wavelength between crests. If we know the kind of wave we are dealing with—for example, light, which is an electromagnetic wave—then to characterize the wave we need only to know one of these. If we know, for example, the wavelength, then we can find the frequency. How can we measure such a wavelength, specially if it is very tiny?

The first useful, accurate way of making this kind of measurement was devised by Fraunhofer, about 1820. Fraunhofer was a German physicist, keenly interested in the nature of the light from the sun. After it became clear, from the suggestions of Huygens and the work of Young and Fresnel, that light is a form of wave motion, Fraunhofer devised an instrument known as a "diffraction grating," which can be understood from Figure 13.1. Before consulting the figure we should recall one or two points about wave motion. The first is the principle of superposition, which says that the disturbance due to two or more waves at any point is

316

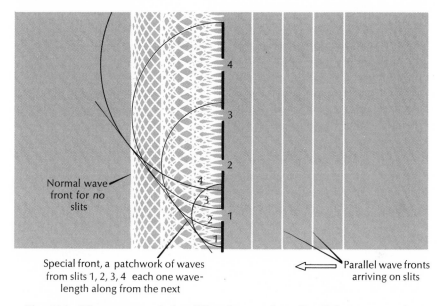

Normal wave front for *no* slits

Special front, a patchwork of waves from slits 1, 2, 3, 4 each one wave-length along from the next

Parallel wave fronts arriving on slits

Fig. 13.1. The concept of the diffraction grating. Parallel waves are inter-cepted by a set of opaque bars with openings 1, 2, 3, 4 between them. Each opening generates new waves that spread out in a circular way. A patchwork wave can be made from slits 1, 2, 3, 4 set in a special direction at an angle de-pending on the separation of the slits and the wavelength. Measuring this angle, for accurately made slits, tells the wavelength.

found by adding up the separate disturbances, with sign included, so that two opposite, equal disturbances add up to zero. The second is the in-herent property of a wave: it is generated by an effect at one place, and that effect spreads to another.

Fraunhofer's instrument involved two major ideas. The first was the creation of a succession of waves accurately parallel to one another, as shown at the right of the figure. This he did by putting a well-illuminated slit in a metal plate at the focus of a lens. The lens then produces a "beam" of light which neither diverges nor converges, and in this beam the waves are all parallel to one another. The second idea was to rule opaque lines on a plate of glass, making the lines very close to one another and (also very accurately) the same distance apart.

To understand why this produces a very valuable device it is first necessary to imagine how light progresses as it leaves a sheet of clear glass with no opaque rulings at all and nothing of any close regularity about its construction. The light that passes through the glass encounters many millions of atoms, each with electrons and each able to influence the original electromagnetic wave which comprises the light. To see what will take place we adopt a suggestion made by Huygens and assume that from any one of these atoms a new center of radiation develops: the resulting summation will then be the wave which is produced further along. In Figure 13.1 we show a construction of what happens when we use this idea. The semicircles are drawn with a little skill. The small ones have a radius of just one wavelength, the next of two wavelengths, the third of three, and so on. It is really easy to see that there is a great concentration of lines in the wave that is advancing straight ahead. This conclusion— which is very necessary, for we *will not* permit our intuition to mislead us about light going straight through a thin piece of glass—is satisfying. Now the lighter lines are different in only one respect. They are the circles that originate from a regular set of openings, spaced accurately, as done by Fraunhofer. It can now be seen that for these, and these only, there is a way to assemble a wave as a patchwork, part from slit 1, part from 2, part from 3, and so on. This wave does *not* go straight ahead; it emerges at an angle and there is a definite relation between the wave-length, the separation of the openings, and the angle. By measuring the angle, by ruling the many lines at known distances apart, and by observing that light is indeed found at an angle, Fraunhofer was able to measure the wavelength of the light.

This was the first spectrometer, though it was only given that name by Schuster long after Fraunhofer's death. A schematic drawing of the whole instrument is shown in Figure 13.2. It is not at all important to us to

Fig. 13.2. Use of the diffraction grating, with two lenses, a slit in a metal plate, and a photographic plate, to form a *spectrometer*.

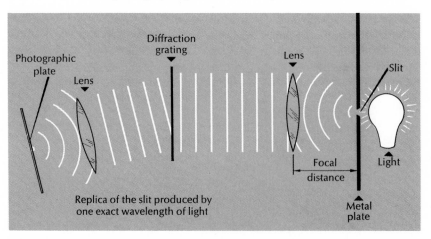

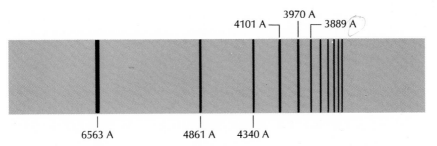

Fig. 13.3 Representation of the photographic record of the Balmer series, using a spectrometer: light emitted by hydrogen atoms. Wavelengths are in Ångstrom units, 10^{-10} meter.

know the details of the apparatus; we need only to know that it can be made, it works, and it accurately measures wavelength.

The exciting thing about this instrument is that with it we can find many sources of light for each of which there are several angles at which this off-axis brightness is found. Each of these "lines" has a different color—in fact, we find that color is a property of the wavelength—red for long waves and blue for short. Still more exciting is that the "lines" found for light made by heating up one particular chemical element are found to be characteristic of that element, so that a fast and sensitive way of detecting an element turned out to be to heat it until it gave out light and then look for its spectrum. In Figure 13.3 we show one of the most famous of all, the spectrum of atomic hydrogen, produced in a discharge tube. The lines are the lines of the Balmer series (already discussed in regard to the Bohr theory) and their wavelengths are given at the side.

It is worth a moment to say one or two other things about this very beautiful technique. It works because one is able to keep the light and obstacles in step. If either gets out, for any reason, the accuracy of the angle gets fuzzy. One might think that the light emitted by an atom would not stay fixed for many waves. It turns out that generally it does, although sometimes it does not, and the reason why it does not is always interesting. Also, the rulings must be very exact. The art of excellent ruling was developed to a high degree in the United States by Rowland. This entry into accurate spectroscopy is another of the first instances of real contributions to science by our emerging nation.

How Light Is Emitted by Atoms

Before we go on to describe some of the very interesting and exciting discoveries made with the spectrometer, it will pay us to think about how light is emitted by atoms. We already know something about it, for one of Bohr's famous postulates, which was needed to reconcile the nuclear atom with the nature of radiation, says that light of a frequency ν is emitted when a transition of an electron between two of Bohr's orbits occurs according to the rule

$$h\nu = E_2 - E_1,$$

where E_2 and E_1 are the energies appropriate to the two orbits and h is Planck's constant. It is a good idea to examine this a little more closely.

We know that Bohr's theory was really only a stopgap kind of stage in thought and that really the behavior of electrons in atoms is determined by a wave-particle duality, which we call "quantum mechanics." According to quantum mechanics the electrons form into patterns around the nuclei of atoms, patterns which also are moving, and which have various shapes. The patterns are capable of being described by interesting, but very elaborate, mathematical expressions and we do not propose to burden the reader with them, although we regret our forbearance, for to us they are very significant and beautiful. We are going to sketch a few of them, as best we can. We are going to tell the reader that the forms of the patterns, their shapes, and the way they are arranged, depend on three whole numbers, which in turn obey two rules, as follows. The first, always called n, can be 1, 2, 3, 4 and so on, never 0. The second, called l, can be 0, 1, 2, 3, etc., and is associated with n in such a way that it is always less than n. Thus if n were 1, then l would *have* to be 0, while if n were 2, l could be either 0 or 1, but not 2. Both n and l are always positive. The third, called m, must be equal to or less than l in size, but it can be positive or negative. Thus we could have a whole arrangement:

$$n = 2; \quad l = 1; \quad m = +1 \text{ or } 0 \text{ or } -1.$$

The reader may wonder why we, who have usually tried to avoid detail, are suddenly packing it in with such intensity. The answer is that these numbers, and the combinations between them, have extraordinary significance. In one sense they are the basis of the whole of chemistry, a statement no chemist will really challenge. The periodic table of the elements follows from these numbers plus two more ideas; the idea of adding one proton to the nucleus to make the next element, and the idea that the electrons will occupy the lowest energy they can find. That this is so was first pointed out by Stoner, and with more illumination by Pauli, who used them in his famous statement that only two electrons can occupy any one of the patterns we have mentioned. We are not concerned with chemistry here, and shall leave the very wonderful development of the table of the elements for other treatment; we *are* concerned with how atoms emit light, and we shall soon find that the patterns of electronic form in the atoms are strongly related to the way in which light and atoms interact.

In Figure 13.4 we show attempts at sketches of the patterns of electrons in atoms. They are not like the patterns of the Chladni plates, but they are related to them in many ways, for they, as well as the Chladni patterns, are both the result of standing waves in a region where the waves are confined. In the plate it is the metal which confines them; in the atom it is the strong electric field of the nucleus which does so. Notice that every time we have $l = 0$ we have a round (spherically symmetrical) shape. Every time we have l bigger the shape becomes more queer. The effect of m is to hold the pattern in a different direction.

Now we must come to the point. How can an atom emit light, which is electromagnetic radiation as Maxwell and Hertz showed? Well, the answer is, to a large extent, what we should expect. The electrons are charges and they are moving, so we have a start. What we must have, also, is some kind of an oscillating, or periodically changing, charge; then we can have radiation. The spectroscopist calls this periodically changing charge an "oscillating dipole." Now it is not too hard to take the mathematical expressions for the patterns we have drawn and see whether, alone or with any combination of them, there is a periodically changing charge. Theorists have done this, and it turns out that for *any one alone* there is *never* such a changing charge: the patterns themselves contain the "postulate" which Bohr had to make, and which was so great a shock to the "classical" physicists, such as Thomson. On the other hand, a *combination* of two patterns may well have an oscillating charge. In particular, a combination of two of them for which l differs by unity has a big oscillating charge. So if we can find some way in which we can effect a *transition* from one of these patterns to another, such that we change l by 1, we should find light involved somehow. We do.

If we want to get light *out,* then we must put the atom into a pattern which has more energy so as to have the energy necessary to give out the light, which itself carries energy. So we heat the atoms, hoping that the heat will "excite" a few of them. Or we bombard them with electrons in a discharge tube, again hoping for some "excited" atoms. When we have these, we wait, and in due time, just as in the case of radioactive decay, the transition will occur and a train of light waves will emerge. Because the patterns are sharp, and have very exact energies, the frequency of the light which comes out is also exact. Thus, with the spectrometer we are able to find out something about the combination of two of the patterns. It is not surprising that of all the ways

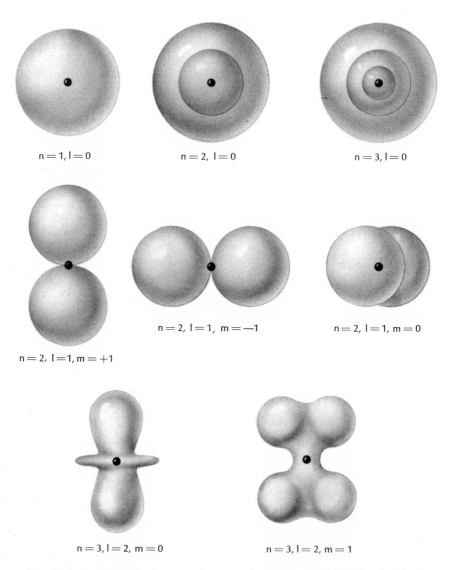

n = 1, l = 0   n = 2, l = 0   n = 3, l = 0

n = 2, l = 1, m = −1   n = 2, l = 1, m = 0

n = 2, l = 1, m = +1

n = 3, l = 2, m = 0   n = 3, l = 2, m = 1

Fig. 13.4. Patterns of electrons in a nuclear atom. The little dot is the nucleus and the shape of the pattern depends on mathematical formulas governed by three integers, n, l and m. Some of the patterns are shown. For $l = 0$ the pattern is spherical; for $l = 1$ pairs of roughly spherical shapes occur. These patterns determine much of the chemistry of atoms.

of getting information about the atom the spectroscope is the most powerful.

If we want to get light *in,* we must reverse the process, which is easier in one way and harder in another. It is easier, in that we do not have to make "excited" atoms, and harder, in that we have to be careful to have the frequency of the light we try to get in (be absorbed) exactly right. It can be done; and the two processes we have just described are studied in terms of *emission* and *absorption* spectroscopy.

We have not really gotten very far into this chapter and yet we are conscious that we have given the reader the basic ideas for understanding a very large part of modern physical science. We are fond of talking about the growth of elaboration from simplicity. Nowhere is this growth more apparent than in this subject. One of the authors has a sharp memory of an encounter with Dr. Goudsmit, one of the really great minds in the interpretation of the spectra observed in this way. At that time the author was trying to make sense out of the energy levels of atomic nuclei, and in asking advice from Dr. Goudsmit he began talking about the frustration of not being able to interpret them. Dr. Goudsmit then asked: "Are your levels many and complicated?," to which the answer was "no, not really." Dr. Goudsmit observed, "Then it will be hard to understand them, for if one wants to elucidate a spectrum, one should have many lines in strange arrangements, and then one can test out hypotheses and find the truth." This may seem a surprising answer, but it is not to one who has interpreted spectra. Let us think about it for a moment and see what develops. The great power of spectroscopy is the accurate measurement of wavelength or frequency, and the great value of this power is the relationship of the measurements to the atomic patterns. What can we hope to discover? We can begin with the Balmer series, shown in Figure 13.3. With relatively little trouble we can measure the wavelength of a dozen or so of the lines of this series, and we can see whether our formula, depending only on integer numbers, actually works or not. In Table 13.1 we give some measured values and some values calculated from theory, using the integers shown.

The units are in terms of 10^{-10} meter, called Ångstrom units. It is clear that there is no freak agreement involved; the series faithfully obeys the relation. The relation we have used to make the calculation can be found in Chapter 11. It is seen that one term in it always involves a fixed value of 2. Why not 1, or 3, or 4? Why not, indeed?

If we devise a spectroscope that will work in the ultraviolet range, we will find a whole new series, for which the first number is 1. This was originally discovered by Lyman. In the infrared, where again the eye cannot detect the light, proper techniques reveal series with the

Table 13.1

n	Observed	Calculated	Relation used
3	6563.07	6563.07	
4	4860.90	4861.57	
5	4340.57	4340.63	
6	4101.73	4101.90	
7	3970.07	3970.22	
8	3888.99	3889.20	
9	3835.35	3835.53	
10	3797.91	3798.04	
11	3770.78	3770.77	

$$\frac{1}{\lambda} = \frac{2\pi^2 \mathrm{m}\, e^4}{c^2 h^3 \left\{ 1 + \dfrac{m}{M} \right\}} \left[\frac{1}{2^2} - \frac{1}{n^2} \right]$$

first number 3 (the Paschen series) and 4 (the Brackett series). So the simple beginning of the Balmer series leads to more and more confirmation. Now the formula we quoted from Chapter 11 has many terms in it and is most impressive, but from among these terms we can select the interesting term, the mass of the hydrogen nucleus, which appears in the denominator. In 1932, Urey, Brickwedde, and Murphy noticed that the lines of the Balmer series itself had a second set of values, very nearly the same as the normal values. They were so sure of their measurements that they were forced to conclude that for these lines the nucleus of hydrogen was different. They tried using a mass of just double, and then working out the formula. The agreement was perfect! They had discovered an isotope of hydrogen; we called it *deuterium*. So even in the Balmer series discovery was latent. The isotope of hydrogen has a nucleus in which there is one proton and one neutron, and this discovery helped to solidify the discovery of the neutron.

The reader may ask why we do not say anything about the number m. The answer is that this number is concerned with the direction in which the pattern is pointing and if we have no direction established it can have no effect. But if we apply a magnetic field, we can choose the direction, and then there should be some difference between the various values of m. There is. This effect of a magnetic field on the "spectral line" was discovered by Zeeman, even before all the theory was established. The effect works out exactly as one would expect it to from the nature of the patterns for different values of m. Even more interesting, the effect of the magnetic field can sometimes be shown to come from within the atom itself; this enables measurements of the magnetic fields inside atoms to be obtained, and tells us in still more detail about the structure of the atom.

The reader can tell from the note of enthusiasm which has crept into the writing that we feel this accurate study of light to be potent in telling about the structure of the source of light: generally about the atom. We want to go on to discuss the use of spectroscopy in the study of stars, but before we do so would like to widen the topic a little more.

The Diffraction of X-rays

When an attempt is made to use the same trick Fraunhofer used in studying light to discover the character of X-rays, it proves to be very hard, though it has been done. In 1912, it occurred to V. Laue, a German physicist, that crystals provided a regular array of obstacles in the form of the atoms themselves. He worked out the formidable theory for the way *diffraction,* as the phenomenon observed by Fraunhofer is called, would operate for a three-dimensional crystal. He suggested to two experimenters, Friedrich and Knipping, that they try it out. It worked! A beam of X-rays, made narrow by two small holes in lead plates, and sent through a crystal, emerges along a whole beautiful pattern of angles as well as straight ahead. We like these patterns so well that we show one in Figure 13.5. This particular picture is very modern, and far removed from those obtained earlier by Friedrich and Knipping; it is the pattern of fibers of DNA, the hereditary substance of all living things. Just as the crystal of salt used by Friedrich and

Fig. 13.5. Representation of the X-ray diffraction pattern of DNA (left) and the twined helices of DNA (right).

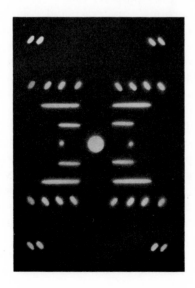

Knipping showed the effect of the regular array of atoms, so do the fibers of DNA. The structure of this giant molecule, as deduced partly from this kind of work, is shown alongside the diffraction pattern.

As often happens, an altered way of thinking revolutionized this use of X-rays. One of the rare father-son teams in science, W. H. and W. L. Bragg, devised a very much simpler way of looking at this diffraction and invented a truly practical and convenient method of studying X-rays, a method called crystal spectrometry. In doing this they opened up two huge fields of work: the study of crystals and the study of X-rays themselves. From the study of X-rays, Moseley was able to deduce that the correct way to arrange the chemical elements was in terms of integers, now recognized as those which describe the number of protons in the nucleus. Compton showed that when X-rays collide with electrons they do so as if they were particles, not only as if they were waves. He thus opened one of the paths which led to the wave-particle duality, which is at the core of quantum mechanics. The whole character of the structure of crystals, of organic molecules, of liquids, was exposed to careful work in which X-rays were used to probe the nature of matter. We do not intend to go on along this path, for we want to look at the universe, but we would have been wrong if we had failed to point it out.

The Use of Spectroscopy To Study Stars

We have said enough to suggest to the reader that the features of atoms which we have designated as "patterns," properly called "orbitals," or, even more spectacularly, "eigenfunctions," are exact and complicated. If we can study the light which is given out when two of these orbitals conspire to do so, we can find out a great deal about the orbitals. Now the stars are the pre-eminent sources of light in the universe, and so it is not a bit surprising that the study of this light by means of the spectroscope should be very revealing of knowledge about the stars. We can start with Fraunhofer himself, and with our own star, the sun. It is clearly easy to illuminate that slit in Fraunhofer's apparatus with sunlight and then we should be able to see what is there. We expect to see, as Newton had seen with a prism, the familiar spectrum of colors from red to violet. We do indeed see it, but we see more; we see a myriad of fine lines, quite black, crossing the spectrum. These lines, known as Fraunhofer lines, have the characteristic sharpness associated with the spectral lines of atoms, and so it is tempting to see whether their wavelengths mean anything in terms of the lines we can produce in the laboratory. It turns out that they do and that we can identify over sixty chemical elements as responsible for the lines. These include one new element, *helium*, whose name denotes its discovery by Lockyer in the spectrum of the sun (the Greek word for *sun* is *helios*).

The reader may ask: "Why are the lines dark, if they come from the sun?" They are dark because, at the last moment, just as the light is starting on its way to us, it has to go through a strange superatmosphere, the atmosphere of the sun. This atmosphere, unlike ours, is hot, dense, and very extensive, and in it we find the hot vapors of almost all the elements. These vapors, right at the edge, are hot enough to give out light, but they are also able to absorb it. So they exact a tax on the sun's radiance at exactly the wavelength at which they would absorb, in the laboratory, under the same circumstances. Thus we have a powerful method of studying the atmosphere of the sun.

We can use the same technique on the planets, and we already know much about the atmospheres of Mars and Venus. Mars has only a slight atmosphere, about one-thirtieth as dense as ours, while Venus has a dense atmosphere, probably hotter than ours. The moon has almost no atmosphere at all.

Energy Distribution in Hot Substances: "Black Body" Radiation

We have described the way in which individual spectral lines appear as black absorption regions in the spectrum of ligh' from the sun. One can ask: "What is the spectrum of light which is not absorbed?" It is a very good question, for much of our knowledge of the stars come from their color and brightness, rather than from the lines such as described by Fraunhofer. To answer the question we have to enter two areas of physical science which we have previously skirted: these are concerned with the way in which energy is divided up in a hot body, and the way in which light is given up by atoms in such a hot body. We cannot avoid thinking about these, for we do know that a star is hot and that there are large numbers of atoms in it. We must look at a star somehow, meaning that we must look at some radiation from it. Now the radiation can be either one of two kinds, though not all kinds, because our atmosphere lets only two kinds through: the light we can see, and a bit more, and some rather short radio waves. Both are most interesting, and both are concerned with the things we are about to discuss.

The distribution of energy among the atoms in a hot body is a famous problem which has been worked on by a very eminent set of physical scientists: Maxwell, Boltzmann, Gibbs, and Jeans, among others. The result is usually known as the Boltzmann equation, and we can readily give the basis for it, though we would rather not give the actual derivation. The basis is so simple that the reader will wonder that anything so profound as a formula with a name to it could result. We have remarked on the growth of complexity before this; here is another example. The basis for the relationship is threefold. We say that in the hot body the number of atoms is fixed, the total energy is fixed, and the way the energy is divided is in the most likely way. This last simple statement is usually dignified with the words "maximum probability." The result of theoretical treatment is shown in Figure 13.6.

The reader will see that this relationship is rather like the one for radioactive decay, with the exception that time is not involved, while energy *is* involved. The similarity is not by chance; both are involved with probability, and this kind of diminishing relationship is very often encountered where chance is the underlying factor. In order to make the rather cold representation of the graph seem a little more dramatic we have shown the distribution a little differently in the second part of the figure. Here we have represented the energy upward, and the dots represent the number of molecules which are in that energy zone. It looks a little more real.

Fig. 13.6. The relative number of molecules having an energy of some value. There are more at low energy and fewer as the energy increases. A hot body has more molecules at higher energies and a cold body has almost all at low energies. In the inserts a pictorial representation of the distribution has been given.

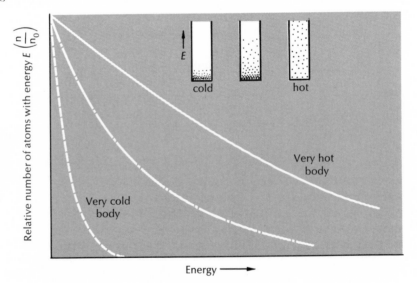

In any event, we are also going to give a formula for this distribution which will raise the tone of the book considerably. The formula is

$$\frac{n}{n_0} = e^{-E/kT}$$

where

$n =$ number of atoms with energy E

$n_0 =$ number of atoms with zero energy

$T =$ temperature (Kelvin)

$e =$ number defined below

$k =$ constant, known as Boltzmann's constant

The reader will note that we have been careful to show a graph and a kind of picture before this piece of mathematics. If we had not done so we might have induced considerable tension. Now it is quite true that our formula has the strange symbol e in it. For our purposes we really do not care about it, but we propose to tell the reader what it is.

$$e = 1 + \frac{1}{1} + \frac{1}{1 \cdot 2} + \frac{1}{1 \cdot 2 \cdot 3} + \frac{1}{1 \cdot 2 \cdot 3 \cdot 4} \cdots$$

Why do we worry about a horribly complicated number like this? The answer is that it really is not so horribly complicated. Let us look at a number like π. It is true that the state of Illinois very nearly legislated the value of π as a simple fraction (it passed the House unanimously, but the Senate caught it), but this number is anything but that. We must write

$$\pi = 3 + \frac{1}{10} + \frac{4}{100} + \frac{1}{1000} + \frac{5}{10,000} \cdots$$

The only difference is in the denominator. In our decimal system the denominator is arranged so that we can write the number in a compact shorthand way, and this is an advantage. The denominator of the number e is arranged to be very simple for any changing character it might have to represent. We can write a series for e^x. It is:

$$e^x = 1 + x + \frac{x^2}{1 \cdot 2} + \frac{x^3}{1 \cdot 2 \cdot 3} + \frac{x^4}{1 \cdot 2 \cdot 3 \cdot 4} \cdots$$

Now if we take the derivative of this, to see how it changes, we find that the derivative is also the same series. (The reader with a little mathematical aptitude can try it). So it is not really surprising that this number e might find a place in some kinds of mathematics. It does, and we have taken the time to shed a little light on it. In reality, though, it is true that we are not really concerned with e at all, only with the way in which energy and temperature appear in the formula. They appear as a *power*. In Chapter 2 we discussed mathematical relations in terms of whether or not they are "lively" in regard to the effect they have. Usually a power is very lively. This is true in this case. If the energy E is large compared to the term kT, then the total result is very small. This shows in the graph. If E is equal to kT then the ratio of the number at the energy E to that for zero energy is 0.37, about one third. If E is quite small compared to kT the ratio is 1.

We are a little sorry to inflict all this on the reader. Still, it only looks complicated; it really is not and it is most important. Is it true? Yes. The Boltzmann formula has been tested by experiment in several ways. Stern measured the actual speeds of molecules in 1922; more recently Havens and Rainwater measured the speeds of neutrons. Both experiments verified the formula.

Atmospheres of Planets

While we are on the subject of this very important formula, we can point out that it underlies the nature of the atmospheres of planets, and perhaps can explain the lack of atmosphere on the moon. In the chapter on potential energy we discussed the potential energy of the bob of a pendulum in the gravitational field of the earth. Measuring from the surface of the earth we found it to be mgh, where g is short-hand for $\dfrac{GM}{R^2}$, which is determined by the mass of the earth, the constant of gravitation, and the radius of the earth. Now if we include potential energy in our Boltzmann formula, we can write a relation:

$$\frac{n}{n_0} = e^{-mgh/kT}$$

in which we have put the term mgh in place of the energy term. The result is the same as the graph we have drawn, only now we see that the energy part contains the mass of the molecule which is part of the atmosphere. Suppose it should happen that m is very small; then mgh might be quite small compared to kT, and for such a case the number of molecules for which h is big is quite large, which is another way of saying that the atmosphere is spread out. If the atmosphere is so spread out that quite a lot of the molecules can be very far up, then they have a good chance of getting away from the earth altogether. A good many of them will collide, fortunately, so as to get high speeds, and these may be high enough to go all the way out and so escape. Thus light molecules have a better chance to get away for two reasons: they have a spread-out atmosphere and they can collide and get high speed.

In Figure 13.7 we show how the atmosphere around the earth looks, assuming that the major factor in describing it is the way the Boltzmann formula works. We see that, for the three kinds of gases that we have drawn, the number of molecules gets less as the height increases. For nitrogen and oxygen, the number gets to be very few at 100 miles; for radon, the number has reached zero long before that; while for hydrogen, the atmosphere would like to extend farther. Now it is not quite so simple as this because the atmosphere is getting hot and cold each day as the earth turns and the sun shines upon it. So there are winds and lots of mixing; but even so, there will be a broad behavior much as would be seen if the three atmospheres in the figure were just pushed into each other.

When we look at other planets we see that the mass of the planet and its radius are important. Mars, for example, is about half the radius of the earth and about one-tenth the mass. This means that $\dfrac{GM}{R^2}$ is four-

Fig. 13.7. The earth's gravitational field causes the distribution of molecules in the atmosphere. A dense gas like radon lies close to the surface. Hydrogen is spread out and some of it actually escapes.

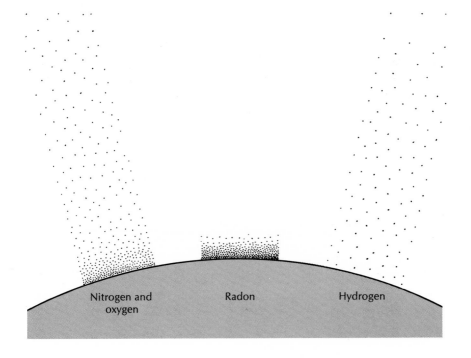

Nitrogen and oxygen   Radon   Hydrogen

tenths of that on the earth. The temperature is somewhat less, but not very much, and the result is that Mars can just about retain an atmosphere, which is preferably composed of heavier gases, including carbon dioxide, not very much water, which is relatively light, and no hydrogen at all. The exact amount of atmosphere on Mars is not really known. Recent measurements have tended to make it seem smaller, but it does have an atmosphere, perhaps of about one-thirtieth the density of ours.

On the other hand, Venus is almost the twin of the earth in radius and mass, though it is hotter, at least we think so. All the evidence we have shows that Venus has a very rich and dense atmosphere.

We can also consider the moon. This has one-fourth the radius of the earth and one-hundredth the mass. So the effect of gravity is about one-sixth that of the earth. It is very cold, except when it is in sunlight, when any gas molecule would have a good chance of gaining energy. All this seems to have conspired to make the moon free of atmosphere, at least to a very great degree. Maybe some radon lurks around in small amounts, but not much else.

Radiation from a Hot Body

Some time ago we began with this heading, or one like it, including the words "black body" and we are now ready to discuss it. It should be easy and it is almost very easy, but not quite. If we think about a hot substance, with the various atoms in the various forms of energy—and we introduce the idea that the atoms which are in high energy conditions can give out radiation, while those in low energy conditions can absorb it—we should be able to think about the way in which light, or radiation of any kind, is given out—or absorbed, for that matter. A little thinking shows that it is not quite so simple; there are always more atoms in the lower energy conditions, if the Boltzmann relation is right, and so there should always be more energy being absorbed than emitted. Yet we would like to think that such a hot body could be in a condition where it was emitting and absorbing at the same rate. One of the truly great insights of that truly great mind, Einstein, was the realization that the very presence of radiation would stimulate other atoms to emit, so that the fewer number would radiate a bit more. Not only that, by making it necessary that the amount stimulated exactly balanced the unbalance in the numbers, Einstein was able to find the rule necessary to state how the hot body will emit radiation of various wavelengths. This rule had been deduced quite differently a few years previously by Planck, and experimentally verified.*

---

* Actually it was the other way around—Planck rather reluctantly deduced what must be happening, in order to explain the experiments of Lummer and Pringshein.

Using Planck's and Einstein's reasoning, we find the relationship shown in Figure 13.8. Notice the profound effect of temperature on the way the line is drawn. The higher temperature not only increases the amount of energy given out in an extremely "lively" way, but it also moves the wavelength of most emission toward shorter (bluer) wavelengths.

We intend to add one more aside, and then we can go back to astronomy. Many years after Einstein made his suggestion, actually in quite recent years, the idea took very practical form in an instrument called a "laser." This instrument works by building up a population of excited atoms in a crystal (or gas or liquid), and then stimulating the emission from them by light. The burst of light obtained is very bright, and because it can be made to go in a direction controlled by the crystal structure, or the shape of the vessel, it is confined to a very narrow beam. Lasers are very much in use today for a variety of purposes, ranging from communication to "welding" the detached retina of the eye back into place.

This is all the technical discussion we need. The reader may wonder why the charming words "black body" ever appeared. The reason is that curves of Figure 13.8 are only part of what might happen. If the hot substance had a tendency to give out light of only a few special wavelengths, like a neon sign, the formula would not really work. So the formula was made to apply only to those substances without such tendencies. Since any one wavelength is colored, the kind of substance we

Fig. 13.8. Energy radiated from a hot body in relation to wavelength. The hotter the body the more it radiates at shorter wavelengths.

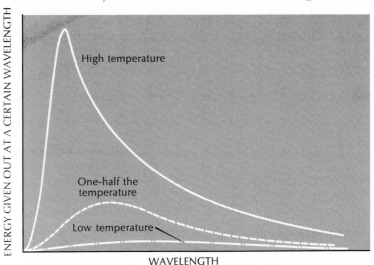

must think about must not have any color. It could have been called a "white body," meaning one that emits everything, or a "black body," meaning one that absorbs everything. The two are the same. The word "black" won out. Psychologists may be able to make something of this choice; the authors cannot. In any event, it adds some spice to the language of physical science.

Stars: Their Distance, Brightness, and Size

To look at stars we must gather light or radiation from them. We do not intend to burden the reader with a description of telescopes, except to say that all such instruments involve some method of collecting the radiation from a broad beam and sending it into a narrow spot. It can be done with lenses, mirrors, or arrays of antennas. The process is horribly hindered by the earth's atmosphere, 100 miles of absorbing gas, smog, and turbulence; thus it is amazing that so much has been learned.

We have one direct and easily explainable way to measure the distance of a star. If we look at it at two different times one-half year apart, when the earth is at opposite sides of its orbit, we are looking at it from two points 186 million miles apart. The direction of the star will change if it is close to us, and by noting the direction change and doing a little elementary surveying we can measure how distant the star is. This requires very great accuracy in measurement, for the distance to the nearest star is 290,000 times the diameter of the orbit of the earth around the sun. But astronomers can do it and have measured several thousand distances in this way.

Another way is not so easy to justify, but it has much more of the flavor of modern astronomy, and suits the theme of this book beautifully. Stars vary in brightness, and it becomes legal to think out reasons why. One class we will discuss later does so for a simple reason: the "star" is really two stars, rotating about each other; one is bright and the other dark. When the dark star comes across the face of the bright one there is a decrease in the light we get. Obviously we can get a great deal of information from these stars. For the moment let us put them aside. Another class varies quite differently. In Figure 13.9 we show the two kinds of variation for contrast. In the first, represented by Algol, the brightness takes a sharp dip and then recovers; it is fixed at other times. For δ-Cephei, the brightness rises to a peak in a gradual way and then falls rapidly. We are tempted at once to explain the case of Algol as that of a dark partner traversing a bright star; but we cannot do so for δ-Cephei. On the other hand, we are at liberty to think about what makes a star bright, and we can think of the star as pulsating in size. If we do this, and formulate a

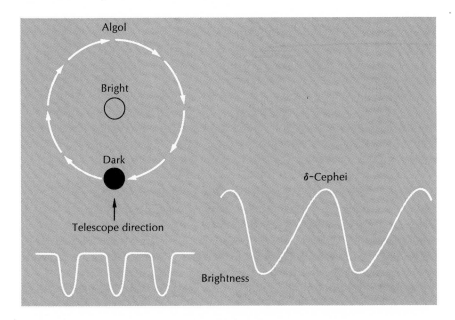

Fig. 13.9. Contrast in the brightness patterns of two variable stars. The dark-bright pair (Algol) is easy to interpret. The Cepheid variable is harder to account for, but theory suggests that the periodicity is related to brightness, so these variables can be used to measure distance.

theory, the very interesting result is that, for stars like δ-Cephei, the interval between the brightest times is exactly related to the actual brightness of the star; the brighter it is the longer the interval between the peaks of brightness. There are enough stars of this class of known brightness to check the theory, and it works. So we know that regardless of how bright it may appear to us, a Cepheid variable star of a certain period has an absolute brightness that we know. In Eddington's words, the Cepheid variable is a "standard candle." Now light loses its intensity —just as gravitation, or an electric field from a charge—as the *inverse square* of the distance. It is thus no trick at all to measure the actual light we get, measure the period, and calculate the distance away to give us this much light, knowing (from the period) how much light started out. So we can use the Cepheid variables to give us distance also.

In this way we can accumulate a catalog of distances and brightness, and make an estimate for many stars of their actual luminosity—in terms of that of our own sun, for example. When this is done another thing is noticed, and that is the relationship to the *color* of the star. If the light from the star is looked at with the spectroscope, some stars seem to be reddish, and some very blue. A chart known as the Hertzsprung-Russell diagram, relating brightness to color, can be prepared, and it looks something like Figure 13.10. Before we discuss the astronomical implications of this diagram, we have to go back for a moment to "black body" radiation. If the reader will look for a moment at Figure 13.8, it will appear that the hotter the body, the shorter the wavelength of the most emission. Going to shorter wavelengths means going from infrared (the hot but not glowing poker) to red (the glowing poker) to white (the light bulb), and in each case the amount of blue light gets greater as the temperature increases. Thus any measure of the "blueness" or "redness" of the light really is a measure of the temperature of the outside of the star. For those stars which have mostly red light, whose "color index" is high, the temperature is low; for those which have a low color index, meaning lots of blue and not so much red, the temperature is high. So we can think of the Hertzsprung-Russell diagram in relation to the temperature of stars.

Now if we turn back to the Hertzsprung-Russell diagram again, we see that most of the stars fall into a curved band, which we are tempted to suggest is a "line." Stars on this line are said to be on the *main sequence.* Two other classes of stars exist: those which are bright and red, and those which are faint and white. Classifying stars in this way also suggests that we should be able to deduce something about the stars from so doing.

Fig. 13.10. Representation of the Hertzsprung-Russell diagram relating luminosity to color and temperature.

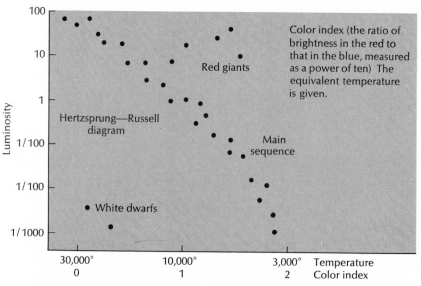

We can. We can see in the Hertzsprung-Russell diagram the story of the evolution of the stars.

To understand this statement we need more astrophysics. If we return to the eclipsing variables—like Algol, not the Cepheids—we see that we are in a position to use Newton's laws to deduce information from the rotation of the two stars about each other. We can; all we need to do is to assume that the constant of gravitation is the same out there, and that all the laws we know are the same. We can then calculate the masses of the two stars, and from the way the eclipsing is related to the orbits we can estimate the sizes of the stars. So now we know the mass as well as the luminosity and can see if they are related. They are indeed. One of the famous laws of astrophysics is the mass-luminosity relation. This says that the more massive a star the brighter it is: brightness increases as the cube of the mass. Such a result is a surprise and is very informative. If a star simply burned more or less equally, we might think that the brightness might increase with the mass, but why so violently? The answer seems to be that the bigger the star, the more rapidly is its fire going—meaning that it will more rapidly use itself up. Thus if a star somehow develops large mass and great brightness, it has less time to continue to shine, for it is "overdoing" and will spend itself before too long. Thus those stars at the upper left extremity of the Hertzsprung-Russell diagram are stars with not much more time to go.

The question now arises as to what happens when a star overdoes it and uses all its fuel. We can clearly see that it continues to put out light, but the light is now redder. This means that the surface temperature has fallen, and the only way in which the star can continue to be bright is for it to have a much larger surface. So the star moves to the right on the Hertzsprung-Russell diagram, at the same time expanding very greatly in size. It becomes a "red giant." However, this is not the end of its evolution. There is another phase of matter, one not yet producible in the laboratory, but predictable theoretically, in which the electrons and protons are closer together and the density of the star is vast, nearly a million times that of normal substances. In the process of shrinking down to this condition there is a release of energy and the star shines. It has so tiny a surface, however, that, even though it has a high temperature and so is emitting white light, it is very faint. It is then a "white dwarf" and is at the end of its road.

So the life history of a star is as follows. It is made by the condensation of gas and dust, primarily by gravitation. As its size increases in this way its interior gains energy until some kind of fuel ignites, and the star is on its way. Depending on how big it is when this happens, it will find a place on the main sequence, and there burn for its appropriate lifetime. If it is small it will last long; if it is large it will soon burn out. Then it finds a second way to burn, with a great expansion, and finally it collapses to a "white dwarf," shining brightly, but as a minute object.

The Fuel of Stars

One very easy measurement which gives us some notions about the fuel of stars is that of the heat we get from the sun, our own star. This heat measurement is known as the "solar constant" and is about a million ergs per square centimeter per second. Because we know how far we are away from the sun we can find out how much heat the sun is giving out *in toto*. As we might expect, it is great. It is so great that if the whole amount of the sun's heat were derived from normal sources like coal or oil, then the sun would burn into a clinker in only a few thousand years. So it is not that kind of energy. Attempts to suggest the kind of energy it is have been made many times; it is assumed that it must be nuclear. By nuclear energy we mean energy derived from reactions in which mass is lost and the energy is generated. It would not be right to say that anyone *knows* the reactions which are at work, but the plausible reactions are really not many; in fact, attention has focused on only three. These are the conversion of hydrogen into helium, the coalescence of three heliums into carbon, and the use of carbon as a catalyst to convert four hydrogens into helium, the carbon itself being returned back to carbon at the end.

None of these reactions will take place at all unless the temperatures are very high. Even at a temperature of 20 million degrees the reaction rates are so slow that each of the three reactions which are needed to convert the hydrogen into helium takes something like a thousand million years. This sounds like a long time; yet it is this very length of time which makes the idea seem reasonable; we have to gain considerable energy by a process which takes billions of years. Here it is.

In some way, when the hydrogen-to-helium process, which we can associate with the main sequence, approaches the end of its cycle, the other two processes become important. There is a change in the way the star distributes its energy-producing regions, apparently with a considerable expansion. This is the transition to the "red giant." As this form of energy is used up, the collapse to the "white dwarf" takes place.

At least so we think at present; we may find more information some day and this may be changed.

The Use of Theory and Observation

Nowhere in science is the mixture of theory and experiment, or rather observation, so strongly in evidence as in modern astronomy. Think about it for a moment. The ways in which we can study the stars are greatly limited. We can measure their positions with an accuracy limited by our atmosphere and our telescopes. We can look at their spectra. We can see if the light they emit is odd in some way, as, for example, vibrating more in one plane than in another, or of a wavelength different from what we expect. We can note any changes that take place over the course of time. This very small group of techniques is in strong contrast to the rich variety of experiments which we can perform on, let us say, a crystal of salt. We could fill two pages with just the list of methods of study of salt crystals. As a result, the astronomer has a very intriguing life forced upon him. He can relatively quickly master all that has been observed about some star, or kind of star, and then he must *think*. He cannot go *see*. The result has been that some of the sharpest minds in theoretical analysis have become interested in astronomy. They have taken the knowledge available from what might be called terrestrial, or earthbound, experiment and theory, and resolutely used it to figure out how a star *must* work. All the laws of mechanics, of gravitation, of emission and absorption of light, of magnetic action, of nuclear reactions are assimilated by the astrophysicist into the best possible theoretical account which he can devise of the nature of a star, or a galaxy, or a planet. It is accurate imagination *par excellence*.

We might wonder what kind of success is to be had by this method. The answer is that the same kinds of success as have been achieved in atomic and nuclear physics are achieved here, only on a more limited scale. The essence of this approach of limited experiment and extensive theory is that new advances occur only as certain confidences are attained, and perhaps only as new measurements which accordingly become relevant are made. The ability to test theory by separate lines of experimentation is also often denied to the astronomer. Nevertheless, the whole approach to stars and atoms is really the same: we can never *live* in either an atom or a star; we must therefore think accurately about what each of them is like.

This leads to the question of the degree of certainty of the conclusions reached by astronomers. It would be foolish to assert that an astronomer is as certain of the details of his statements as the atomic physicist is about his atom. The astronomer cannot *know* that the constant of gravitation has remained unchanged for all the time he needs to consider (and indeed an attractive suggestion has been made that it has not), but he can show clearly how he has applied all our knowledge of Nature to the stars he has studied, and he can defend his ideas in terms of confidence in his correct use of that knowledge. Any other scientist who can show that he has misused the laws of Nature can *prove* his work to be doubtful. So the astronomer does have checks on his ideas, checks which are respected by other scientists. He is, like all scientists, at the mercy of new discoveries which reveal more. This is one reason why astronomers are so vitally interested in the potential of the space age. For example, an observatory outside our atmosphere could be used to observe the light which is now absorbed by that atmosphere, and greatly extend the evidence we have; we could measure angles more accurately, too. Already telescopes in balloons at very high altitudes are telling us new things about the planets. Nevertheless, the attitude of most astronomers is that they do not expect a whole series of revolutions in thinking—perhaps one or two, and that is fair enough.

Before putting this discussion aside, it is in order to comment on the respectability of this kind of scientific operation in which the data are limited and the thinking about them is very deep. It is, of course, respectable in astronomy. It is also very respectable in nuclear physics and in atomic and molecular physics. It is a little less respectable in chemistry, but the successes of theoretical physics as applied to chemistry have been very good, and the respectability is increasing. On the other hand, in biology this method has not enjoyed much recognition, a situation which is changing fast. Living things have been shown to be controlled by the precise behavior of molecular structures, which are not readily visible to the eye, though they are not so hard to perceive as atoms or nuclei. These molecules exert their influences in ways which have been recognized for a long time as genetic, and for a long time the subject of genetics has had a more than usually firm theoretical foundation. So even in biology one begins to find a *Journal of Theoretical Biology* and groups of scientists

Fig. 13.11. An open spiral galaxy.

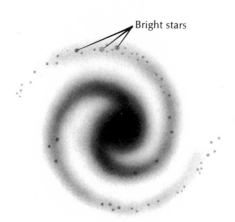

Bright stars

Fig. 13.12. Edge-on view of a galaxy.

taking obvious interest in it. Thus the attribute of astronomy of thinking deeply about knowledge won in an inaccessible realm is not confined to that science, though it may be found there more than in others.

Galaxies, the "Red Shift," and the Origin of the Universe

If we suppose that a star which is at the very top of the main sequence is at a distance of a billion light years from us, then we can soon assure ourselves that the amount of light which will reach us is too little to be seen. Yet we see stars at that distance. What we see must therefore be something much more than a single star. It is indeed much more; it is a galaxy, an aggregate of 100 billion stars. We ourselves are in a galaxy, and by looking at it—which is easy, for it is the "Milky Way"—and looking at nearby galaxies, we can make something of a story about them. In Figure 13.11 there is a picture of a galaxy seen from "above"; in Figure 13.12 there is one seen from the side. A diagram of our galaxy, to compare with Figure 13.12, is shown in Figure 13.13. These aggregates of stars, which are forming and changing, are an enormous challenge to interpret. They are rotating, and apparently they have a magnetic field which helps to confine their whole mass in the shape we see.

We are going to consider only one aspect of the study of galaxies, the discovery that they are receding from us, a conclusion drawn from what is called the "red shift."

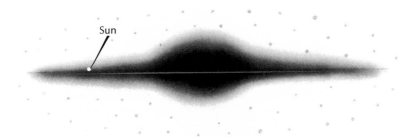

Fig. 13.13. An edge-on reconstruction of our galaxy, showing the place we occupy in it.

Waves Emitted from a Moving Source: The Doppler Effect

Everyone has noticed that changes in pitch occur in the sound of a moving object, a car or train, as it goes by us. As the train approaches the pitch is higher; as it recedes the pitch is lower. This is a manifestation of the Doppler effect, which is found when waves are produced by a source moving in relation to the observer. Briefly, what happens is this: the motion of the object emitting the sound packs more waves into a certain distance as the source approaches, and this makes the wavelength shorter; the reverse occurs as the source receded. It may seem a bit more dignified to look at Figure 13.14, in which the actual pattern of the waves has been drawn. The source of light is supposed to be moving away. The advantage of the figure is that some idea of the numerical relationship can be deduced from it. The essential relationship that concerns us is the way in which the number of waves registered in one second depends on the speeds of the source and of the light. In the upper part of the figure we show the normal arrival of ν waves (in this case a mere 5) in one second at the detector, which we have indicated as being like a TV antenna. We also show how far the star has gone away from the telescope in that one second. Below we show that the stretch of space corresponding to the distance gone by light in one second does not contain all the waves generated by the source in one second; instead, some have been generated too far away to arrive in a second and will arrive too late at the antenna. Thus the ν vibrations will take more than a second to register because in free space the light travels at velocity c, and more distance than c, namely $(c + v)$, has to be covered, meaning more time elapses and the apparent frequency at the antenna goes down. So the frequency falls. It can be seen from Figure 13.14 that in addition the wavelength increases. Because the longer wavelengths of light visible to the eye are red, when we see the light from a star going away from us we actually see a shift of that light in wavelength toward the red.

Of course, for a star coming toward us the wavelength is less, the frequency higher, and there is a shift to the blue. The whole phenomenon is called the Doppler effect.

Astronomy has made great use of the Doppler effect. For example, it can be used to study the rings around a planet or the rotating of galaxies. One most interesting use has been in the study of the receding motion of stars and galaxies. Earlier in this chapter we pointed out that the light emitted by an atom had a set of quite characteristic frequencies which would appear as sharp and definite lines in a spectroscope. These lines can be identified both by pattern and wavelength. Many patterns are quite unmistakable. In particular, the element calcium emits two lines designated H and K and these are recognizable. In Figure 13.15 we show the two lines as observed for each of five galaxies with their distances in light years. The speed of recession is also given.

These shifts to the red, first discussed in this way by Hubble, are found to be the same for all sorts of spectral lines, not only these from calcium. It has been found that the more distant the galaxy, the faster the reces-

Fig. 13.14. The receding light source emits vibrations in a second, but the telescope finds these vibrations spread over a distance c (light) *plus* v (source). The ratio is $\dfrac{c + v}{c}$ or $1 + \dfrac{v}{c}$. The *change* depends on the ratio of the velocity of the star to that of light. This is the Doppler effect.

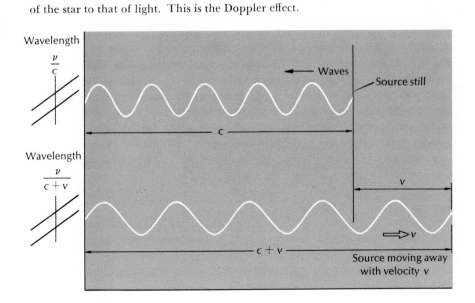

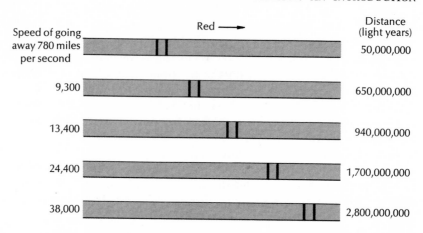

Fig. 13.15. The red shift for five galaxies. The two lines appear more and more in the red. The farther the galaxy the more rapidly it is going away.

sion; now we are up to huge distances and to speeds of recession of half the velocity of light.

This finding clearly starts us thinking about the origin of the universe. We need not believe that the galaxies are going away from *us;* we would see the same thing if everything were getting farther apart, meaning that the universe is expanding—almost one has to say "exploding," for velocities as high as half that of light are not small. If we trace backward in time the motions of the galaxies we can try to decide what was there at the start. The way our ideas gained in this way fit together is not bad, but, of course, it cannot be as accurate as a puzzle. All the same, something like 13 billion years ago (and estimates of this number keep going up) there was a much smaller, denser universe. How did it start? It is perhaps most interesting that we can dare to think about it in terms by which we believe we can make a decision. (Perhaps we really cannot, but we like to try our wits.) So we can consider one hypothesis which says that relatively suddenly, with a "big bang" (a gross understatement), the universe began. It was vastly energetic, certainly made of units which are subnuclear. As soon as it started, it began to expand, as it must, and the expansion has not stopped. In expanding, the energy changed to less exciting forms, the nuclear particles appeared, the elements formed and the operation of the laws of Nature caused the formation of galaxies, stars, planetary systems, and all that we can see with our varied kinds of telescopes and spectroscopes. It is exciting, and breathtaking, and something like it must have happened.

The reader will certainly comment that so much of this depends on interpretation. It does. All of this could change if it were found that the red shift was caused only by distance and not by speed. It may even develop that the majestic pattern of expansion begins to verge on the absurd. New techniques by which the emission of radio waves from hydrogen gas are detected are bringing some surprises, among them the discovery of still faster speeds of recession and still greater distances. In twenty years the incoming knowledge may not fit with any ideas we now have. In this extreme of our scientific scope, we should not be too arrogant. It maybe that we cannot explain the cosmos in terms that we now know. The excitement to the scientist is not over. He does not seek to find his views changed by the necessity of discovery, but at the back of his mind he knows that such can happen and it contributes toward keeping him alive.

Suggestions for Further Thought.

1. Write an essay on quasars.
2. Relate the early moments of the universe to fission, radioactivity and the present chemical elements.
3. Discuss the Doppler effect and the significance of the red shift to the evolution of the universe.
4. Compare the kind of equipment and elaboration of study needed by Galileo with that needed today. Who provides the extra material? What sort of return on the dollar is expected?
5. Discuss the character of revolutions introduced by science. Have they always resulted in human betterment? Illustrate your answer with examples.

References

E. G. Ebbighausen, *Astronomy* (Columbus, Ohio: Merrill, 1966).

Arthur S. Eddington, *Stars and Atoms* (Oxford: Oxford at the Clarendon Press, 1927).

Thornton Page (ed.), *Stars and Galaxies* (Englewood Cliffs, N.J.: Prentice-Hall, 1962).

14

Practice in Numerical Description: Problems

We have made the point in the text that numerical description is necessary to the physical scientist. This rather bare statement does not have much impact. It is really necessary to make the operation of numerical description acceptable by a certain amount of practice and drill, and in this chapter we propose to introduce this practice. Before beginning to do so, it is very tempting to show a way in which numerical description does have an impact. Anyone who has literary leanings can read the source material for himself: it is Daniel Defoe's *Journal of the Plague Year*. In this Defoe describes vividly the whole event of the London Plague of 1665, and the drama which it contains is carefully linked by Defoe to the number of deaths due to the plague, in what parish they occurred, and how the number rose. Since an epidemic of plague is, in a very real sense, a life and death matter, the observations of a bulletin that the number of deaths last week sharply increased may easily mean the question as to whether to stay or to try to move, and to say that the numbers on these bulletins are not important is clearly not true.

Without trying to portray the drama of the London plague, let us look at how the figures might appear in one parish in London and see how we can look at these in an emotional and concerned way and then as students of what is happening. Here is an imaginary table of what might have appeared.

Suppose we lived four miles away from this parish, and nobody had been taken ill. Up to May 15 we might not be concerned. By June 15 we would definitely be worried and also, almost certainly by June 15, there would be plague deaths near home. By July 30 the situation is obviously desperate and without doubt the epidemic has started to be serious even on our own street. Then in September the numbers fall and it becomes clear what the course of the epidemic is likely to be. The October num-

346

April 15, 1665	2 deaths
″ 30	10 ″
May 15	19 ″
″ 30	25 ″
June 15	106 ″
″ 30	250 ″
July 15	1200 ″
″ 30	2500 ″
August 15	3000 ″
″ 30	2800 ″
September 15	1750 ″
″ 30	800 ″
October 15	25 ″

bers came as a huge relief. It is not at all hard to reconstruct the feelings of fear and tension. Defoe does it magnificently.

Now to look at these scientifically, we need some way to assess them rapidly and clearly. One of the best ways is a graph. The time of the bulletin is measured along the horizontal axis (the abscissa) and the number of deaths on the vertical (the ordinate). The result is shown in Figure 14.1. The insignificant start grows slowly and relentlessly until,

Fig. 14.1. Growth and decay of an epidemic, used to illustrate how a knowledge of numbers and how they change can be literally a life and death matter.

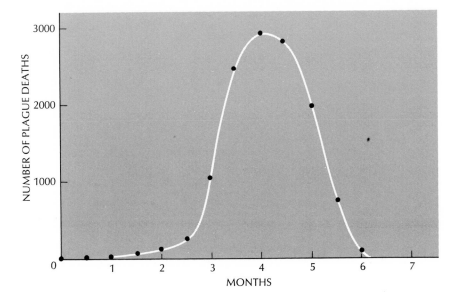

at three months, there is a clear rise which sweeps up, hesitates, and then falls rapidly. The thick dots form a pattern, and the physical scientist promptly wants to say that something is going steadily along between the dots: people are dying, and so he runs a line through the dots as we have done. Then he asks why the line does what it does, and in this instance he cannot answer: it takes a biologist to give the answer.

The answer is that plague is caused by a bacterium which infects fleas, rats, squirrels sometimes, and man. The best hosts for the fleas are the rats, and if the fleas are infected, the rats begin to take sick and die. In the process lots of bacteria grow, in fleas and in rats. Then a few people are unfortunate enough to harbor infected fleas: they get sick and die, about half of them. At first it does not seem that many people are ill, but each sick person breeds more bacteria which infect more fleas which then infect more people, and more die. After a while the infected people who do not die form a group who are immune, for they have antibodies against the bacteria. So though the fleas bite, the bacteria do not affect the immune group, and the increase in bacteria slows down, so that the rate of infection grows less. Finally, when enough rats have died and enough immune people are left, the epidemic starts down. It goes sharply, and soon it essentially dies out. All this story shows in the numbers and the graph, impersonally and coldly perhaps, but still there.

With this example of numerical description we can go on to the practice we need.

Almost anyone who finds himself taking a required course in physical science is there for just about one reason, and one which really does not make sense. Somewhere, way back around age ten to twelve, he, or rather more generally, she, developed an aversion to mathematics and numerical things. Often this aversion is produced by a teacher or a parent or an elder brother, and mostly unintentionally. Such an aversion has big effects. It is like the discovery that other children can run faster, which discourages athletics, or the piano teacher who storms about false notes, which discourages musical performance. So it did not take many times of "getting it wrong" to encourage a preference for reading books or drawing drawings rather than staying with those wretched equations.

Now equations in themselves are indeed wretched, a statement which at once turns some mathematicians against us. But what is not wretched is Nature. And one aspect of Nature is a very beautiful regularity which can be seen in many ways. Some of these ways can be described so compactly and simply in terms of symbols and something akin to, but not the same as, mathematics, that it is a shame to shut this aspect of Nature away from our senses, and even worse, our intellects. Because of this need for symbolic description, it will pay off to try to replace our aversion by pleasure. It has to be positive pleasure: it will not do to "get by." Nature is too wonderful to be taken casually. It should be all or nothing.

Let us therefore start out right. The first thing to understand is that we are not going to be involved with "getting it right." No one is going to rap any knuckles, even figuratively. Instead, what we will do is get the hang of some very simple ways in which symbols are used to represent ways of behavior.

We start with somebody walking. He starts down a road. We are interested in how far he goes as our watch runs on. We can say that how far he goes is in terms of yards and we measure time with our watch in seconds. We imagine watching him move away, passing various markers, and also we imagine watching the second hand of the watch sweeping around. What we do in physical science is use two symbols and one number to represent on paper what the walker does. We use the symbol s for distance (it could be *any* symbol, such as 柏 , which is the Chinese name of one of the authors, or a Greek letter) and the symbol t for time, and we then put $s = 3t$, which means that the walker moves 3 yards every 1 second. This equation really is compact, and rather good. It will not mean very much if all we do is look at it. A very good thing would be to get a stopwatch and a football field, which is already marked out, and try it ourselves, making up our own symbolic relation. However, there is usually no football field near, so we do the next best thing. We represent it graphically. One way is by marking out seconds along the paper, as shown in Figure 14.2, and then making pedestals at each second, of height which represents the distance he goes. Thus we can see what we get for 0, 1, 2, 3, and 5 seconds. We will find s to be 0, 3, 6, 9, and 15 yards. Making pedestals of the right relative heights we get a picture as drawn. To get the feel, fill in 4 and 6.

Another way is to dot the value of s along an "axis" upward and the value of t along an "axis" horizontally. By this we mean directions ↑ and →, respectively. What happens is shown in Figure 14.3. Again, to get the feel, fill in 4 and 6 seconds.

Fig. 14.2. The relations $s = 3t$ set out in pedestals.

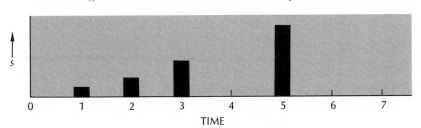

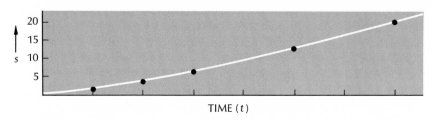

Fig. 14.3. The relation $s = 3t$ set out in dots. Because it is also true for *all*
values of t, a line through the dots can be drawn.

Now we made a bland assertion about Nature. We said that she was
often very regular in her behavior. Our walking man is a part of Nature.
So we feel confident that if we had looked at our watch at $2\frac{1}{2}$ seconds
he would have gone 3 times $2\frac{1}{2}$, or $7\frac{1}{2}$ yards. Actually he will have gone
a definite distance for any time, if he does not stop to tie his shoelaces on
the way. We can represent this very easily by drawing a line through the
points, as in Figure 14.3. Then we can read up until we hit the line and
then across until we hit the distance. It will tell us where he reached.

Now, on the same paper, make pedestals and mark points for two other
possible relations, $s = 1t$ and $s = 4t$.

Notice how the numbers 3, 1, and 4 change the actual figure but not the
form of the figure. These "numbers" are often called (rather loosely)
"constants." If we care to denote any number such as 3, 1, or 4 by a
symbol, say G, then we have $s = Gt$.

When such a relationship holds we say that distance is proportional to
time; in symbols, s is proportional to t.

Quite a bit of physical science is concerned with simple proportional-
ities; for example, speed is proportional to time in a falling body; current
is proportional to electric field in a conducting wire. However, we cannot
settle for this degree of simplicity: we need to examine two more relations
at least.

If, instead of the man walking, we had used our watch to time a car
just starting up, we would not have seen the same thing at all. Instead,
the car would cover lots more distance for the longer the time. The sort
of thing we might have found would be represented by $s = 2t^2$.

This is different. Applying our two methods of representing this relation, we find a different behavior, changing more as time goes by, for the
pedestals. We have left 4 and 6 seconds to be filled in. The graph,
Figure 14.5, of course, also looks different; once again, fill in 4 and 6
seconds.

As before, we know that the car was behaving regularly, so that the
distance gone at $2\frac{1}{2}$ seconds or $3\frac{1}{2}$ seconds can be found. The easiest

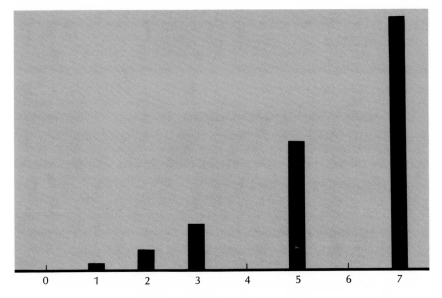

Fig. 14.4. Representation of $s = 2t^2$ by pedsetals.

way to find it is to join the points on the graph with a line and then do as before, read up from the proper time to the line and then across to the distance.

Now plot $s = 4t^2$ on the same graph, as before. In making these plots graph paper and rulers are not necessary. Just make good sensible esti-

Fig. 14.5. Graphical representation of $s = 2t^2$.

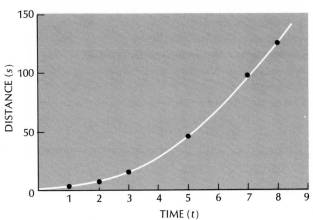

mates of distance, using ruling on the page and the width of a pencil, or the length of a bobby pin. The important thing is the form of the relation. In this kind of plotting, without graph paper, the points will not lie exactly on the line. Never mind, go ahead and draw a good-looking line anyway.

Notice that the numbers 2, 1, and 4 do not change the form, but they magnify or diminish the values appropriate to the relation. We can, as before, represent these numbers by a letter, say c, and then $s = ct^2$.

The last relation we need to look at is very important indeed. It is the form of the law of gravitation, of electrostatics, and of magnetism. Since we are going to discuss it at some length later, we propose simply to give a formula for it. It is

$$F = \frac{10}{r^2}$$

The symbol F is useful to represent force and the symbol r to represent a distance away from some object causing the force. This relation is so important that we intend to use three ways to study it. The first is the pedestal trick. It is shown in Figure 14.6.

We notice that for $r = 1$, F is $10/1^2 = 10$; for $r = 2$, F is $10/2^2 = 2.5$; for $r = 3$, F is $10/3^2 = 1.11$. You can fill in (approximately) 4 and 6.

The second way is again a graph, shown in Figure 14.7. We plot it exactly as before. Notice that the force gets less as the distance increases, and also that for zero distance there is so huge a force that we could not possibly plot it. In fact, the force is infinite. This sort of thing bothers a mathematician, but it is a futile worry in physical science, for no object that can cause a force can have zero size.

Fig. 14.6. Representation of an inverse square law.

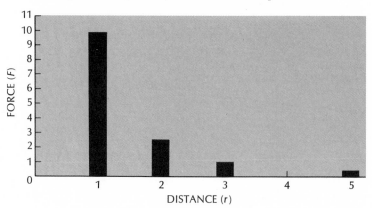

DISTANCE (r)

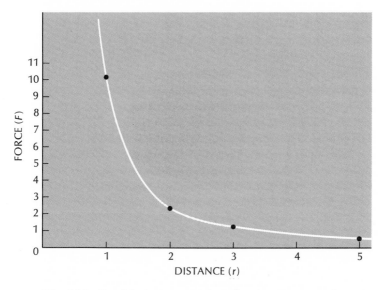

Fig. 14.7. Graphical representation of an inverse square law.

Now both the graph and the pedestals fail to represent something about this relation, which is that r can have any direction. To try to overcome this problem draw a set of circles of radius 1, 2, 3, 4, 5, and 6 units rather lightly in pencil. Fill in the center ring, as we will suppose this to be the smallest radius possible. Now put 200 dots rather close to the first ring, 50 rather close to the second ring, 22 rather close to the third, 14 rather close to the fourth, and so on. The end result ought to look something like Figure 14.8. If the reader is good at drawing and art in general, he can replace the dots by a graded shading so that a better impression is produced. In any event, this kind of rapid fading away is characteristic of this relation.

The relation is called an *inverse square relation*.

We can now go on to think about some of the relationships of physical science.

The Meaning of Mathematical Expression in Physical Science

By now such relations as $v = at$ and $F = ma$ will be disturbing the reader's equanimity. These relations do have an exact meaning, and to a person who intends to practice science professionally the exact meaning is most

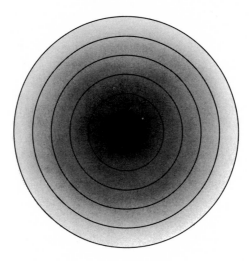

Fig. 14.8. The inverse square law. The shading in the center is much deeper than out at the edge. This is the character of something which depends *inversely* on distance.

important. For us a somewhat lessened exactness is all we need, and some few remarks about this may help.

In each relation there are two things to look at: *form* and *magnitude*. It is easiest to give examples. Thus

$$v = 2t \qquad v = 10t \qquad v = at$$

all have the same form, but the magnitudes are different. We can check this very easily by putting in some easy numbers, like 1 or 10 or 2. Take the first. Put $t = 1$. Then the value of v would be 2. Take the second. Put t $= 1$ and the value of v is 10. The magnitude is different; 10 is bigger than 2. But while the magnitudes differ, we are always multiplying t by some number, so the form is the same. On the other hand, relations such as $s = \dfrac{at^2}{2}$ and $F = \dfrac{q_1 q_2}{r^2}$ have quite different forms.

The relation $s = \dfrac{at^2}{2}$ has a great dependence on t. If $t = 1$, then s is small. If $t = 10$, then s is 100 times larger. If $t = 100$, s is 10,000 times larger.

Again, the relation $F = \dfrac{q_1 q_2}{r^2}$, where we have r on the bottom and squared, is quite different in form. In order to make F have a big value, r must be *small*. So the smaller r is, the bigger F is. This is quite a different form.

WHY ARE WE SO UNCONCERNED OVER MAGNITUDE?

It may seem surprising that a scientist, who deals so much in accuracy and precision, is willing to look at only a part of a mathematical relation. The reason is that, first of all, we want to gather the ideas. In the science of mechanics the all-important idea is that acceleration is the feature of motion which matters the most. The first clue to this came from Galileo and can be seen in his relation $v = at$. The form of this tells us the importance of a, the acceleration; the magnitude would depend on whether Galileo measured his distances in cubits or feet, and his time in drops of water or seconds or hours. Also, in suggesting this first attention to form we are doing just what an experienced physical scientist does. If he opens up a new book and sees new mathematical relations, he first looks at the way the relationships appear. Only quite a bit later does he test the relations with numbers. So we take the same approach here.

UNITS

Quite clearly, units will be concerned with magnitude. Thus a car which does 60 miles per hour does 60×1760 yards per hour, or 105,600 yards per hour. In feet per second, the same car, at the same speed, does 88. To keep units consistent, and to get numerically significant statements out of mathematical relations, is quite a discipline. It contains no profound ideas but can become tricky and frustrating. The ability to interconvert units and handle relations correctly is essential to a specialist. For us it is not essential, because, once again, we are concerned with ideas. Later in this chapter special attention to units has been given; the reader can follow the subject further by reading there.

COMMUNICATION BETWEEN SPECIALIST AND LAYMAN

One of our objectives is to make communication between our reader and a specialist possible. Fortunately it is not so hard as is commonly supposed. Many of the ideas of a science, or of any relatively accurate subject, like economics or music, can be conveyed as ideas, while the reasoning behind the ideas or the practical results of the ideas may be much harder to convey. Thus we shall not have any great trouble understanding why a satellite does what it does, and the idea can be readily transmitted. But to instruct a crew how to shoot off and control a missile to put a man in a particular orbit is something else again. Thus we propose to separate ideas and numbers, and for this reason we stress the *form*, or the relations.

MEASURING RATES: THE DIFFERENTIAL CALCULUS

If we consider a car starting up, or a falling body, or a growing population, we are confronted with a rather interesting mathematical problem. The problem is to measure something at an instant and not over a *range*. It has been solved by the following thought process: we start out by measuring over a range and we shrink the range until it is an instant. When we do this we find we can set up some rather simple rules. The rules are given the name of the *differential calculus*.

Let us start with an example. A falling body, starting from rest, falls a distance s in feet during a time t in seconds, given by the relation $s = 16t^2$.

Now, for the first idea, the velocity is defined as distance/time. Let us make the relation pictorial with a graph, as in Figure 14.9. Now suppose we have to know the velocity at 5 seconds. How do we find it out? We can make a try by saying that velocity is distance/time and say that in 5 seconds the body falls 16×5^2, or 400 feet. Then we divide by 5 and get 80 feet per second.

But someone disagrees with this. He says we should have measured how far it goes in the time from 4 seconds to 5 seconds, and divided this by one second. Well, this is easy. We have:

$$4 \text{ seconds} \quad 16 \times 16 = 256 \text{ feet}$$
$$5 \text{ seconds} \quad 16 \times 25 = 400 \text{ feet}$$

Difference = 144 feet, velocity = 144 feet in 1 second = 144 feet per second. *It is not the same.*

So someone else says we should have measured how far it goes in the

Fig. 14.9. Graph of distance $(s) = 16t^2$. The velocity, the ratio of distance to time *at* 5 seconds, is required.

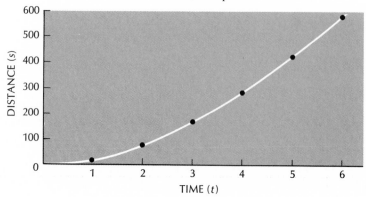

time from 5 seconds to 6 seconds, and divided this by one second. We have:

$$5 \text{ seconds} \quad = 16 \times 25 = 400 \text{ feet}$$
$$6 \text{ seconds} \quad = 16 \times 36 = 576 \text{ feet}$$

Difference = 176 feet, velocity = 176 feet in 1 second = 176 feet per second. *It is not the same.*

All this looks very confusing, and it is. So we stop and think. The whole trouble is that the distance changes very fast as the time changes, and that it changes more and more all the time. Suppose we said that we would measure the distance gone between 5 seconds and 5.1 seconds, and divide by 0.1 seconds. This mean we almost measure at an instant—not quite, but almost. Try it.

$$5 \text{ seconds} \quad 16 \times 25 = 400.00$$
$$5.1 \text{ seconds} \quad 16 \times (5.1)^2 = 416.16$$

Difference = 16.16, time = 0.1 seconds, distance/time = 161.6.

This is better, because it is between 144 and 176 and makes more sense, but perhaps it, too, is not right. Why not try the distance gone between 5 seconds and 5.01 seconds? Then divide by 0.01, a short time, to be sure, but still a time. This is even closer to an instant. Try it.

$$5 \text{ seconds} \quad 16 \times 25 = 400.00$$
$$5.01 \text{ seconds} \quad 16 \times (5.01)^2 = 401.6016$$

Difference = 1.6016, time = 0.01 seconds, distance/time = 160.16.

This is better yet, though not the same. What we see is that this trick gives us velocities which are less each time, but less in a way which suggests that they will not go below a certain *limit*. If we try 5 seconds and 5.001 seconds we get the distance/time = 160.016, and for 5 seconds and 5.0001 seconds we get 160.0016. The magic number we seem *to approach but never get below* is 160.

Where this kind of division of one number by another occurs, so that both numbers get less together as we make the bottom number smaller, there may well be *no change* in the ratio as the two numbers get less and less. Such a case is spoken of as *having a limit*. It was Newton's idea that the velocity at 5 seconds would be found by taking the distance gone from the 5 seconds to some very tiny time beyond 5 seconds and dividing by the very tiny time. He said "You can make the tiny time as small as you like, the result will be the same."

Today we have a special notation for the tiny quantities. The tiny distance we call *ds* where the *d* is a prefix meaning "tiny change in" and the tiny time we call *dt*, where again the prefix *d* means "tiny change in." Do not confuse d with distance. In this book d will never represent distance, diameter, dog, or any profanity—only "tiny change in." So we get

$$\text{Velocity, } v, = \frac{ds}{dt}$$

also

$$\text{Acceleration, } a, = \frac{dv}{dt}$$

This idea of a limit of a ratio is the basic idea of the differential calculus. It is called the *derivative*.

Measuring Summations: The Integral Calculus

There is one other important requirement for numerical description; with it we will have all the mental equipment necessary to understand a great deal of physical science. This is the need to express a summation, even when the thing we wish to add up is changing. Suppose we have the relation between distance and velocity given by an equation. Also suppose we know the velocity at many times, but we need to know distance. We put

$$v = \frac{ds}{dt}$$

In this, dt means a tiny change in time and ds a tiny change in distance which happens in that time.

Now we can multiply any equation by equals on each side and we do not change the statement of truth which it contains. Multiply by dt. So

$$vdt = \frac{ds}{dt}dt = ds, \text{ because the } dt\text{'s cancel.}$$

or $ds = vdt.$

This tells us that we can find the tiny bit of distance gone by multiplying the tiny bit of time by the velocity. Now if we did this, starting at zero time and continuing to measure the tiny distance gone for a succession of tiny times, we would get:

$$ds_1 = v_1 dt_1$$
$$ds_2 = v_2 dt_2$$
$$ds_3 = v_3 dt_3$$
$$ds_4 = v_4 dt_4$$

Adding up all the tiny pieces on the left will give us the whole distance gone. Now suppose we do not know the left-hand side, but we do know the values of v_1, v_2, and so on, and of course we would make up a whole lot of equal tiny times dt. So our problem becomes that of adding up the *right-hand side,* and to do that is a shade harder.

The person reading all this very symbolic and rather remote material may wonder why it is necessary or even conceivably interesting. In a sense it is impossible to give a reassuring answer, because really one has to have a certain amount of preliminary interest anyway. That is one of the reasons for describing this material in a late chapter. To try to give an answer we can say that there are many cases where the end result is really of more value than the detailed nature of the process. We can take a rather exaggerated analogy. If we deal out four hands of cards, the act of dealing each card is interesting, and the dealer has to think about it. But the really interesting thing is each final hand when dealt. A card sharper knows that the actual process of dealing is vital to him and he pays great attention to the individual acts of his fingers. But most honest people just want to be sure that thirteen cards have been dealt to each of the four players. So with the case of the summations we are working at. We do indeed have to know the nature of each detailed process, but we also need to know the whole result at the end. So when we are after the summation, in science we turn toward the process we are describing: the process of the integral calculus.

Whether this helps or not, at least the reader has had a short respite from symbols.

Now to return to our example, suppose we plot a graph of velocity, v, versus time, t, as in Figure 14.10.

We have chosen the rather interesting case where the velocity changes very markedly as the time gets bigger. Ordinarily, falling bodies, or simple systems, usually do not have quite so complicated a relationship. Now we suppose that someone asks us "how far did your car (or bicycle, or whatever) get in ten seconds?" If we think for a minute we can see there is no reason not to give the answer: we know all about the speed at all the times that matter. Yet it is not just a matter of quick glance and a decision—or rather, it really is, but only after we know the method to be used.

The method is this: we tackle it a bit at a time. We divide up the graph into a set of strips, as drawn in Figure 14.10. The times at which we made the division we have labeled as 0, t_1, t_2, t_3, . . . , and so on to t_9. In the earlier part of this section we concluded that we could gain a great deal of knowledge by seeing what happened for these short intervals and then deciding to make them shorter (and, in this case,

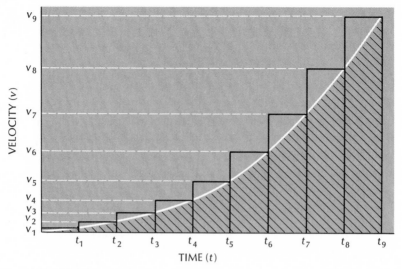

Fig. 14.10. Addition method of finding distance gone for a changing velocity.

deciding to add more of them). When we do this we notice that we can multiply the individual velocities by the individual times and add them up:

$$v_1(t_1 - 0) + v_2(t_2 - t_1) + v_3(t_3 - t_2) \ldots ,$$

and when this is done we get a set of steps as in Figure 14.10.

This is not quite the same as the summation we are after, because the steps are artificial and we should be going along the line. But by making the steps very short and very many, the artificial nature gets less, *and we can lessen it as much as we please* by increasing the number and diminishing the size. When we have made the number huge and the size small, then the addition of all the vast numbers of products will be the same as what we want, and in this case will be the distance gone, *s*. We write

$$s = \int_0^{v_9} v\,dt$$

The numbers at top and bottom of the integral sign are the finishing and starting points, respectively.

It is also constructive to notice that, in terms of geometry, this addition of many tiny steps is the same as the area between the line, the time axis, and the last time, the area we show shaded in Figure 14.10. This trick is especially useful if we have a simple geometrical way to find the area. Where we have a straight line graph, for example, the area is that of a triangle, and is 1/2 (base × height). This is the basis for our saying that kinetic energy is

$$\tfrac{1}{2}v \times mv = \tfrac{1}{2}mv^2.$$

$$\downarrow \quad \downarrow$$

base   height

All of this reasoning, of course, underlies the *integral calculus*.

The Application of Physical Principles to Actual Problems

Up to the present we have stayed with the bargain we made very early with the reader: in exchange for understanding the principles correctly we agreed to introduce no problems. Now we are at the very end of the material we want to cover and we think there may be some hardy souls who feel that they should be able to see how the principles actually work: in short their appetite has been whetted for some problems. Also we have some sympathy for those many students who are engaged in more formal physics courses and who are being exposed to problems. So, in this chapter we intend to discuss the nature of "solving" problems. It will rapidly appear that, while the laws of Nature have great beauty, man-made exercises for student underbodies do not. In spite of this, the approach to many very interesting applications of physical laws to real cases is not very difficult, and can be quite pleasant.

Measurement, Units, and Equations

In Chapter 2, where we introduced the idea of numbers and algebra as an aid to abstract thinking, or, preferably, "accurate imagination," we stuck resolutely to ideas, and said nothing about how numbers go into relationships between them. It is soon found that some thought has to go into how this is done—it is actually quite a lot of thought, and because this rather disciplinary aspect of science seemed to get in the way of realizing the beauty of the ideas of science, we postponed discussing it.

Suppose you have the habit of walking home from work, and that one day a friend, who rides a bicycle, joins you just as you leave. It would not be absurd for the two of you to get into an argument about how far it is to walk. To settle the argument you might agree to count your paces, while he might read off the odometer on his bicycle. If

your home is one mile away, and if you walk one-yard paces, then at
the end of the walk you will be carrying the number 1760 and he will
be observing that he has just 1. Now the distance is just the same for
both of you, and anything which involves motion, such as force,
acceleration, potential energy, and so on, will be involved in some way
with this distance. Which number do you use: 1 or 1760? Even worse:
suppose that instead of walking a yard at each stride, you knew you
walked four feet, and suppose it were on your conscience to tell your
friend the distance in yards. Something would have to be done to
the number laboriously accumulated in your head, to get it into yards.

Clearly we are introducing a subject which truly is a "discipline,"
to quote a much over-worked word among educators, and we sympa-
thize with any reader who starts to turn the pages rapidly at this point.
On the other hand, those who do stay with them may feel a certain
sense of power at the end which they might have missed otherwise.

The clue to the proper use of these numbers is to return to the way
in which numbers developed. It was never any problem with integers,
which represent single definite things. It takes great skill to represent
one apple by any means other than the number 1. So if we have two
apples in stock and buy three more, there is no problem about the
total of 5 being equal to $2 + 3$. But as soon as we introduce fractions
we change all that, because now there is a choice as to what to divide
by. In other words, an apple can either be 1 *or something else*—say,
4, meaning it is the sum of four quarters. So we have to think about the
way we introduced these more complicated numbers into relationships.

We need to remind the reader that we are suffering at this moment,
though perhaps he is not. We do love the beauty and form of the
laws of Nature, and we really know that when a planet sweeps around
the sun it is not doing so in order to make some mathematical equation operate: it is simply obeying the laws. Here is where the use
of numbers to aid our thinking may make life harder for us than it
need be. Perhaps there is a better way to visualize the way Nature works.
If there is, no one has ever made a success of it, and we are left with
the tradition of our means of discovery. So we must dig in and see how
to use these numbers mathematically so as to make sense physically.

The first simple rule is that our way of measurement must be consistent, and that we do not measure the same thing, or a closely related
thing, differently at different stages. Thus if we have to calculate a
distance from the knowledge of speed for a certain time, we must not
use miles per hour for the speed and seconds for the time. The result will not be false, but it will be strange and hard to assimilate, and
we have to learn the discipline of watching each operation with this

criterion of consistency. This sounds easy, but it is not, because there are generally a lot of operations.

The second rule, which really follows from the first, is that the adjustment of measurements must be consistent. Thus a fast car, known to be doing 100 miles per hour, may actually be timed by an expert with a stop watch reading seconds. The "raw data," therefore, is mongrel: it has hours *and* seconds in it. It will not matter how we make the figures consistent, so long as we do. This we can easily check. Suppose the car was timed for 50 seconds. In an hour we have 60×60, or 3,600 seconds. So 50 seconds is $50/3,600$ or $1/72$ hour. Then the distance gone, s, is given by the formula

$$s = \text{velocity} \times \text{time}.$$

(We shall be very wise if we see that all formulas fit our ideas of what is reasonable—here we notice that our definition of velocity was distance/time, so that we get

$$\text{velocity} \times \text{time} = \frac{\text{distance}}{\text{time}} \times \text{time} = \text{distance}$$

which checks. Also we note that a high speed and a long time make for a great distance, so that on two counts we check. We intend to return to this aside later.)

Completing our calculation, we find that

$$s = 100 \times 1/72, \quad \text{or} \quad 1.39 \text{ miles}.$$

Now suppose we had elected to work in seconds. Then we face the problem of how many miles the car does in one second. This must be much less than the mile in an hour, and will be $100/3600$, or $1/36$ mile per second. Again we will be wise to check this for reasonableness. A car going 60 miles per hour does one mile in a minute, or $1/60$ mile per second. Our car is faster, and does more of a mile per second—it is sensible.

The calculation now goes:

$$s = 1/36 \times 50 = 1.39 \text{ miles}.$$

This very simple calculation shows up some strong messages we want to impart. The first, and by far the most important, is that we must be maddeningly deliberate. The slower the better. This is not unique to scientific calculations. A good music teacher generally slows his pupils down. Also there is no hurry—certainly not for us. Let us make it clear that we have a great aversion to the idea that finding out how the laws of Nature work is somehow competitive, and that we shall be judged by the speed with which we get the "answer." No single more misguided idea than this exists in the whole of the teaching of physical science. Every operating research scientist knows how slowly and carefully he must make the calculations with which he makes his final conclusions. The practice of many great men is to make the calculation, and wait as much as a month, and repeat it as differently as possible, and to try to get a friend to go over the whole once more before it appears in public. Even so, some of the greatest men have erred: for example Einstein, who corrected one error he made some six years later.

Our second message is that we should use as many varieties of thinking which will bear on the problem as possible. If the procedure is all mathematical, then we should use an equivalent physical way to reason. See if they agree. Use "common sense" to check both.

The third, a really trivial suggestion, is that we should have no impatience in the writing down of numbers. Hurry with words, not numbers. An incorrect copying of a number is obviously as big a "goof" as any incorrect reasoning. This leads naturally to the subject of computation itself, which we can now consider.

COMPUTATION: USE OF APPROXIMATIONS; POWERS OF TEN

Unfortunately we can never escape the toils of arithmetic. What has to be done with numbers must be done resolutely and, we fear, often. Fortunately, almost nobody is as bad at arithmetic as one of the authors, as his wife will testify in regard to bridge scores, and yet he has survived to do many calculations and even to do some correctly. One reason why this has proved to be possible is that physical arithmetic is not like accounting arithmetic; it is not done to catch every cent, but is done to show the kind of behavior which results from Natural Law. Very often the calculation can be grossly simplified and still the insight obtained is quite adequate. Almost every physical scientist has this skill: the ability to do shortened approximate calculations, to gain an idea of the *kind* of thing which must be happening instead of the pure and exact working out of all the figures. This readiness to do "rough" calculation surprises many students who see it in their scientific professors for the first time. It makes good sense, because often an accurate result is laborious to obtain, and, if the conclusion is trivial, as it often is, not worth considering.

As a start, it is quite legal to reduce all the numbers in a calculation to numbers between zero and 10, eleven in all. Arithmetic with such numbers is not too tough. Suppose we go back to our car, and how far it will have gone in 50 seconds. Doing it by the first way, we start with 100, which conveniently has just 1, so we have an easy start, and then we see we have 1/72 hour. We don't like 72, it is awkward, so we call it 70. Then our result is roughly $100 \times 1/70$, or 10/7, which is a division most people can do in their heads, particularly if all we are asking is the first number, or at most the first two. Even the authors can see that the first number is 1 and the first two 1.4. For many purposes, the conclusion that the car went over a mile may be all we want, and the result 1.4 may be quite enough to give us the "feel" of the speed and time.

Now we know that the reader has developed one objection already. He has noticed that we have treated 100 as if it were 1, but later we replace it as 100. What are we up to? This is a very easy matter, but it needs some explanation. One of the great beauties of the system of numbers we use, and one not employed by the Romans, to their lasting detriment, is that at some designated number, in our system it is ten, we make a shift in writing, usually by moving one to the left, and in this way we can accumulate numbers compactly and make simple rules for arithmetic. We do not intend to change this very adequate system, but we are confronted with the enormous range of size offered to us by Nature, from the nucleus of the atom to the set of atoms comprising the Universe. To keep the spirit of the shift to the left, or for small numbers, to the right, we have to use a more compact notation, which involves representation of these shifts as "powers of ten." We will illustrate this and then try to explain it. We write 100 as 10^2, 10,000 as 10^4. For numbers smaller than unity (one) we write 1/100 or 0.01, as 10^{-2}, 1/10,000 or 0.0001 as 10^{-4}. For big numbers the power of ten is equal to the numbers of zeros, for those less than unity in the decimal system the number is one less than the number of zeros. Now we may take a number like 139 and call it 1.39×10^2. This is not any gain, but the velocity of light, which is 29,980,000,000 centimeters per second, is better written as 2.998×10^{10}. The number of electrons in the universe, thought to be 10^{72}, is even better.

In physical science we have to adopt this system, and it is easy to see that it has the effect of separating the number of zeros, or the number of zeros after the decimal point, from the number itself.

Thus one comes to do calculations in two parts, the number and the power of ten.

Now we promised to explain powers of ten. By now we feel that we really do not need to. The only matter which should be mentioned is that each power of ten is represented by a number, and that there is no difference between these numbers and squares, cubes, etc. The negative powers refer to 1 divided by various numbers of ten, and because 1/10 is much less than 1 we do not think of it as the separation

point between numbers larger than 1 and those less than 1. We reserve
10^0, or the equivalent, 10^{-0}, for that position. This has the effect of
making the decimal point not quite the same indicator as we might
expect, for we set 0.1 as 10^{-1}, and so the number of zeros after the decimal point is one less than the power of ten. For numbers greater than
unity the number of zeros equals the power of ten.

WORKING A PROBLEM: DATA AND RELATIONSHIPS

No physical problem exists without information being supplied: such
information is called *data*. This information is in the form of relevant facts, usually as numbers or as numbers and the units. The reader
may wonder why on earth we take time to say this glaringly obvious
fact, and indeed he has good cause to wonder. The reason we introduce it is because the vast majority of physical problems which we are
concerned with really are not solvable, and one reason for this is that
the amount of data needed may be far too great to manage. Let the
reader take a sheet of paper and, without doing anything to it, let it
fall. The resultant motion will be interesting. It is even more interesting to do it a second time and notice that the paper does *not* transverse
the same path twice. To solve the "problem" of a falling sheet of paper
is thus sure to be tough. We are certainly going to need to know all
about the density of the air, the shape of the paper, any air currents in
the room, as well as the knowledge Galileo developed about falling
bodies. Thus it is good practice before starting a problem to look carefully at what knowledge is given. It may be wiser to abandon the
whole thing at the start, and to do so will be normal among physicists.
We may conclude, on the other hand, that we have enough to make a
try at a solution. If we do, then the next thing to do is to recast the
problem in a form suitable for introducing the relationship of our laws
of Nature. Often this involves no change; often it does involve a change.
Always our attitude of mind becomes that of watching the consequence
of the relationship and not only the original statements.

Let us take an example. Suppose we want to know how much a
200-lb. astronaut will weigh when he gets to the moon. This is a nice
compact way of saying what we are interested in, but we shall be wise
to look at it to see what information we must ask for. Do we have it?

Now weight is the force exerted by whatever body is pulling us. On
earth it is the earth, on the moon it is the moon. The force will be
given by the law of gravitation, the relationship we have been harping
on above. We can write it down:

$$F = G \frac{M \times m}{R^2}$$

and the reader knows that G is the constant of gravitation, M the mass of the earth, m the mass of the astronaut, and R the distance from the center of the earth to the astronaut. It looks as though we are going to need to know everything in this formula, plus all about the moon, and it looks pretty tedious. Better leave it to the National Aeronautics and Space Administration. However, before we give up we notice that all we are asking is what happens to this one astronaut. If we could compare his weight on the moon with that on earth, we would be happy; we would have obtained what interests us. So, if we use subscripts for "moon" all the way through, we see that his weight is F_m, where

$$F_m = G \frac{M_m \times m}{R_m{}^2}$$

Suppose we divide this by the first relation. We can always divide equal by equals without altering truth. Then

$$F_m/F = \frac{M_m}{M} \times \frac{R^2}{R_m{}^2}$$

and we see that we do not need to know the gravitation constant or the mass of the astronaut, we only need to know the mass of the moon, the mass of the earth, and the two radii. Now we can ask for this information, and we are a bit more ready to work the problem than we were. *What we have done is to recast it.* To know that this step is necessary, and that the greatest point of reward in doing such problems is in this process of recasting, is the most important basis of approach which most people have to have if they are to solve problems.

Incidentally, we were quite fast about some mathematics in the paragraph above. This is not because we are especially bright, but because we have done it before. What we must ask the reader to do, if working problems is to be part of his life, is to go at the above mathematics slowly and see that we are right. Scratch pads are needed for this, and actually there is even some fun associated with it.

To return to the problem. We are now at the end of ingenuity. We must go somewhere and find the things we need to know. Here they are:

Ratio of mass of moon to mass of earth = 0.01.
Radius of earth = 4,000 miles.
Radius of moon = 1,000 miles.

Therefore:

$$F_m/F = 0.01 \times \frac{16}{1}$$

We thus deduce that F_m/F is 0.16, and for a 200-lb. astronaut, F is 200 lb. We then calculate F_m as 32 lb.

Now the reader may well exclaim that the above problem *did* contain the need for some trickery, that it did not just follow from the laws of Nature as we have tended to claim in the past. We had to be initiated into the secrets of "recasting" before the problem could be solved. This is not quite true. Just the same result is obtained without any skill at all; by using the law of gravitation. It is just longer, that is all, and we have to discover for ourselves that the constant of gravitation is not relevant to the question we have asked. In order to make good on our assertion we are now going to work the problem absolutely straightforwardly and show that the result is not different.

Now we need to know the mass of the astronaut and the constant of gravitation. The former introduces a little confusion because we have permitted a custom to grow up in which the mass of a body and its weight are given by the same number, a custom which has been richly cursed by generations of students. When we say, as we did above, that the weight of the astronaut is 200 lb., we are requiring ourselves to remember that whenever we concern ourselves with motion we must introduce the effect of the earth's gravity on the body. Generally, while shopping, or in checking on our diet, we only want to compare, and we get lazy. If we consult the formula above, we soon see that the force exerted by the earth on a mass of 200 lb. is $\dfrac{G M \times 200}{R^2}$, and this is certainly not 200.* This is the accursed custom that has made so many students develop a hatred for physics. It is not our fault, any more than it is our fault that we use the word "square" to refer to a geometric figure on one occasion or a kind of person on another. Then if we accept that the mass of the astronaut, m, is 200 lb., the other new number we need is the value of G, the constant of gravitation. We are going to save the reader a lot of trouble by giving this value in the units we have used so far, involving pounds for mass and feet for distance. In terms of this measurement G is 1.03×10^{-9} poundals feet^2/pounds^2, the mass of the earth is 13.1×10^{24} lb., of the moon 13.1×10^{22} lb. The radius of the earth is 2.1×10^7 feet, of the moon 5.0×10^6 feet.

Now we can see directly that the force on the moon is

$$F_m = \frac{1.03 \times 10^{-9} \times 13.1 \times 10^{22} \times 200}{(5.0 \times 10^6)^2} = 200 \times 5.3$$

---

* The force measured in this way, on the system using pounds for mass, feet for distance, and seconds for time, has units called poundals.

and the force on the earth is

$$F = \frac{1.03 \times 10^{-9} \times 13.1 \times 10^{24} \times 200}{(2.1 \times 10^{7})^{2}} = 200 \times 32.$$

This last may be vaguely familiar to some readers, as it is the mass time the acceleration of free fall in feet per second per second, or 200×32. It is useful to find this number, as it is one check on our calculation. The ratio of the two, in round numbers, is 0.16, as before. The two calculations check. Thus we see that the result is the same as that obtained by recasting the problem.

One illustration is not really enough, and the previous example, while within the scope of the material we have developed in the text proper, is really not as good as a starting problem as it seemed at first: it is too much involved with trickery and units. Here is another, which may prove to be better. Suppose we calculate the force exerted on a single proton as it reaches the nuclear radius of uranium. This force is repulsive, because the proton and the nucleus are both positively charged, and we suppose that the proton has just not entered the region of influence of nuclear forces.

The force must be calculated from Coulomb's Law, so we put, using F for the force, q for the charges, and R for the distance from the proton to the center of the uranium nucleus,

$$F = \frac{q_1 \times q_2}{R^2}$$

Here is our relationship. What must we have for data? Well, we must know the values of the two charges, and we must also know the value of the radius. The charges are not too bad, for we know that uranium has 92 protons in its nucleus, and the charge of one proton is 4.8×10^{-10} electrostatic units, which are the units designed to work in the above formula for force. To obtain R we can either demand that we be told, or we can remember that the nuclear radius is given by the formula

$$R = 1.5 \times 10^{-13} A^{1/3} \text{cm}.$$

which is in the text. For uranium A is 238 and the cube root of 238 is very nearly 6, as can be seen by trying it out, so that R is very nearly $6 \times 1.5 \times 10^{-13}$. Now we have everything we need and can make the calculation. Here it is:

$$F = \frac{4.8 \times 10^{-10} \times 92 \times 4.8 \times 10^{-10}}{(9 \times 10^{-13})^{2}}$$

To make this something we can assimilate, we tidy it up, first by getting the various powers of ten collected into one power of ten. We must remember that we add them if they are multiplied and substract them if they are divided. Thus we get

$$\frac{10^{-10} \times 10^{-10}}{10^{-13} \times 10^{-13}} = \frac{10^{-20}}{10^{-26}} = 10^6$$

Division by a negative power of ten is an operation of division by something less than unity, so it makes a bigger number. This is why the 10^{-26} on the bottom appears up above as 10^{+26} and gives the big figure.

Now for our purposes we can put $4.8 = 5$, $92 = 90$, and the numbers are then $\frac{5 \times 5 \times 90}{9 \times 9}$, or $\frac{250}{9}$, or, roughly, 30. The final result is there:

$$F = 30 \times 10^6 = 3 \times 10^7.$$

The units in which this number is measured are now our concern. We have set up the form of Coulomb's Law so that a unit charge at a unit distance from another unit charge produces a unit force. If the charges are electrostatic units and the distance in centimeters, the unit of force is the dyne. If we are still linked to gravity in our intuition we want to know how this compares with what something weighs. Well, a dyne is very nearly one millionth of the weight of a kilogram, which is 2 lb. in the degree of roughness we have above. So our poor little proton experiences a force equal to about the weight permitted on the transatlantic airlines for baggage. Since nuclear forces are able to overcome this force and pull the proton into the nucleus, they must be even stronger, although they operate over a very tiny range of distance.

While we are about it, we can calculate the force due to gravity between the proton and the nucleus of uranium. The formula we already know. We use M_U and M_P for the mass of the uranium nucleus and the proton, respectively. The relationship between them becomes

$$F = \frac{G \times M_U \times M_P}{R^2}$$

and we must be told the mass of the proton and the uranium nucleus plus the value of the gravitation constant. The value of R we already know. The mass of a proton is 1.6×10^{-24} gram, and that of uranium, of atomic weight 238, is 238 times greater, or 384×10^{-24} gram, so we have the masses. The gravitation constant, in this kind of units, is

$$G = 6.7 \times 10^{-8} \text{ dyne} \left(\frac{\text{centimeter}}{\text{gram}} \right)^2.$$

So we can calculate F as follows:

$$F = \frac{6.7 \times 10^{-8} \times 3.8 \times 10^{-22} \times 1.6 \times 10^{-24}}{(9 \times 10^{-13})^2}$$

$$= \frac{6.7 \times 3.8 \times 1.6 \times 10^{-54}}{81 \times 10^{-26}} = 4.7 \times 10^{-29} \text{ dyne.}$$

The reader will have no difficulty in seeing that this is of a completely different size from the electrostatic force, and, of course, even more different from that of the nuclear force. It is this kind of calculation which is the basis for the statement we made much earlier in the text—that "gravity" is a very weak force.

While we are calculating forces in this kind of way we can see what sort of force would be exerted if we took all the protons and all the electrons in one cubic centimeter of water and set them along opposite edges, just one centimeter away from one another. This is a strange idea, but it cannot but suggest something about the kind of force holding matter together if it is indeed electrical as we have suggested.

The relationship is once again very easy, it is Coulomb's Law.

$$F = \frac{q_1 \times q_2}{R^2}$$

and we have set R as one centimeter, so that is easy. Thus we have to be told the value of the two charges, or rather of either one, for they are accurately equal, except in sign. The number of molecules in 18 grams of water (obtained by adding H_2O in terms of the atomic weights, as $2 + 16 = 18$) is 6×10^{23}, a formidable number known as Avogadro's number. In one cubic centimeter of water there is one gram, so we find there are $\frac{6 \times 10^{23}}{18}$, or, roughly, 3×10^{22} molecules. Now each molecule has 10 protons, and 10 electrons. Thus the value of q_1 and of q_2 is 30×10^{22} times the charge of each one, which is 4.8×10^{-10} electrostatic units. Thus the two charges are, again roughly, $5 \times 10^{-10} \times 30 \times 10^{22}$, or 150×10^{12}, or 1.5×10^{14}.

Then we see that

$$F = \frac{1.5 \times 10^{14} \times 1.5 \times 10^{14}}{1^2}$$

and is, again roughly, 2×10^{28} dynes. This is the weight of about 4×10^{22} lb., because we have said previously that one dyne is one-millionth of the weight of 2lbs., and one-millionth is 10^{-6}. Consider what a gigantic force this is. An ocean liner, weighing 100,000 tons, weighs only 2×10^8 lb. as there are 2,000 lbs. in a ton, so this force is greater than the weight of this very large object by 2×10^{14} times. To make any comparison at all we have to begin to think of the weight of something close to the size of the whole earth. All this in less than a teaspoon of water. It may come as a slight shock to the reader that the weight of the whole earth is only about 100 times larger than this force in the small space of a cubic centimeter of water!

This calculation does not simply show the great force latent in the charges of atomic material. It also shows why no charge can remain away from an opposite charge for long: the forces of attraction are so great. Matter only *appears* to be neutral; it is another of the great illusions.

SUMMARY AND POINTS OF WISDOM

In reality we have now covered all the necessary requirements for making calculations and attempting to do problems. Before we go on to some more illustrations, let us summarize the points we have made so far.

First we must see whether there is a relationship relevant to the problem we are asked to do. In other words, we ask if we can see some form of the laws of Nature which can be sensibly used on the problem. The falling sheet of paper cannot be tackled, because the relationship for the motion of a light, flexible body through the air under the influence of both gravity and local air currents is not one we know. So we must leave it alone. This does not mean that there is any mystery about how it falls; it means that we have to have a whole set of complicated data, and that the solution would be extremely laborious and only worth attempting if there were some real ultimate motive.

Second, we must recast the problem to suit the exact needs we have in mind. No rule for this process can be given, but it must be consciously done and time must be given to it, or the total time will be longer than we want. In the process of recasting we seek to reduce our wants from the relationship to those which concern us, and to eliminate all others. Also, we consciously try to replace the original reality by something closer to the abstraction of mathematics. For example, if we are asked to do one of the old cheeses in physics texts, to inquire about the stability of a ladder up against a wall, we replace the wall and the ladder by artificial geometric lines of great rigidity, of the same proportionate length, and draw arrows representing the forces on the "ladder" due to whatever causes. Then we look at this quite new diagram, in which the whole thing is, so to speak, held by forces in mid air. The way in which this is possible proves to tell us what we are asked to know about the ladder.

Third, and nastiest, we have to examine the way each number is to be inserted into the relationship to see that the proper convention for measurement applies to our figures. This is about 70 per cent of the trouble, and physics teachers are usually careful to take 0.7 per cent of their time in explaining it. In truth, the laws of Nature are so powerful and beautiful that the student almost at once is as competent as the professor. A good professor should love this, but there are some others.

Fourth, it is wise to be slow. Be slow, and always use as many secondary ways of looking at the question as possible. Check against other points of view, against common sense, and against other ways of getting the same result. It is true that $\frac{5 \times 10}{2} = 50/2 = 25$, and it is also true that $\frac{5 \times 10}{2} = 5 \times 5$, which again is 25. Running through this kind of check is always of the greatest value. It can be applied to much more subtle things than simple arithmetic, and the process is one which should be formed into a habit if the reader cares.

As an example, the reader may consider the formula for the time of oscillation of a pendulum: it is

$$T = 2\pi \sqrt{\frac{l}{g}}$$

where l is the length of the pendulum and g is shorthand for $\frac{G \times M}{R^2}$, where G is the gravitational constant, M is the mass of the earth, and R^2 is the distance to the center of the earth. Notice that it does not depend on the mass of the bob of the pendulum, which is rather a surprise. One can think about this as follows. Imagine *two pendulums* of exactly the same length, with bobs of exactly the same mass. Start them swinging. They will swing at the same rate. Now, in your mind, imagine them fused into one. The rate is unaltered. But remember, the fused pendulum now has one bob of twice the mass. By this quite indirect way we can see that the rather strange result is not so unexpected. This kind of constant alertness is part of the fun, and is an essential quality of a competent physical scientist.

Fifth, the beginner doing these exercises will always seem to be at a disadvantage in comparison with even the moderate expert. If some reserve of psychological adjustment could be called on to counteract that feeling of inferiority, the student would find that the glaring omissions which the "expert" does not seem to see, but which completely block the student, can be supplied if the student will ask for the information. Only by long experience does a patient, kindly, practicing scientist realize that things which are second nature to him are fresh and new to a student. Here is the area where aggression and initiative on the part of the student is of the greatest help to the "expert," and we make a plea that persistence and inquiry be used rather than retreat and defeat.

Sixth and last. Have a mortal dread of arithmetic. Battle it constantly and never let up. Induce your friends to check it for you if possible. Never relax, and as with anything for which you have a real fear, always vanquish it.

SOME MORE ILLUSTRATIONS

Because we do not want the reader to start on any problems for himself yet, we can put in a few more illustrations.

The first is really almost the simplest problem in Nature, the motion of one electron in an electric field. Let us see how it accelerates, and how long it takes to move in various ways. Before we begin, we remind the reader that the insertion of numbers into relationships is 70 per cent of the trouble. So we propose to state some very simple ways in which such numbers can reliably be used. Electrical quantities can be measured in many ways: the one we will use is quite old and not very fashionable among engineers, but it shows the relationships very simply. We will measure the charge in electrostatic units, the electric field in quaint units called "statvolts per centimeter," the distance in centimeters, and the time in seconds. When we do this the forces are naturally in dynes, and one dyne is about one-millionth of the weight of 2 lb. If we should ever get into problems of energy, the unit of energy we develop in this system is the *erg,* and about 40 million ergs make up a gram calorie, if we want to think about heat as well as other forms of energy. So long as we do not want to work magnetic problems, we can get along very well with this limited system. When we get into magnetic effects we have to lose some of the simplicity. For now, let us stop being frustrated and go ahead.

Suppose we apply an electric field of 1 statvolt per centimeter, which incidentally is about the field between the prongs of a plug as we plug it into the light socket. Then the force on an electron of charge e in this field intensity E is, as the reader knows,

$$F = Ee$$

and we need to be reminded that the actual charge of an electron is 4.8×10^{-10} electrostatic units, or as we shall say, 5×10^{-10}.

The force is then $1 \times 5 \times 10^{-10}$, or 5×10^{-10} dyne. This seems to be very small, but we must remember that we are on the scale of small things. Let us calculate the acceleration. To do this, we equate force to mass times acceleration, and so we must know the mass of the electron. This, we shall soon see, is very far from simple, but for now let us use the figure available from texts, 9×10^{-28} gram, or as we shall say, roughly 10^{-27} gram. Then the relationship for acceleration, $F = m \times a$, tells us that

$$5 \times 10^{-10} = 10^{-27} \times a$$

$$a = \frac{5 \times 10^{-10}}{10^{-27}} = 5 \times 10^{17} \text{ cms. per sec. per sec.}$$

The reader can see at once why electrons are useful if we want to do things quickly. This is an enormous acceleration. Let us figure how long it takes to get to 1/100 of the speed of light, or 3×10^8 centimeters per second.

For this, the relationship is

$$\text{Velocity} = \text{acceleration} \times \text{time}$$

which we can check for reasonableness, by recalling that an acceleration over a long time will give a big velocity, and a big acceleration will give a big velocity, so the relation seems sensible.

Putting in the numbers we find that

$$3 \times 10^8 = 5 \times 10^{17} \times t$$

$$t = \frac{3 \times 10^8}{5 \times 10^{17}} = 6 \times 10^{-10} \text{ second.}$$

This is amazingly short, and it explains why we were so coy about the mass of the electron. If in one-billionth of a second the electron is going at somewhere near the velocity of light, the effect of this speed will be felt in making the mass increase, as suggested by the theory of relativity. So that the mass of the electron in such calculations is not so simple. We are not going to attempt relativistic calculations, though they are really not very hard, only a bit tiresome.

These simple calculations suggest some of the reasons why electrons form a very exciting part of matter. To think about the way they actually behave in matter we need to consider another simple problem. This is: What is the distance apart of molecules, or in simple cases, atoms, in regions of matter where we expect electrons to move? Suppose we calculate how far apart the atoms in the simplest metal, lithium, are spaced. To do this we should, by rights, know something about the actual structure of lithium. But it turns out that, once again, we can find out what we need to know, without excessive exactness. What we propose to do is to say that the atoms are spaced evenly and consider a cube of side one centimeter. Figure 14.11 will help, though it is not essential.

Suppose that in one edge of the cube there are n atoms, as shown. Then in a face, there are n^2, and in the whole cube n^3. So if we can find the number in the whole cube, this can be used to tell us the number in an edge, and then if we divide the length of the edge by this number we should find the distance apart. We can check by starting with the distance apart, say x. Then the number in an edge is $1/x$ because we have a side of length 1 for a centimeter cube. Then the total number is $(1/x)^3$. In either event we must now find the total number. We do this by asking what is the mass of a one-centimeter cube of lithium. The tables will list this as the density of lithium, and it is 0.5 gram. Now we have to know

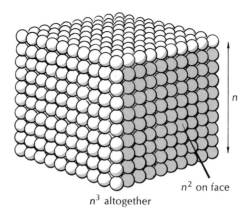

n

n^2 on face

n^3 altogether

Fig. 14.11. The number of atoms in a cube of regular atomic array.

the mass of one atom of lithium. If we knew the mass of one hydrogen atom we could find the mass of lithium, for the chemists have found the atomic weight of lithium to be 7, which for this book is the ratio of the mass of an atom of lithium to that of hydrogen. So one datum we must be told is the mass of hydrogen atom. It is 1.6×10^{-24} gram.

Then the mass of a lithium atom is $7 \times 1.6 \times 10^{-24}$ gram, or roughly 10×10^{-24}, or 10^{-23} gram. Thus the number of atoms in a cube of lithium is $0.5/10^{-23}$, or 0.5×10^{23}, or 5×10^{22}. So $n^3 = 5 \times 10^{22}$. To find n we have to find a cube root, which can generate tension in us. We make it easy by writing the powers of ten in easy multiples of 3, namely 10^{21}, and say that $n^3 = 50 \times 10^{21}$. Now all we have to do is to find the cube root of 50 and some rapid trial and error puts it between 3 and 4. We will call it 4. So $n = 4 \times 10^7$ and $x = 1(4 \times 10^7)$ which is 2.5×10^{-8} cm., a very small number. Our check method says that $(1/x)^3 = 7 \times 10^{22}$, and we find $1/x = 4 \times 10^7$, so, again, $x = 2.5 \times 10^{-8}$ cm. This number is generally written in different units. We call 10^{-8} cm. one Ångstrom unit, abbreviated Å, and so we find $x = 2.5$Å.

If the reader will bear with us, we would like to go a little further with this line of calculation. We are leading up to a little elementary "solid state physics," and our next thought concerns how fast an electron will be going, in the field we spoke of before, if all it does is to go from one atom to the next. We need not be too accurate about where each atom starts and stops, let us just say that the electron goes a distance equal to the spacing we just calculated. Now if we go back to the equations of motion we developed a long time ago, we find that we have expressions for acceleration and time but nothing simple for speed and distance.

However, we *do* recall something about potential energy and kinetic energy, and we also recall that electrical forces are of the kind we called conservative, and so have a potential energy. Let us find the change in potential energy as an electron moves in the electric field through this distance. The value will be force times distance, and we already know the force: it is 5×10^{-10} dyne. The distance is 2.5×10^8 cm., so the change of potential energy is $5 \times 10^{-10} \times 2.5 \times 10^{-8}$ dyne cm., or 12.5×10^{-18}. These units we call ergs. The number is very small, but so is the electron. Now we also remember that the loss of potential energy, for a conservative force, is equal to the gain of kinetic energy, and the expression for kinetic energy is $\frac{1}{2}mv^2$. So we have, $\frac{1}{2} \times 9 \times 10^{-28}v^2 = 12.5 \times 10^{-18}$, which leads to

$$v^2 = \frac{25 \times 10^{-18}}{9 \times 10^{-28}} = 3 \times 10^{10}, \text{approximately.}$$

Thus the speed developed, which is the square root of 3×10^{10}, is about 1.7×10^5 centimeters per second, or quite close to one mile per second. In other words, in this very tiny distance the electron has gained a prodigious speed. It is not a bit surprising that an electric current develops very quickly.

To keep on one more step, let us now ask about the size of the electric field which the electron will encounter when it gets near the next atom. To figure this we do have to know something about the size of the atom. Let us suppose it to be about one-third the distance apart of two atoms, or, since we like easy numbers, 1 Ångstrom unit, or 10^{-8} cm. Then the electric field is the field due to the one charge which is on the atom, left there by the electron when it became free, and so is

$$E = e/r^2 = 5 \times 10^{-10}/(10^{-8})^2$$
$$= \frac{5 \times 10^{-10}}{10^{-16}}$$
$$= 5 \times 10^6 \text{ statvolts per centimeter.}$$

In other words, this electric field is five million times larger than the feeble effect of some battery we have connected to the metal to produce a current.

The reader is now in a position to understand the basis for the first theory of conduction of electricity in solids, devised by Drude in 1904. Drude supposed that between collisions the electron moved only in the electric field produced by the battery, but that whenever a collision with an atom took place the event was so huge that the electron lost all "memory" of its motion in the field of the battery and violently started a totally new flight in any direction whatsoever. During this flight, however, the field of the battery reasserted itself, and the electron developed a speed because of it, a speed directed toward the positive pole of the battery, and which, after many collisions resulted in the final achievement of the goal—reaching the other end. This theory, as the reader can well see, has to be considered as very much of an approximation, as indeed it is; nevertheless, it gave valuable insight into the processes that take place in a metal and enabled Drude to examine several of the characteristics of the conduction of electricity in metals, notably the relation to heat conduction and the way in which electromagnetic waves, such as light waves, can be expected to react with metals.

The reader may have tired of all this by now. If he still has any interest left, here are a few problems he can try. They are not chosen as exercises at all, but rather because they illustrate something of inherent interest. We give skeleton solutions with each problem, so the reader should not develop too many frustrations.

Some Problems

PROBLEM 1

Given that the relation between speed and temperature in a swarm of molecules is

$$\tfrac{1}{2}mv^2 = (3/2)kT,$$

where m is the mass of a molecule, k is Boltzmann's constant, and T is absolute temperature, calculate the speed of a molecule at 27°C. Use hydrogen, oxygen, and radon as examples of molecules.

Skeleton Solution

Mass of a proton is 1.6×10^{-24} gram. It is to be found in most tables. A hydrogen molecule has two of them. An oxygen molecule has two atoms, but each is 16 times more massive. Radon has only one, but it is about 230 times more massive.

Boltzmann's constant, also from tables, is 1.4×10^{-16} ergs per degree, $27 + 273 = 300$, cheers.

So

$$\tfrac{1}{2} \times 3 \times 10^{-24}\, v^2 = 1.5 \times 1.4 \times 10^{-16} \times 300$$

$$v^2 = \frac{4.2 \times 10^{-14}}{10^{-24}}$$

$$v = 2 \times 10^5 \text{ cms. per second.}$$

You are on your own for the others.

Oxygen: $5 \ \times 10^4$
Radon: $\ 1.9 \times 10^4$

PROBLEM 2

Suppose that for the purpose of communications it is desirable to have a satellite which goes around at the same rate of rotation as the earth and so stays in the same place in the sky. Can it be at any height, or is there only one height possible?

Information point: the linear velocity, v, or rather, the speed, around the orbit of a body at radius r rotating at ω angle (radians) per second is $v = r\omega$.

Skeleton Solution

For a circular orbit, speed, v, radius, r, the mass $\times$ acceleartion is $\dfrac{mv^2}{r}$, m being the mass of the satellite. This equals the force of gravity of Newton's Second Law and the Law of Gravitation. So

$$\frac{mv^2}{r} = \frac{GM_E m}{r^2} \qquad M_E = \text{mass of earth}$$
$$G = \text{constant of gravitation.}$$

We thus have

$$v^2 = \frac{GM_E}{r}$$

Clearly the mass of the satellite does not matter.

For a "hanging" orbit ω, the angular velocity is the same as mother earth. It is 2π radians, the whole circle, in 24 hours, or $24 \times 60 \times 60$ seconds. So we have

$$v = r\,\omega$$
$$v^2 = r^2\,\omega^2$$

and substituting above:

$$r^2\,\omega^2 = \frac{GM_E}{r}$$

$$r^3 = \frac{GM_E}{\omega^2}$$

Now ω is fixed by the length of the day, G is fixed, and M_E is also fixed. And so r must be fixed. There is only one height possible.

For the numerically curious, $G = 1.03 \times 10^{-9}$, $M_E = 13.1 \times 20^{24}$, $\omega = 6.9 \times 10^{-5}$. The units are G in poundals feet ^{2}/pound^2, M_E in pound, ω in radians per second. A radian, being a ratio, has no unit. Our finding: The satellite must be 27,000 miles from earth's center.

PROBLEM 3

An electron, traveling at one-tenth the speed of light, smashes into a dense target —lead or tungsten. It is stopped when it has gone one-tenth of a millimeter, a few sheets of paper in thickness. How much of its energy is radiated? This energy is in X-rays, so we can estimate how efficient an X-ray machine might be.

Skeleton Solution

The energy radiated per second by an accelerated charge is $\dfrac{2e^2a^2}{3c^3}$ where e is the charge, a the acceleration, and c the velocity of light. Consistent units will be e in electrostatic units, a in centimeters per second per second, and c in centimeters per second. The energy will be in *ergs*.

So we need to know a. We must make the assumption that a is constant, for we have no suggestion to the contrary. Let t be the time taken to become stopped. Let v_0 be the starting speed; it is zero at the end. The average speed is then $\dfrac{v_0}{2}$, so the time taken, t, is related to the distance to stop, s, by

$$\frac{s}{t} = \frac{v_0}{2}$$

$$t = \frac{2s}{v_0}$$

Now by the definition of uniform acceleration,

$$a = \frac{\text{final velocity} - \text{initial velocity}}{\text{time taken}}$$

$$= \frac{0 - v_0}{t}$$

$$= \frac{0 - v_0}{\dfrac{2s}{v_0}} = -\frac{v_0{}^2}{2s}$$

So

$$a = -c^2/100/2 \times 1/100 = \frac{-c^2}{2}$$

The energy radiated per second is then $\dfrac{2}{3}\dfrac{e^2c^4}{4}\dfrac{1}{c^3}$, remembering the square of a negative is positive. This is $\dfrac{e^2c}{6}$ per second. Now the time taken to stop, t, is

$$\frac{2s}{v_0} \quad \text{or} \quad \frac{2s}{c/10} \quad \text{or} \quad \frac{20s}{c}$$

The total energy radiated is thus $\dfrac{e^2c}{6} \times$ time radiating,

$$= \frac{e^2c}{6} \times \frac{20s}{c} = \frac{10}{3}e^2s$$

This is an intriguing result, because it is seen to depend mostly on the distance of penetration of the electron.

Putting in numbers, we find that the energy radiated

$$= \frac{10}{3} \times (5 \times 10^{-10})^2 \times \frac{1}{100}$$

$$= 0.8 \times 10^{-20} \text{ erg.}$$

The original energy of the electron was $\frac{1}{2}mv_0^2$, and so was

$$\frac{1}{2} \times 9 \times 10^{-28} \times (3 \times 10^9)^2 = 40.5 \times 10^{-10} \text{ erg.}$$

The ratio is thus $\dfrac{0.8 \times 10^{-20}}{4.5 \times 10^{-9}} = 2 \times 10^{-12}$.

So X-ray machines are not likely to be efficient.

PROBLEM 4

The process of nuclear fusion is one in which light nuclei are rearranged into forms of great stability. Doing so releases energy. Taking as an example the reaction

$$_1H^2 + {}_1H^3 \rightarrow {}_2He^4 + {}_0n^1 + \text{Energy}$$

Estimate the energy released per kilogram and compare it with chemical energy of the nature of TNT.

Information supplied: Atomic masses are as follows:

$$_1H^2 = 2.0147$$
$$_1H^3 = 3.0169$$
$$_2H^4 = 4.0039$$
$$_0n^1 = 1.0090$$

Energy per reacting molecule in normal chemistry is 6×10^{-12} erg.

Skeleton Solution

The energy developed, E, obeys the famous Einstein relation $E = mc^2$, where m is the amount of mass converted into energy. In the above reaction the balance sheet is

2.0147	4.0039
3.0169	1.0090
5.0316	5.0129

So the difference is 0.0187.

Now the atomic mass of chemistry, originally a relative number, has been found to refer to 6×10^{23} atoms. Thus the actual mass of an atom whose listed atomic mass is 1.0000 is $\dfrac{1.0000}{6 \times 10^{23}}$. So the actual mass of 0.0187, the difference above is

$$\frac{0.187 \times 1.0000}{6 \times 10^{23}} = \frac{18.7 \times 10^{-3}}{6 \times 10^{23}} = 3.1 \times 10^{-26} \text{ grams.}$$

This number, times c^2, is the energy released per reacting pair. It is $3.1 \times 10^{-26} \times 9 \times 10^{20} = 28 \times 10^{-6}$, which is four million times bigger than the energy of normal chemistry.

Now in 5 grams $(2 + 3)$ there are 6×10^{23} reacting pairs. In one kilogram there will be $\dfrac{1000}{5}$, or 200 times this many. This is 1.2×10^{26}. The energy released is $28 \times 10^{-6} \times 1.2 \times 10^{26}$, or 3.4×10^{21} ergs.

In one kilogram of TNT-like material, the reacting molecules rarely add up to less than 20 atomic masses. In such a mass there would be 6×10^{23} reacting pairs. In one kilogram there are $\dfrac{1000}{20}$ or 50 such. The energy released is therefore

$$6 \times 10^{-12} \times 50 \times 6 \times 10^{23}, \quad \text{or} \quad 1.8 \times 10^{14} \text{ergs}.$$

The ratio nuclear/chemical $= \dfrac{3.4 \times 10^{21}}{1.8 \times 10^{14}} = 2 \times 10^7$, approximately.

This is 20,000,000. It is not surprising that the invention of the H-bomb, which permits far more than 1 kilogram (2.2 lb.) to be set off, does introduce awesome thoughts. Incidentally, a 2-lb. blast of TNT is a tidy bang in itself.

PROBLEM 5

The carbon extracted from many present-day sources of living material is found to give 10 counts per minute over background counting rate, per 0.1 gram sample. Carbon from fossils is found to give 0 counts per minute. A sample from the center of a redwood tree is found to give 7 counts per minute. How old is the tree?

Skeleton Solution

The formula for radioactive decay is $\dfrac{dn}{n} = -\lambda \, dt$, where n is the number of radioactive atoms present, λ is the decay constant, and dn is the number decaying in a time dt.

In 100 milligrams of carbon we select a standard number of carbon atoms. Some of these, a very small number, are radioactive, because the nitrogen of the air undergoes a nuclear reaction to make ^{14}C. This form of carbon is radioactive, with a 5,300-year half-life. In modern living material this is "fixed," and it amounts to 100 counts per gram. In fossil fuel it has all decayed and gone. In the redwood there are $7/10$ of these atoms left. So the age of the redwood is such that $7/10$ are not yet decayed. If we plot a simple graph, using 5,300 years as the time to go to one-half, it looks like Figure 14.12. From our graph we estimate that the redwood is 3,000 years old.

PROBLEM 6

What sort of temperatures are needed for a thermonuclear reaction?

Information supplied: a thermonuclear reaction for a light element might start at half the energy needed to make contact with the nucleus. Potential energy for two charges of size e, at a distance r apart, is e^2/r.

Skeleton Solution

Choose the reaction

$$_1\text{H}^2 + {}_1\text{H}^3 \rightarrow {}_2\text{He}^4 + {}_0n^1$$

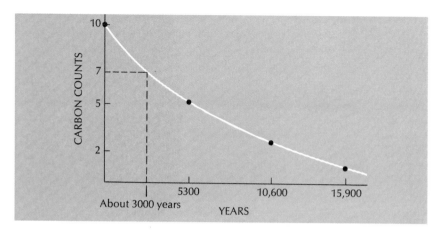

Fig. 14.12. The radioactive decay of ¹⁴C used to compute the age of a redwood tree.

The radius involved is given by

$$r = 1.5 \times 10^{-13} A^{1/3}$$

A is 2 and 3, respectively, and for both of the cube root is about 1.4 to our degree of approximation. So $r = 1.5 \times 10^{-13} \times 1.4$ cm., or 2.1×10^{-13} cm. Each nucleus has this radius, so the separation of the two positive charges as they make contact is $(2.1 + 2.1) \times 10^{-13}$ cm. The potential energy of the repulsion is $\dfrac{e^2}{r}$, or $\dfrac{(5 \times 10^{-10})^2}{4.2 \times 10^{-13}}$, or approximately 6×10^{-7} erg.

If this is a thermal energy, then

$$\frac{3}{2} kT = \frac{1}{2} mv^2$$

where k is Boltzmann's constant, T is the absolute temperature, and $\frac{1}{2}mv^2$ is the kinetic energy. So we have, using $k = 1.4 \times 10^{-16}$ erg per degree,

$$3 \times 10^{-7} = 1.4 \times 10^{-16} \times \frac{3}{2} \times T$$

$$T = \frac{2 \times 10^{-7}}{1.4 \times 10^{-16}} = \frac{2}{1.4} \times 10^{9}$$

$$T = 1.4 \times 10^{9}, \text{ or } 1.4 \text{ billion degrees.}$$

That this can be achieved in the H-bomb is also impressive.

PROBLEM 7

One hundred people listen to a lecture in a room 45 feet long by 30 feet wide by 18 feet high. No doors or windows are open. What happens to the temperature of the room?

Information: an average person generates 100 watts as heat. The specific heat of air is 0.25. When a mass of M grams, having a specific heat S, is warmed with Q calories, the temperature rise is T, where

$$Q = SMT$$

We also need to know that a cubic centimeter of air weighs 0.0013 gram, so that a cubic meter weighs $100 \times 100 \times 100$, or 10^6 as much, or $1.3 \times 10^{-3} \times 10^6$, or 1.3×10^3 grams.

Skeleton Solution

1 calorie, which is arranged to make the above formula work for $S = 1$, $M = 1$ gram, and $t = 1°C.$, is related to watts as follows:

$$\text{1 calorie per second} = 4.2 \text{ watts}$$

So

$$100 \text{ watts} = \frac{100}{4.2} \text{calories per second}$$

$$= 23 \text{ calories per second}$$

For 100 people, this is 2.300 calories per second.

Now approximately 3 feet = 1 meter, so the room is 15 meters by 10 meters by 6 meters, and it contains 900 cubic meters. Thus M, the mass of the air, is $900 \times 1.3 \times 10^3 = 1.17 \times 10^6$ grams. Note that this is about a ton, usually a surprise. We can thus see that in one second we have

$$2.3 \times 10^3 = 0.25 \times 1.17 \times 10^6 \times T$$

$$T = \frac{2.3 \times 10^3}{2.9 \times 10^5} = 7.9 \times 10^{-3}°C.$$

If we like Fahrenheit degrees, we multiply by $\%$ to get, in round numbers,

$$T = \frac{1}{100}°F. \text{ per second.}$$

This means that in two minutes the temperature in the room is up one degree, not a bother. In 20 minutes it is up 10°F., and this is uncomfortable. It is usually at about 20 minutes that someone looks for a window to open.

PROBLEM 8

How much food do we have to eat to produce our 100 watts of metabolic energy?

Information: We suppose that we eat rather less potent stuff than TNT, say one-tenth as potent. This is 6×10^{-13} erg per reaction. Also the atomic mass involved we suppose to be 20, as before.

Skeleton Solution

One watt is 10^7 ergs per second. So we need 10^9 ergs every second. Because reactions $\times$ energy of each must be equal to 10^9 per second, there will be a relation

$6 \times 10^{-13} \times$ reactions $= 10^9$, or we need

$\dfrac{10^9}{6 \times 10^{-13}}$, or 1.6×10^{21} reactions per second.

In 20 grams there are 6×10^{23} reacting pairs, so we need $\dfrac{1.6 \times 10^{21}}{6 \times 10^{23}}$ or roughly 5×10^{-3} gram per second. In a four-hour period (the time between meals) we have 3600×4 seconds, or 14,000, roughly. So between meals we use up $3 \times 10^{-3} \times 1.4 \times 10^4$, or 40 grams, of this foodstuff. In a whole day it is more like 250. This is a little more than a half a pound. This explains why dieting is so miserable: it takes a long time to lose weight, whereas we can easily add weight by eating. It is not pleasant to reduce the food balance to less than zero, and this only takes off about half a pound a day.

Reference Materials

Chapter 1

Jeans, Sir J. H. *The Growth of Physical Science.* 2nd ed. New York: Cambridge University Press, 1951.

Snow, C. P. *The Two Cultures.* New York: Cambridge University Press, 1963.

Zinsser, Hans. *Rats, Lice, and History.* New York: Bantam Books, Inc., 1960.

Chapter 2

Dantzig, T., ed. *Number, the Language of Science.* Garden City, N. Y.: Doubleday & Co., Inc., 1956.

Hardy, Godfrey H. *A Mathematician's Apology.* rev. ed. New York: Cambridge University Press, 1967.

Hogben, Lancelot T. *Mathematics for the Million,* New York: W. W. Norton & Co., Inc., 1946.

Logsdon, Mayme I. *A Mathematician Explains.* Chicago: University of Chicago Press, 1936.

Chapter 3

Fermi, Laura, and Gilberto Bernardini. *Galileo and the Scientific Revolution.* New York: Basic Books, Inc., 1961.

Galilei, Galileo. *Dialogues Concerning Two New Sciences,* trans. by Henry Crew and Alfonso de Salvio. Evanston, Ill.: Northwestern University Press, 1952.

Galilei, Galileo. *The Sidereal Messenger,* trans. by E. S. Carlos. London: Dawsons of Pall Mall, 1960.

Omer, Jr., Guy C., *et al. Physical Science: Men and Concepts.* Boston: D. C. Heath and Co., 1962.

SCIENCE AND ITS RELATION TO SOCIETY

Bronowski, Jacob. *Science and Human Values.* rev. ed. New York: Harper & Row, Torchbooks, 1965.

Dubos, René Jules. *The Dreams of Reason: Science and Utopias.* New York: Columbia University Press, 1961.

Hobsbawm, E. J. *The Age of Revolution.* Cleveland: World Publishing Co., 1962.

Lapp, Ralph E. *Atoms and People.* New York: Harper & Row, 1956.

Rowe, A. P. *One Story of Radar.* New York: Cambridge University Press, 1948.

Smyth Report. Princeton, N. J.: Princeton University Press, 1946.

Snow, C. P. *Science and Government.* Cambridge, Mass.: Harvard University Press, 1961.

Zinsser, Hans. *Rats, Lice, and History.* New York: Bantam Books, Inc., 1960.

Chapter 4

Gamow, George. *Biography of Physics.* New York: Harper & Row, Torchbooks, 1964.

Holton, Gerald J., and D. H. D. Roller. *Foundations of Modern Physical Science.* Reading, Mass.: Addison-Wesley, 1958.

Ripley, Jr., Julien A. *The Elements and Structure of the Physical Sciences.* New York: John Wiley & Sons, 1964.

Chapter 5

Omer, Jr., Guy C., *et al. Physical Science: Men and Concepts.* Boston: D. C. Heath and Co., 1962.

Stoner, E. C. *Magnetism and Atomic Structure.* New York: E. P. Dutton & Co., Inc., 1926.

Chapter 6

Magie, William F. *A Source Book in Physics.* New York: McGraw-Hill Book Co., Inc., 1935. Cambridge, Mass.: Harvard University Press, 1963 (8th printing.)

Tyndall, John. *Faraday as a Discoverer.* New York: Thomas Y. Crowell, Apollo Edition, 1961.

Chapter 7

Holton, Gerald J. *Introduction to Concepts and Theories in Physical Science.* Reading, Mass.: Addison-Wesley, 1958.

Tyndall, John. *Heat: A Mode of Motion*. New York: D. Appleton and Co., 1915.

Gamow, George. *Matter, Earth and Sky*. 2nd ed. Englewood Cliffs, N. J.: Prentice-Hall, Inc., 1965.

Chapter 8

Gamow, George. *Biography of Physics*. New York: Harper & Row, Torchbooks, 1964.

Tyndall, John. *Heat: A Mode of Motion*. New York: D. Appleton and Co., 1915.

Chapter 9

Gamow, George. *Matter, Earth and Sky*. 2nd ed. Englewood Cliffs, N. J.: Prentice-Hall, Inc., 1965.

Omer, Jr., Guy C., *et al*. *Physical Science: Men and Concepts*. Boston: D. C. Heath and Co., 1962.

Chapter 10

Fermi, Laura. *Atoms in the Family: My Life with Enrico Fermi*. Chicago: University of Chicago Press, 1954.

Gamow, George. *The Atom and Its Nucleus*. Englewood Cliffs, N. J.: Prentice-Hall, Inc., 1961.

Pollard, Ernest, and W. L. Davidson. *Applied Nuclear Physics*. 2nd ed. New York: John Wiley & Sons, 1951.

Rutherford, Ernest. *The Newer Alchemy*. New York: The Macmillan Company, 1937.

Chapter 12

de Broglie, Louis. *Matter and Light: The New Physics*. New York: Dover Publications, Inc., 1955.

Heitler, Walter. *Elementary Wave Mechanics with Application to Quantum Chemistry*. New York: Oxford University Press, 1956.

Chapter 13

Ebbighausen, E. G. *Astronomy*. Columbus, Ohio: Charles E. Merrill Books, Inc., 1966.

Eddington, Arthur S. *Stars and Atoms*. Oxford: Oxford at the Clarendon Press, 1927.

Lodge, Sir Oliver. *Pioneers of Science*. New York: Dover Publications, Inc., 1960.

Page, Thornton, ed. *Stars and Galaxies: Birth, Aging and Death in the Universe*. Englewood Cliffs, N. J.: Prentice-Hall, Inc., 1962.

Schwartz, George, and Philip W. Bishop, eds. *Moments of Discovery*. New York: Basic Books, Inc., 1958.

Shapley, Harlow, and Helen E. Howarth. *A Source Book in Astronomy*. New York: McGraw-Hill Book Co., Inc., 1929.

Young, Louise B. *The Mystery of Matter*. New York: Oxford University Press, 1965.

Suggested Readings

This list includes six books of a biographical nature, two pertaining to historical development of a science (astronomy and nuclear physics), two for general reading, and one of a humorous nature.

Curie, Eve. *Madame Curie*. New York: Pocket Books, Inc., 1959.

Dubos, René Jules. *Pasteur and Modern Science*. Garden City, N.Y.: Doubleday & Co., Inc., 1960.

Fermi, Laura. *Atoms in the Family: My Life with Enrico Fermi*. Chicago: University of Chicago Press, 1954.

Koestler, Arthur. *The Sleepwalkers*. New York: Grosset & Dunlap, Inc., 1963. (An extract of this book, entitled *The Watershed . . . A Biography of Johannes Kepler . . .*, has been published under the Science Study Series by Doubleday & Co., Inc., Anchor Books).

Lives in Science, Scientific American Book, New York: Simon and Schuster, Inc., 1957.

MacDonald, D. K. C. *Faraday, Maxwell, and Kelvin*. Garden City, N.Y.: Doubleday & Co., Inc., 1964.

Nathan, Robert. *The Weans*. New York: Alfred A. Knopf, Inc., 1960.

Romer, Alfred. *The Restless Atom*. Garden City, N.Y.: Doubleday & Co., Inc., 1960.

Shapley, Harlow, Helen Wright, and Samuel Rapport. *Readings in the Physical Sciences*. New York: Appleton-Century-Crofts, Inc., 1948.

Tyndall, John. *Faraday as a Discoverer*. New York: Thomas Y. Crowell, Apollo Edition, 1961.

Weisskopf, Victor F. *Knowledge and Wonder*. Garden City, N.Y.: Doubleday & Co., Inc., 1962.

Index

393

DATE DUE

AP 19'8			
OCT 12 1985			
FEB 24 '87			
GAYLORD			PRINTED IN U.S.A

Withdrawn From
Ohio Northern
University Library